HIGH-ALUMINA CEMENTS AND CONCRETES

HIGH-ALUMINA CEMENTS AND CONCRETES

by

T. D. Robson

Ph.D., B.Sc., F.R.I.C., M.Inst.F.

CONTRACTORS RECORD LIMITED
LENNOX HOUSE . NORFOLK STREET . LONDON W.C.2

JOHN WILEY & SONS, INC.
440 PARK AVENUE SOUTH . NEW YORK 16 . N.Y.

MCMLXII

FIRST PUBLISHED IN 1962

THE CONCRETE LIBRARY
Advisory Editor : J. SINGLETON-GREEN
M.Sc., M.I.C.E., M.I.Struct. E.
A.M.I.Mech.E., F.Inst.H.E., M.Soc.C.E. (France)

Set in eleven point on twelve point Monotype Imprint and made and printed in Great Britain by F. J. Parsons Limited of London, Folkestone and Hastings.

PREFACE

The total annual output of high-alumina cement is a very small fraction of the world production of Portland cement. However, this is a special cement, possessing certain valuable properties, and times of shortage (such as World War II) have shown how vital a part it plays in many applications. Concrete made with ordinary aggregates and high-alumina cement is slow-setting but extremely rapid-hardening and it also has high resistance to many aggressive agents. When a refractory aggregate is used, the concrete is suitable for continued service at high furnace temperatures. These main properties, (1) rapid development of strength, (2) chemical resistance, (3) refractory bond, are responsible for most of the attention paid to high-alumina cement.

The technical literature about individual aspects of high-alumina cement is indeed very extensive but the information available is widely dispersed and, it is believed, has never been collected in a reasonably adequate fashion. This cement has been the subject of excellent chapters in works devoted to cement and concrete, but it was felt that a need existed for a volume dealing only with high-alumina cement and the concretes made from it. Even so, certain aspects may not be given in the detail sufficient for some readers and therefore the opportunity has been taken to provide an extensive list of references so that the path to further information is made easier. It is therefore hoped that this book will form a time-saving guide to the publications in many countries on high-alumina cement.

Originally developed for its resistance to sulphates (and probably still pre-eminent in this field), high-alumina cement soon revealed exceptional rapid-hardening properties, thus creating a considerable interest in its use for structural concrete. The advantages and limitations of this type of cement for structural work in certain climatic and industrial situations have been fully discussed, together with the underlying principles, and a better understanding of the latter should

5

lead to the correct use of high-alumina cement when its rapid-hardening or chemical resistance properties are required.

One of the most rapidly developing applications of high-alumina cement is in the preparation of refractory concretes or refractory castable mixes which, by choice of aggregate and type of cement, can be readily formulated to give satisfactory service at temperatures up to 1800°C. To deal exhaustively with this subject would require more space than is available, but an attempt has been made to discuss all the basic methods and properties and to include all the major applications. Many aspects of refractory castable technology have already been adequately reviewed in the technical literature and comprehensive references have again been given.

The chemistry of high-alumina cement has not been explored too deeply, except where it appears to be of practical significance, and most of it is confined to Chapters II and III. By so doing it is hoped that this book will be useful to readers whose degree of interest or whose approach to the subject may vary widely.

The Author is grateful for the helpful suggestions he has received from the Universal Atlas Cement Division, United States Steel Corporation, particularly in dealing with the manufacture and properties of cement made in the U.S.A., and he is also deeply indebted to Ciments Lafarge, Paris, for much background information. Acknowledgement, is made in the text to technical journals throughout the World, and to the many writers whose papers and articles have been consulted and quoted. Thanks are also due to Mr. E. Davison, B.Sc., A.M.I.C.E. who kindly undertook to produce the figures.

CHAPTER 1.—THE MANUFACTURE OF HIGH-ALUMINA CEMENTS

CONTENTS

The Manufacture of High-Alumina Cements

1. Nomenclature.

In countries where English is spoken, the type of hydraulic cement with which this book will deal is called Aluminous Cement, High-Alumina Cement, or Calcium Aluminate Cement. The main cementitious constituent is always monocalcium aluminate ($CaO.Al_2O_3$).

The term Aluminous Cement has perhaps been the most popular, and it is also used in many other languages, e.g. " Ciment alumineux " (France), " Tonerdezement " (Germany), " Cemento Alluminoso " (Italy), " Aluminiumcement " (Netherlands), " Hlinitanový cement " (Czechoslovakia), and " Cement glinozemisty " (U.S.S.R.). Nevertheless, some justifiable criticism has been directed against the use of Aluminous Cement as a generic name, on the grounds that other types of hydraulic cement (including Portland cement) contain some alumina and could therefore qualify as " aluminous."

High-Alumina Cement is now the preferred name in England, although even this is not entirely free from objection since, in the refractory field, confusion can arise between High-Alumina Cement (which is used as a bond in refractory castable mixes) and plastic aluminous fireclay mixes, which have no hydraulic-setting properties but are sometimes described as " high alumina refractory cements " or " alumina cements."

Possibly the best description is Calcium Aluminate Cement — a designation which is commonly used in the U.S.A. (in Finland also it is called Aluminatcement). Since the essential feature of this class of cement is that the cementitious properties are derived (either wholly or to a major extent) from calcium aluminates, this last name seems to be fully descriptive and unlikely to cause ambiguity.

However, in the subsequent text it is proposed to make free use of the abbreviation H.A.C. to denote High-Alumina Cement. T.S.Z. (for Tonerdeschmelzzement) is already used similarly in the German literature.

2. MANUFACTURERS' TRADE NAMES

In the manufacture of Portland cement the raw materials are merely clinkered in the kiln, but most of the H.A.C. produced today has been completely fused during manufacture. This is the origin of the Trade Mark " Ciment Fondu " for the H.A.C. made in England. It should be noted however that one frequently finds " ciment fondu " is used to represent all high-alumina cements instead of merely indicating the product of a particular manufacture. A somewhat similar situation may arise in other countries when " cemento fuso," " cemento fundido," or " schmelzzement " are used to denote the broad class of high-alumina cements.

Trade Names for the H.A.C. now made by manufacturers throughout the World include " Lumnite " (U.S.A.), " Rolandshütte " (Germany), " Istrabrand " (Yugoslavia), " Citadur " (Hungary, Czechoslovakia), " Fundido Electroland " (Spain), " Alcement Lafarge " (Scandinavia), " Fondu Lafarge," (France), " Lightning " (England) and " Ciment Fondu " (England). High-Alumina Cement is also produced today in the U.S.S.R., Italy and Japan.

3. HISTORICAL BACKGROUND TO HIGH-ALUMINA CEMENT MANUFACTURE

Calcium aluminates were prepared by heating mixtures of alumina and lime or marble in 1848 by Ebelman[1] and in 1856 by Sainte-Claire Deville[2]. The latter mixed his product with water and corundum aggregate in order to mould crucibles which could be heated to very high temperatures. At this time he was therefore aware of the hydraulic properties of calcium aluminate and he also anticipated (by about 70 years) its use as a refractory bond. In the same year Winkler[3] published information on the hydraulic properties of calcium aluminates although Frémy[4] in 1865 is often credited with the pioneer work in this field. The setting and hardening properties of the less basic calcium aluminates were certainly confirmed and investigated by Michaelis[5] in 1869 and in 1906 by Schott[6], who showed that very high strengths were obtainable.

The first isolation of monocalcium aluminate itself may well have been accomplished by Sainte-Claire Deville in the course of his synthetic mineralogical studies, by Le Chatelier[7] or by Dufau[8]. This compound was also separated by Shepherd, Rankin and Wright[9] during their study of equilbria in the lime-alumina system.

10

However, the first manufacture of a product which we might now recognise as a commercial high-alumina cement was proposed in two very early patents, one German and the other British. In 1882 L. Roth, of Wetzlar, obtained a patent for obtaining a cement by " burning " bauxite with siliceous materials and lime[10], while in England (1888) an interesting patent was granted to a curious syndicate consisting of a doctor of medicine, two merchants, a manufacturing chemist and a metallurgist[11]. A " calcareous aluminous frit " was prepared by moulding into bricks a mixture of Irish bauxite and lime, and then firing these bricks in a kiln (a method substantially the same as that used many years later in Hungary for the commercial production of high-alumina cement). The fritted bricks were then to be ground with granulated blast-furnace slag to produce a product described (erroneously) by the inventors as " a cheap and reliable cement of the class known as Portland cement."

Meanwhile the French Society for the Encouragement of National Industry had been concerned at the serious decomposition of Portland cement structures in certain areas and in 1853 they offered a prize for work aimed at a solution to this problem. By 1898 J. Bied considered that the expansion and decomposition of existing concretes in these areas, and in sea-water, was due to chemical attack by sulphates, and he devoted many years to the search for a cement which would resist this attack[12]. He realised that a cement based on calcium aluminate instead of calcium silicate would fulfil certain chemical requirements which, according to earlier work by Vicat, were necessary to obtain an " indecomposable " cement.

The work of Bied in the laboratories and in the Le Teil works of J. and A. Pavin de Lafarge (now Ciments Lafarge) eventually led to the patenting (in May 1908) of a suitable method for the commercial manufacture of high-alumina cement from lime and bauxite[13]. This manufacture, in a hot-blast cupola furnace, had been satisfactorily operated by 1913 but extensive tests were carried out in the following years, by the Lafarge Company and by the appropriate French Government department, before the cement was placed on the general market in 1918-1920. Although primarily developed as a sulphate-resisting cement, its ultra-rapid hardening properties were soon evident and a considerable amount was supplied during the 1914-1918 World War for the construction of gun emplacements and shelters.

Touché[14] has described the prolonged testing of this French high-alumina cement (Fondu Lafarge) in the highly sulphated area traversed by the Nice-Coni line of the P.L.M. Railway. In 1916, mortar specimens were half-immersed in the sulphate waters found at the Col de Braus tunnel and in some cases the sand in the specimens was replaced, either partly or entirely, by crushed anhydrite in order to increase the severity of the test. Over 7000 tons of high-alumina cement was also employed for concrete construction in anhydrite and gypsum soils or in sulphate waters. In 1922, Féret[15] was able to produce tests over a period of 10 years and in the same year Séjourné[16] declared that the " indecomposability " of high-alumina cement in sulphates was beyond question.

Spackman (and Conwell), in the U.S.A., had commenced experiments in 1902 for the laboratory preparation of calcium aluminates using a relatively low grade aluminous material and limestone which were calcined together in a small kiln or fused in graphite crucibles. Subsequently he produced his aluminates on a semi-commercial scale by grinding the raw materials, moulding into bricks and firing with added fuel in a shaft kiln[17]. The Aluminate Patents Co. was formed in 1909 to exploit the Spackman patents (which were held up for a time by interference proceedings arising from the Bied patents). However, Spackman did not propose to use calcium aluminate as a cement but merely as an additive to lime, natural cement, or plaster in order to accelerate the hardening and improve the strength of these materials[18]. " Alca " cements or " Alca Lime " based on this principle appeared for a time on the American market between 1910 and 1917, but the commercial manufacture of a true high-alumina cement was not started in the U.S.A. until 1924.

Spackman did not investigate the individual aluminates present in his product but Bates, at the U.S. Bureau of Standards, made several different calcium aluminate compositions by sintering finely ground limestone and calcined alumina in a small (2 ft. x 20 ft.) rotary kiln. Although the amounts of impurities such as silica, magnesia, and ferric oxide in the product were varied for experimental purposes, the total iron oxide content never exceeded about 3 per cent, and it was therefore possible to carry out runs at temperatures from 1360°-1500°C. without fusing the clinker[19]. Bates (and also Endell[20] in Germany) concluded that only two of the calcium aluminates occurring in the lime-alumina system formed cements which were of practical use.

Finally, a historical summary would be incomplete without further reference to the fundamental work in the U.S.A. of Shepherd, Rankin, and Wright on the lime-alumina-silica system[9]. This was of prime importance not only to workers in the Portland cement field but also to those who have since been concerned with high-alumina cement.

12

4. Methods Proposed for the Manufacture of High-Alumina Cement

(1) *Fusion under reducing conditions with simultaneous production of cast-iron.*

The furnaces originally used in France were really cupolas or very small blast-furnaces, consisting of a vertical cylindrical steel shell fitted with water-jackets to reduce the wear on refractories. The charge of bauxite and lime or limestone lumps, together with coke, was added through the top at fairly regular intervals. A hot air blast was applied to the charge through tuyères situated in the lower part of the furnace, and the combustion of the coke under these conditions reduced a high proportion of the ferric oxide present in the red bauxite to metallic iron. Combination of the lime and alumina in the raw materials to a molten calcium aluminate " slag " occurred simultaneously and this, together with the molten iron, was tapped off continuously into a pan-conveyor where clinker " pigs " were formed by cooling[21]. The air-blast was pre-heated by passing it through a metallic recuperator in which the exit gas from the furnace was burned. Practically all the iron was easily separated from the clinker but Patrouilleau[22] patented the use of magnetic separation for removing the finer particles of iron from the cement after the clinker " pigs " had been ground. These " water-jacket furnaces " eventually ranged in height from 10 ft. to 25 ft. and in diameter from 30 in. to 60 in.[23], producing about 10-35 tons of high-alumina cement clinker per day, and consuming up to 1680 lbs. of coke per ton of clinker[24].

Elsewhere several early attempts were also made to effect the same result in an ordinary blast-furnace. In 1904 the Pennsylvania Steel Company tried to smelt aluminous Mayari iron-ore from Cuba. Their first attempts were regarded as a failure because of the very high coke consumption (about 4700 lbs. per ton of iron produced) but the slag produced contained about 30 per cent alumina and, after reaction with lime, some was used as an addition material in place of the more expensive Spackman aluminates. In 1924 further trials gave better results and Kinney, Joseph and Wood in 1927 obtained a suitable high-alumina cement slag together with cast iron, from a small blast-furnace charged with bauxite, limestone and low-silica iron ore, and scrap-iron[25].

Between 1925 and 1928 the manufacture of H.A.C. in a blast-furnace was studied and perfected in large-scale experiments at the Rolandshütte Works, Wiedenau, Germany, using an air-blast preheated to 550°C. Hessian, Istrian or French bauxites, together with limestone, were used at various times in the charge, which also contained

13

sinter and calcined pyrites, or Krivoi-Rog iron ore and iron-scrap. The coke consumption, at first rather high, was later reduced to 1940 lbs. per ton of cast-iron. Industrial production was then started by Eisenwerke Kraft, near Stettin, and essentially the same process has been used since 1951 by Metallhüttenwerke Lübeck, A.G. in manufacturing their " Rolandshütte " brand of H.A.C. at Lübeck-Herrenwyck.

Apart from the early Lafarge patents[13] many other inventors have since patented processes which produce high-alumina cement and cast-iron simultaneously. Mathesius[26] in 1922 obtained a comprehensive patent covering, amongst other things, the reductive fusion of limestone and bauxite, or bauxite residues, in various furnaces including blast-furnaces. He also claimed that, in this process, excess silica in the raw materials could be removed as ferro-silicon, thus maintaining the silica content of the H.A.C. slag at a desirably low level. Eckel[27] also proposed manufacturing in a large blast-furnace fitted with the usual hot-blast stoves, gas-recovery, etc., using low-silica iron ore, bauxite, and limestone. The cast-iron and molten cement were tapped separately and intermittently to allow time for the metal to separate in the furnace. In addition he patented the reductive fusion, either in a blast-furnace or in an electric furnace, when sufficient carbon was present not only to reduce the ferric oxide but also to reduce some of the silica[28]. This permitted the use of high-silica raw materials (c.f. the Mathesius patent). Ruzicka[29] proposed to manufacture H.A.C. and cast-iron in a blast furnace with an air-blast (either cold or hot) which could be enriched with oxygen. His charge was a mixture of bauxite, limestone, iron, and a special coke or " artificial charcoal " which had a very low ash content and therefore contributed little or no silica to the slag. It will be seen later that if H.A.C. contains too much silica in its composition, the rapid-hardening properties are adversely affected, and accordingly there are many patents claiming to solve this problem[30].

Séailles[31] used an electric furnace in 1930-1934 to produce almost white calcium aluminate by reductive fusion which removed the iron compounds from the raw materials in the form of cast-iron and ferro-silicon. In more recent times Bederlunger[32] has also claimed that a suitable high-alumina cement may be prepared from a raw material containing only 23 per cent alumina and as much as 40 per cent. silica, by reductive fusion in an electric-arc furnace with separation of ferro-silicon. The resultant slag is re-melted with lime to give a cement clinker containing 41 per cent alumina and no more than 13 per cent. silica. Fox (1937) also suggested a two-stage process

14

by which bauxite or laterite was first fused with limestone or chalk in a blast-furnace, so that the major portion of the iron in the bauxite could be separated from the slag. The latter was then re-fused with additional aluminous material in a separate " correcting furnace " so as to produce a calcium aluminate slag of the desired cement composition[33].

A calcium aluminate slag is obtained, by reductive fusion, as an intermediate product in the manufacture of alumina by the Pederson process[34]. Bauxite, limestone, coke and some iron ore are melted in an electric-arc furnace and the resultant products are pig-iron and the calcium aluminate slag from which alumina and aluminium are subsequently obtained[35].

(2) *Fusion under reducing conditions with simultaneous production of phosphorus.*

The simultaneous production of a slag corresponding in composition to high-alumina cement, and of phosphorus or phosphorus derivatives, is a possibility which has attracted considerable attention during the past forty years and numerous patents have resulted. Phosphorus is normally obtained by electric furnace fusion of calcium phosphate, under reducing conditions, in presence of silica so that, when the phosphorus has been distilled off, the residual slag is of the calcium silicate type. It should obviously be feasible to obtain phosphorus and a calcium aluminate slag by suitably altering the raw materials or even, it has been suggested, by fusing the usual calcium silicate slag with aluminous material.

One of the early patents[36] stated that previous processes, in which adjustment of the siliceous slag composition took place in the furnace, led to increased energy consumption and loss of phosphorus. It therefore recommended that the slag should be tapped off and that the required aluminous material should then be added — in a separate furnace if necessary. Another variant[37] suggested adding to the furnace sufficient iron ore or iron-scrap to combine with all the phosphorus. Alumina and lime were also added in order to obtain a calcium aluminate slag together with ferro-phosphorus (iron phosphide) as the second product.

In most cases, however, the inventors have sought to keep the formation of ferro-phosphorus to a minimum, and processes which involve reductive fusion of a mixture of calcium phosphate and ordinary red bauxite, although readily producing a calcium aluminate slag, suffer from the disadvantage that much of the phosphorus combines with the iron originally present in the bauxite. The difficulty could

15

be overcome by using a low-iron or white bauxite but this is expensive, and it has therefore been proposed[38] to carry out a preliminary reductive fusion of red bauxite, carbon and lime so as to eliminate iron as metal and thus obtain a low-iron calcium aluminate. In a subsequent operation this slag is then fused with phosphate, under reducing conditions, giving a high yield of phosphorus and a final slag with the composition of high-alumina cement.

Experiments have also been carried out in which mixtures of calcium phosphate and aluminium phosphate have been fused under reducing conditions[39]. It was claimed that, if the silica content of these raw materials was sufficiently low, a good high-alumina cement could be prepared by grinding the resultant calcium aluminate slag[40]. Another suggested furnace charge is calcium phosphate, aluminium phosphate, lime and cork[41].

Aluminium phosphate occurs naturally, although suitable deposits are very restricted in distribution when compared with the occurrence of calcium phosphate. Its use in this type of manufacture presents obvious advantages and comparatively recently King[42] has patented the simultaneous production of phosphorus and high-alumina cement slag by employing a mixture of naturally-occurring aluminium phosphate and calcium phosphate, or of aluminium phosphate and lime.

(3) *Simple fusion.*

After developing the " water-jacket " furnace method of manufacture, the Lafarge Company patented the use of a reverberatory furnace[43] into which bauxite and limestone lumps were fed through a vertical shaft situated above one end of the hearth. A flame played on the ramp of solid materials at the bottom of the shaft and a pool of molten cement therefore collected in the horizontal reverberatory section. Such furnaces, which are still used extensively for modern manufacture, are fired with pulverised coal, oil, or a combination of both. The furnace atmosphere may, at times, be slightly reducing, neutral, or oxidising, and therefore a variable proportion of the ferric oxide present in the bauxite is reduced to ferrous oxide but not to metallic iron. The presence of dark ferrous compounds in the clinker made from ferruginous bauxite, imparts to high-alumina cement the familiar deep-grey colour. The colour may vary somewhat according to furnace conditions without effect on the cementitious properties, but Séailles[44] patented an oxidation process for subsequently adjusting the shade of colour.

In this type of reverberatory furnace all the combustion gases

16

must pass up through the burden of lump material in the vertical shaft or stack, and Dumas[45] some years later, in proposing a similar furnace, provided for alternative gas exits when the normal gas path was obstructed.

Another suggested improvement[46] consisted in feeding the raw materials first into a short rotary kiln whose discharge was connected to the inlet shaft of the reverberatory furnace. A similar invention[47] involved the use of a preparatory calcining furnace (e.g. a rotary kiln) in which dehydration and decarbonation of the raw materials would take place before they were passed to a fusion furnace (either reverberatory or rotary). In order to prevent fusion in passage between the furnaces, the duct carrying the hot gas from the reverberatory section was kept separate from the duct carrying the calcined materials. The use of an externally operated conveyor device for transferring materials between the calcining and fusion furnaces, and the insertion of a regenerator in the intermediate hot-gas duct, have also been patented[48].

The complete fusion of bauxite and limestone in a rotary kiln was the subject of numerous patents by Spackman, by Ciments Francais, and later by British Portland Cement Manufacturers Ltd., Polysius and others[49]. These patents made various claims for improvements in this method of manufacture, e.g. dividing the rotary kiln into three zones. Dehydration and decarbonation took place in the first zone which was lined with bricks of high thermal conductivity so that the temperature did not exceed 1000°C. The materials were fused in the second or high-temperature zone, and the molten cement escaped at the junction with the third zone which comprised an air-cooled hearth surrounding the initial part of the flame. Another proposal was for a kiln closed at the lower end but provided with near-by holes in the shell through which the molten cement was tapped. It has also been claimed that when high-alumina cement is made by fusion in a rotary kiln, the raw materials may be fed in lump form, thus avoiding the costly fine grinding and intimate mixing required at this stage during Portland cement manufacture. For many years the commercial production of high-alumina cement in the U.S.A. has been effected by complete fusion in a rotary kiln, and the process is described later in greater detail.

A considerable quantity of high-alumina cement has been made in the past by fusing the bauxite and lime in electric furnaces. It is of course, possible, with this manufacture, to arrange for reduction of iron oxide and silica to ferro-silicon[31][32], but the reduction caused by the carbon electrodes alone usually stops at the ferrous oxide stage, giving the cement a dark colour if red bauxite is employed. Early patents refer to resistance furnaces with iron electrodes immersed in the melt[50] but it is usually considered that the low conductivity of the calcium aluminates necessitates the use of electric-arc furnaces. Such furnaces, with two or three carbon electrodes, gave satisfactory results in regions where current was relatively cheap (e.g. Finland, Switzerland, Savoie and Pyrenées in France). Leonhardt[51] has described the process used in Finland in 1935. The arc furnaces, fitted with three electrodes of large cross-section, operated at low current-density and the power consumption was about 800 K.w.h. per ton of cement (figures as high as 2000-2500 K.w.h. per ton have been quoted for manufacture elsewhere). Calcined bauxite and lime were added to the furnace in the form of small lumps and the molten product was run into ingots for slow cooling. Further information about the early manufacture in electric furnaces has been given by Rengade[21], Blanc[24], Biehl[52] and Brissaud[53].

(4) *Sintering or clinkering*

The early work of this nature by Snelus, by Spackman, and by Bates has already been mentioned and it was soon discovered that the lime and alumina of suitable finely-ground raw materials could be combined to calcium aluminates at temperatures well below the melting-point.

In 1924 Decolland[54] obtained a patent for the manufacture of high-alumina cement, without complete fusion, in a rotary kiln similar to that used for Portland cement. The feed was introduced as a finely-divided slurry and the temperature was kept just below the melting-point. However when ferruginous bauxite is used, it is extremely difficult merely to clinker the raw materials in a rotary kiln. Comparatively slight fluctuations in temperature produce variable fusion causing " rings " which block the flow through the kiln. Usually it is found that the clinkering process proceeds normally in a rotary kiln only when the iron content of the bauxite is very low. The same inventor therefore proposed to lengthen the roasting zone of the kiln, and to reduce the flame temperature by using lignite as fuel, by introducing steam or natural gas, or by incorporating limestone in the fuel. He also suggested removing the refractory lining and cooling the kiln shell at points where " ringing " was most prevalent. Other solutions include playing the flame, not directly into the rotary kiln, but into a chamber preceding the clinkering zone, or the use of producer gas, water gas, or natural gas as fuel[55]. Voisin suggested that waste-heat gases from another manufacturing process could be used to give suitable clinkering conditions in rotary kilns[56].

Patents have also been granted for sintering or fritting processes in which the finely-ground raw materials are held for long periods at much lower temperatures (e.g. 9-11 hours at 900°-1100°C. or 6-8 hours at 1000°C.-1100°C.) in various types of kiln[57]. It has also been claimed that a cement with improved strength could be obtained by calcining the materials in a state of rest for 30 hours and cooling the product slowly over a further 30 hours. In this process the bauxite and limestone did not require to be particularly finely ground[58]. Knibbs proposed to autoclave a finely-divided mixture of bauxite and slaked lime with high-pressure steam, so as to form hydrated calcium aluminates, and then he heated the product for 4 hours at 1100°-1150°C. or 1-2 hours at 1150°-1200°C., i.e. at a temperature well below the fusion point[59].

If the melting-point of the raw mix is raised by reducing the proportion of limestone well below that necessary for an ordinary high-alumina cement composition it is possible to employ higher kiln or furnace temperatures without obtaining fusion[60]. An adjustment to give the correct cement composition can then be made during a second " firing "[61].

Manufacture on a stationary or travelling " sinter-grate " has also been put forward — chiefly in Germany[62]. A mixture consisting of bauxite, limestone, sinter rejects, and solid fuel is ignited at one point and combustion of the fuel proceeds under the influence of air drawn or blown through the perforations of the grate. The bed of materials on the grate may be up to about 1 foot thick.

Numerous patents have claimed beneficial effects, particularly in sintering or clinkering processes, from the addition of small quantities of " mineralisers " to the raw feed. Such materials include alkali-metal salts, calcium chloride or fluoride, cryolite[63], borates[64] and oxides or salts of lead or chromium[65].

(5) *With unusual raw materials.*

The materials customarily used for the manufacture of ordinary high-alumina cement are calcium carbonate (nearly always in the form of limestone) and bauxite (of the quality employed in the aluminium industry). Various suggestions and attempts have been made to substitute some other available material for bauxite as source of the alumina required to form calcium aluminate. Clays[66], slag[67], shales and laterites, are all aluminous, but, although cheap and widely distributed, they contain too much silica to yield directly a good-quality high-alumina cement. Their employment would therefore necessitate a preliminary chemical treatment designed to separate silica from the alumina[69], or else an attempt to remove much of the silica as ferro-silicon by a reductive fusion. Both processes are generally uneconomic at the present time when suitable bauxite is readily available, but a laboratory process has been described[69] in which it was claimed that a good high-alumina cement was produced from kaolin.

During World War II the shortage of imported bauxite in England led to the use of a " synthetic bauxite " for high-alumina cement manufacture. The materials used were the " red mud " obtained as a residue from bauxite treatment in the aluminium industry, and aluminium oxide " dross " skimmed from aluminium melting furnaces. A slurry of these materials was treated with sulphuric acid in a special plant[70], and then neutralised with chalk. After filtration, the solid product was used to replace at least part of the natural bauxite required in the manufacture of high-alumina cement[71].

Nagai has also described a method of using aluminium oxide " dross " by mixing it with lime and raw materials containing ferric oxide (such as burned pyrites, bauxite, or aluminous shale). The mixture was kneaded with water to decompose the aluminium nitride and aluminium metal, always present in the " dross," and then it was sintered at 1300°-1400°C. to give a calcium aluminate which could be crushed to yield cement. A fusion process did not give satisfactory results[72].

He also studied the possible use of alunite (a naturally-occurring potassium aluminium sulphate) in place of bauxite. A mixture of powdered alunite and limestone was heated, then slurried with water and ammonium carbonate or ammonia, before being treated with carbon dioxide. The filtrate was rich in potassium and ammonium sulphates and could be used as a fertiliser. The residue (containing alumina and calcium carbonate) was heated at 1350°C. and gave a good high-alumina cement clinker, in a yield corresponding to 85-95 per cent. of the original alunite[73].

A novel method of making calcium aluminate, together with certain aluminium alloys, employs molten aluminium itself in place of bauxite[74]. Calcium oxide or carbonate is heated below the surface of molten aluminium at 1500°-1600°C. and continuous production of a calcium aluminate slag is said to be possible.

However, it is probably true to say that bauxite remains the only aluminous material used today for the commercial manufacture of ordinary high-alumina cement. Apart from the economic reasons for this, there is also the fact that many alternative materials contain appreciable quantities of alkali. Unless the manufacturing process removes this almost entirely, the resultant cement will probably be unduly quick-setting and will be unable to develop its full potential strength. The use of " synthetic bauxite " in England tended to produce very fast-setting clinker and this was (at least partly) caused by residual alkali originally present in the " red mud."[75] Similar troubles may arise in processes using aluminium phosphate which contains an appreciable quantity of alkali-metal salts. It is no doubt fortunate that bauxite contains hardly any alkali compounds.

Since limestone is a relatively cheap material there is usually little incentive to search for alternatives, but the production of calcium aluminates by heating a mixture of bauxite and gypsum has been suggested. The interest in the process arises because sulphur dioxide, which can be used to manufacture sulphuric acid, is liberated at the same time[76]. Chalk was used, at first, as a raw material for the manufacture in England of H.A.C., but limestone is now employed since the latter was found to be more suitable for the particular manufacturing process.

5. MODERN METHODS USED FOR THE MANUFACTURE OF HIGH-ALUMINA CEMENT

(1) *In The United States of America*

The early work of Spackman, Conwell, and Bates has already been mentioned and " Lumnite " brand of high-alumina cement has been manufactured in the U.S.A. since 1924, first at Northampton, Penn., but now at Gary, Indiana.

In the process used there by the Universal Atlas Cement Division, United States Steel Corporation, the raw materials are bauxite and limestone. The bauxite requires a preliminary crushing and drying before it is ground with the limestone to a fineness of about 15 per cent residue on the 200-mesh sieve. Then the dry powder is fed into a rotary kiln basically similar to that used in the manufacture of Portland cement. A pulverised low-ash coal is used as fuel and completely molten product collects in the lower end of the kiln. This section of the kiln has no refractory lining, but is water-cooled so that a protective layer of solidified clinker forms against the shell. At this point the kiln shell is provided with holes and, at each revolution, molten clinker pours through each hole in turn, down into a trough set in the floor at right angles to the axis of the kiln. Water is sprayed onto a revolving screw in the trough and this quenches and granulates

21

the clinker, which is then conveyed to a stock-pile. The granulate is ground to cement fineness together with a small amount of gypsum. Since 1951 a small addition of retarder/plasticiser has also been made. (Fig. 1).

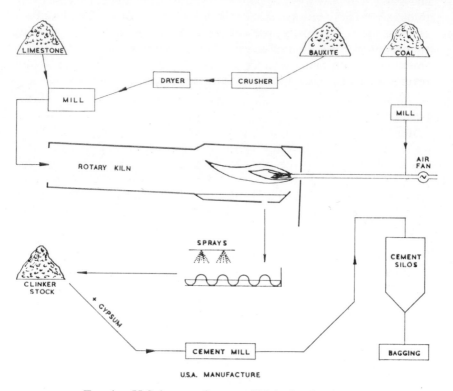

FIG. 1.   U.S.A. manufacture of high-alumina cement.

(2) *In Germany*

Following the work carried out between 1925 and 1928 at the Rolandshütte works, Wiedenau, which has been described previously, commercial production of high-alumina cement was initiated by Eisenwerke Kraft near Stettin.   After World War II the manufacture of " Rolandshütte " brand of high-alumina cement was restarted in 1951 at Lübeck-Herrenwyck, and it has since been made there by Metallhüttenwerke Lübeck A.G.

The cement is produced in ordinary metallurgical blast-furnaces, the charge consisting of lumps of low-silica bauxite, limestone and coke, together with scrap-metal. The latter, combined with iron resulting from reduction of the ferric oxide present in the bauxite,

22

collects in the hearth of the furnace and it is covered by the molten slag (which in this case is a calcium aluminate slag). The ratio of slag/cast-iron is usually 0.6 - 0.7 and the two are tapped off separately 6-8 times per day. The slag is run into ladles and poured into a shallow pit where it cools and solidifies in sheets of fairly uniform thickness. It is then ground to cement fineness with a small amount of gypsum. When making high-alumina cement slag, the furnace campaign is usually limited to 5-6 weeks, since refractory wear is quite severe with this type of charge. At other times the blast-furnaces revert to normal production of cast-iron when the ordinary calcium silicate slag is, of course, produced. The cast-iron made in conjunction with high-alumina cement is said to be similar to high-carbon Swedish charcoal iron.

(3) *In Hungary and Czechoslovakia*

" Citadur " brand high-alumina cement was manufactured at the Felsogalla works of the Hungarian General Colliery Co., by fritting the briquetted raw materials in a brick-kiln. Only a small amount of high-alumina cement is now made in Hungary but the same process is currently employed at the Ladce works in Czechoslovakia.

The bauxite is calcined, mixed with the correct proportion of limestone and then finely ground before being formed into bricks. The latter are then fired in a Hoffman-type kiln at a maximum temperature of 1250°C. and subsequently ground to the requisite cement fineness. The product therefore is not a " fused cement " and the kiln temperature must be maintained very accurately since a relatively small increase may cause undue softening or fusion.

(4) *In Great Britain*

The very early patent of Snelus and his colleagues in 1888[11] does not appear to have been worked in Britain and the next development in this country was the patenting in 1908 (by the Henry S. Spackman Engineering Co.) of calcium aluminate as an additive to improve the properties of lime, wall-plasters, and other cementitious materials[18]. In 1909 J & A Pavin de Lafarge (now Ciments Lafarge) extended to England their previous French patents covering the manufacture of high-alumina cement by fusing bauxite and lime in " water-jacket " furnaces or cupolas[13].

From 1923 to 1925 The Lafarge Aluminous Cement Co., Ltd., distributed French-made " Ciment Fondu " in Great Britain and in January 1925 The British Portland Cement Manufacturers Ltd., started the commercial manufacture of " Lightning " brand high-alumina cement at their Magheramorne works (N. Ireland). It is interesting to note that they used the native source of bauxite which was probably the same as that mentioned by Snelus. The cement was made[49] by fusing bauxite and limestone in a rotary kiln (similar to current manufacturing methods in the U.S.A.) but production of high-alumina cement at Magheramorne ceased at a later date.

In 1926 the manufacture of " Ciment Fondu " brand was started by The Lafarge Aluminous Cement Co. Ltd., at their works at West Thurrock, Essex, England[77], at first in " water-jacket " furnaces and a few years later in the L-shaped reverberatory furnaces which have already been briefly described. The process used today is shown in Fig. 2, the raw materials being limestone and French or Greek bauxite. All materials charged to the furnaces are in lump form to allow reasonably free passage up the vertical shaft for the combustion gases. Bauxite " fines " are therefore briquetted before addition, but even so, the resistance of the stack of solid materials requires the furnaces to be operated at an unusually high positive pressure.

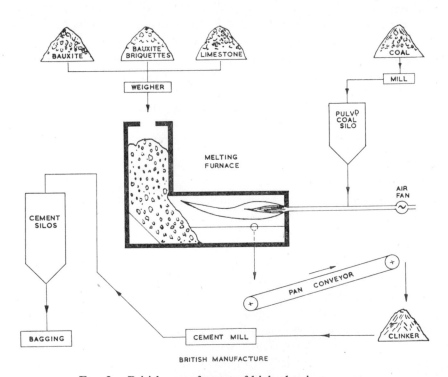

FIG. 2. British manufacture of high-alumina cement.

The molten " clinker " which issues continuously from a tap-hole in the side-wall of the furnace is allowed to cool relatively slowly on a moving pan-conveyor, and the clinker "pigs" which form are crushed to cement fineness without any further addition.

(5) *In France*

Until 1919, high-alumina cement was manufactured exclusively in France by the Lafarge Company at Le Teil, Ardèche, but other firms then started production in electric-arc furnaces at Luchon, Luzières, Argentière la Bessée, and at Bex (Switzerland). Lafarge also used the electric furnace method at Moutiers, but, after further production at Vitry and Bas-Roux, they centred their production of high-alumina cement in 1933 at the Fos-sur-Mer works near the mouth of the Rhone. At the present time " Fondu Lafarge " is made at this works which is now the only site of manufacture in France for ordinary high-alumina cement.

The process and the reverberatory furnaces used are similar to those employed in England, the design of the English furnaces being based on French experience. However, at Fos-sur-Mer, an alternative type of furnace has also been developed which is fired with oil and which is comparable to those used for making glass. Accordingly, with this furnace, the raw materials may be fed in the form of " fines."

(6) *In various other countries*

In the period 1926-28 the manufacture of high-alumina cement was commenced, originally under Lafarge patents, in England, Italy and Spain. The former Italian works at Pula (Pola) is now included in Yugoslavia and " Istrabrand " cement is still manufactured there. In Spain, Cementos Molins make " Electroland " brand of high-alumina cement near Barcelona.

It is believed that high-alumina cement is also made in at least three works in the U.S.S.R. but little information is available about the method of manufacture. It is probable that blast-furnaces are used but reference has been made by Krylov and Pomyan[78] to manu-facture by the V. V. Serov method in a convertor with air-blast and a cooled shell which eliminates the need for a refractory lining.

In the U.S.A., France, and England a specially pure, white high-alumina cement is manufactured in smaller quantities. This type of cement is made from alumina not bauxite and it contains 70 per cent - 80 per cent alumina, which of course is a much higher figure than is found in ordinary high-alumina cements. It is also practically free from silica and iron oxide. This pure cement, which

has a much higher melting-point, is directed chiefly to the refractory market and will therefore be discussed later when dealing with that subject. Less pure forms of low-iron high-alumina cement are also made to some extent in Germany, Italy and Japan.

6. FACTOR DETERMINING THE SUITABILITY OF RAW MATERIALS

(1) *Silica content of raw materials*

Probably the main factor determining the choice of bauxite for H.A.C. manufacture is the silica content, or more accurately, the alumina/silica ratio. In order to yield a high-alumina cement with the ultra-rapid hardening properties customarily required, red bauxite should have a ratio sufficiently high to give a clinker containing not more than about 6 per cent SiO_2.

For the same reason it is often necessary that the silica content of the limestone should not greatly exceed 1 per cent. In manufacturing processes using pulverised coal for melting, it may also be important to use a low-ash fuel which will contribute the minimum of silica to the clinker. Electric furnace melting, or the use of oil or gas fuel, can therefore be valuable in maintaining a satisfactorily low level of silica in the clinker.

(2) *Iron oxide, titania, and magnesia content of raw materials*

The iron oxide content of common bauxite is perhaps less important than the silica content. The iron compounds present in H.A.C. clinker contribute less to the strength development, although they act as useful fluxes in manufacture by fusion and they assist in regulating the setting-time of the cement. A relatively high proportion of such compounds can thus be present in H.A.C. but the alumina/ferric oxide ratio in the bauxite must not be unduly low unless reductive fusion, with removal of metallic iron, is envisaged. Low-iron or white bauxites are more suitable for the manufacture of H.A.C. by clinkering or sintering processes.

Most common bauxites contain about 3 per cent. titania but some (e.g. certain Indian bauxites) contain much higher quantities. Since titanium compounds in the clinker must be regarded as inert, there is clearly an upper limit to the amount of titania which may be tolerated.

Limestone should preferably contain not much more than 1 per cent magnesia since the presence of appreciable quantities in the clinker can adversely affect the strength development. For example Eipeltauer[79] prepared sintered cements of relatively high silica content and found that strength rapidly fell off when they contained between 1 per cent and 3 per cent. magnesia.

26

(3) *Physical properties of the raw materials*

Manufacturing processes which employ electric furnaces, blast-furnaces, cupolas, or the special reverberatory furnaces, require raw materials in lump form. In most of these cases the hardness or strength of the lumps must also be sufficient to prevent crushing under the weight of the charge of solid materials. On the other hand, softer bauxites or limestones can be considered more suitable for sintering or clinkering processes in which the feed is finely ground before going to the furnace.

(4) *Typical analyses of raw materials used for the manufacture of H.A.C.*

Analyses of the raw materials in common use are given in Table I.

TABLE I. TYPICAL ANALYSES OF RAW MATERIALS FOR THE MANUFACTURE OF H.A.C.

Percentage Analysis	Moisture	Loss on Ignition	SiO_2	Al_2O_3	Fe_2O_3	CaO	TiO_2	MgO
French Bauxite	5.0 to 10.0	11.5 to 12.5	3.5 to 6.0	45.0 to 55.0	20.0 to 25.0	0.5 to 3.0	2.5 to 3.5	—
Greek Bauxite	1.0 to 3.0	11.0 to 12.5	2.0 to 3.5	50.0 to 58.0	25.0 to 30.0	0.5 to 3.0	2.5 to 3.5	—
Yugoslav Bauxite	3.0 to 8.0	18.0 to 20.0	2.0 to 3.0	50.0 to 55.0	20.0 to 25.0	0.5 to 3.0	2.5 to 3.5	—
Mixed Bauxites (incl. Surinam Bauxite)	3.5	23.9	3.5	56.1	14.1	—	2.4	—
Limestone (High lime)	0.1 to 2.0	42.0 to 43.5	0.5 to 1.5	0.25 to 1.0	0.20 to 0.60	53.0 to 55.5	—	0.25 to 1.0

LITERATURE REFERENCES

[1] EBELMAN. Ann Chim. (Phys.) 1848, **22**, (3), 227.
[2] H. SAINTE-CLAIRE DEVILLE. Ann. Phys. Chim. 1856, **46**, (3), 196.
[3] WINKLER, J. prakt. Chem. 1856, **67**, 444, 455.
[4] E. FRÉMY. Compte Rendu 1865, **60**, 993.

[5] W. MICHAELIS. Hydraul. Mörtel, Leipzig, 1869, 35.

[6] O. SCHOTT. Doctorate Thesis, Heidelberg, 1906. Rev. Metall. 1908, **5,** (ii), 363.

[7] H. LE CHATELIER. Compte Rendu 1883, 1056.

[8] E. DUFAU. Compte Rendu 1900, **131,** 54.

[9] E. S. SHEPHERD, G. A. RANKIN, & F. E. WRIGHT. Amer. J. Sci. 1909, **28,** (4), 293. G. A. RANKIN & F. E. WRIGHT. Amer. J. Sci. 1915, **39,** (4), 1.

[10] L. ROTH. German Pat. 19800 (1882).

[11] G. J. SNELUS, T. GIBB, J. C. SWANN, H. SMITH & W. WHAMOND. Brit. Pat. 10312 (1888).

[12] J. BIED. Recherches Industrielles sur les Chaux, Ciments, et Mortiers. Dunod, Paris, 1926, pp. 224.

[13] SOC. J. & A. PAVIN DE LAFARGE. French Pats. 320290, 391454 (1908). Brit. Pat. 8193 (1909). Rev. Métall. 1909, **6,** 749.

[14] M. TOUCHÉ. Le Ciment 1926, **31,** (7), 240.

[15] R. FÉRET. Ann. Ponts Chauss. 1922, (4), 2, 5.

[16] M. SÉJOURNÉ. Congres des Chemins de Fer, Rome, 1922.

[17] H. S. SPACKMAN. Proc. Amer. Soc. Test. Mater. 1910, **10,** 315. Engng News Rec. 1922, **88,** (20), 831. Cement Age 1910, **11** (2), 76.

[18] H. S. SPACKMAN ENGINEERING Co. Brit. Pats. 10110, 18345 (1908). U.S. Pats. 1643136, 1643137 (1927).

[19] P. H. BATES. J. Amer. ceram. Soc. 1918, **1,** 679. Proc. Amer. Soc. Test. Mater. 1919, **19,** (2), 440. U.S. Bur. Stand. Tech. Paper 197, 1921.

[20] K. ENDELL. Zement 1919, **8,** 319, 334, 347. See also KILLIG. Prot. Ver. dtsch Portl. Zem. Fabr. 1913, 408.

[21] E. RENGADE. Congr. int. Ass. Test. Mat. Zurich 1931, **1,** 928.

[22] L. G. PATROUILLEAU. Brit. Pat. 210366 (1923).

[23] A. G. FLEMING. Engng J. Can. 1933, 215.

[24] E. C. BLANC. Rock Prod. 1924, 37. Concrete 1928, **32,** (4), 113.

[25] E. REITLER. Tech. Bl. 1935, (25), 452. Cement & Cem. Manuf. 1936, **9,** (9), 190.

[26] W. MATHESIUS. German Pat. 307169 (1922).

[27] E. C. ECKEL. Brit. Pat. 237779, (1924). U.S. Pat. 1591662 (1926). Concrete 1925, **26,** (5), 117.

[28] E. C. ECKEL. Brit. Pat. 268736 (1927).

[29] S. RUZICKA. U.S. Pat. 2184318 (1939).

[30] LONZA-WERKE. French Pat. 726932 (1932). F. KRUPP. German Pat. 93773 (1925). BONTHRON & HAGLUND. French Pat. 643024 (1927). E. L. RINMAN Brit. Pat. 435870 (1934). J. C. SÉAILLES. Brit. Pat. 632164 (1946). L. G. PATROUILLEAU. Brit. Pat. 232898 (1925).

[31] J. C. SÉAILLES. Cement & Lime Manuf. 1947, **20,** (1), 1.

[32] H. BEDERLUNGER. Radex Rdsch. 1955, (2), 394.

[33] C. S. FOX. Brit. Pat. 503225 (1937). Laterite Syndicate. Indian Pat. 26022 (1938). French Pat. 829271 (1937).

[34] H. PEDERSON, H. GINSBERG & W. WRIGGE. Metall u. Erz 1944, **41,** 32.

[35] W. FULDA & H. GINSBERG. Tonerde u. Aluminium, Berlin, 1951, Vol. 1.

36 I. G. FARBEN, A.G.   Brit. Pat. 263124 (1927).

37 W. KYBER.   Brit. Pat. 267518 (1927).   German Pat. 448099 (1925).
    E. URBAIN.   French Pat. 639412 (1927).   E. COLLET.   French Pat.
    639893 (1927).

38 I. G. FARBEN, A.G.   Brit. Pat. 287036 (1928).   French Pats. 626151
    (1927) ; 650412 (1929).

39 K. AKIYAMA.   J. Soc. Chem. Ind. Japan 1934, 37, (4), Supp. 173B.

40 K. AKIYAMA.   Bull. Waseda appl. chem. Soc. 1937, 14, (4), 1, 34.

41 K. AKIYAMA.   Idem 1938, 15, (1), 1, 45 : 15, (4), 15.

42 ALBRIGHT & WILSON LTD. (G. King).   Brit. Pat. 747016 (1956).   U.S.
    Pat. 2859124 (1958).

43 CIMENTS LAFARGE.   Brit. Pat. 222426 (1923).   French Pat. 571328 (1923).

44 J. C. SÉAILLES.   French Pat. 725775 (1932).

45 G. M. J. DUMAS.   Brit. Pat. 257819 (1926).

46 CIMENTS LAFARGE.   Brit. Pat. 222427 (1923).   French Pat. 571329 (1923).

47 CIMENTS LAFARGE & BUREAU D'ORGANISATION ECONOMIQUE.   Brit. Pat.
    225858 (1924).

48 S. KOHUT.   Brit. Pat. 342414 (1929).

49 H. S. SPACKMAN.   U.S. Pats. 1643136, 1643137 (1924).   Brit. Pats.
    222151 (1924), 244756 (1925).   French Pats. 585472 (1924), 607577
    (1926).   B.P.C.M. LTD.   Brit. Pat. 276438 (1926).   G. POLYSIUS.
    Brit. Pat. 286122 (1927).   French Pats. 626583, 625600 (1924),
    634518 (1927).

50 C. E. CORNELIUS.   Brit. Pats. 249554 (1926), 303798 (1929).

51 R. W. P. LEONHARDT.   Zement, 1935, 24, (4), 49.

52 K. BIEHL.   Zement, 1927, 16, 115, 139.

53 A. BRISSAUD.   Chim. et Industr.   1923, 9, 1187.

54 R. DECOLLAND.   French Pats. 573517, 589235 (1924).   Swiss Pat. 108438
    (1924).   Brit. Pat. 211497 (1924).

55 C. PONTOPPIDAN & H. P. BONDE.   Brit. Pat. 235138 (1925).   French Pat.
    592628 (1925).

56 U. B. VOISIN.   Brit. Pat. 270496 (1926).

57 U. B. VOISIN.   Brit. Pats. 243876 (1924), 248282 (1925).   French Pats.
    595090 (1924), 609575, 609825 (1925).   CIMENTS LAFARGE.   French
    Pat. 615113 (1925).   Brit. Pat. 250246 (1926).

58 G. HERTZKA.   Brit. Pat. 265494 (1926).   French Pat. 622535 (1926).

59 N. V. S. KNIBBS.   Brit. Pat. 303639 (1927).

60 U. B. VOISON & E. M. ROCHE.   Brit. Pat. 233698 (1925).   J. C. SÉAILLES.
    Brit. Pat. 640905 (1946).

61 O. ROLFSEN, Brit. Pat. 483770 (1937).   RAMUZ & ROCHE.   French Pat.
    898650 (1944).

62 METALLGESELLSCHAFT, A.G.   Brit. Pats. 375950, 404863 (1933).   Ger-
    man Pat. 616265.   Zement, 1936, 25 (6), 82.   G. S. VALBERG & F. I.
    PIROGOVA.   Tsement, 1954, 20, (5), 10.

63 E. MARTIN.   French Pats. 587343, 597978 (1925).   Brit. Pat. 251618
    (1926).   Monit. Sci., 1926, 16, 97.

64 N. A. TOROPOV & T. M. DIUKO.   Bull. All-Union Res. Inst. of Cements,
    1937, (2), 3.

[65] Seco S. A. Brig., G. Stock. Brit. Pat. 777564 (1953).

[66] —. Pangon. French Pat. 587175 (1923).

[67] H. Loescher. French Pat. 556402 (1922), 561064 (1923).

[68] H. Schoenfelder & H. Ginsberg. Ver. Aluminium-Werke A.G. U.S. Pats. 2939764, 2939765 (1960).

[69] A. W. Schmidt, L. Stuckert & S. G. Feng. Zement, 1942, 31, (33/34), 353.

[70] Anon. Cement & Lime Manuf., 1937, 20, (2), 19.

[71] A. V. Hussey, Chemistry & Industry, 1947, 42, 635, 642.

[72] S. Nagai & T. Harada. J. Jap. ceram. Soc., 1950, 58, (651), 300.

[73] S. Nagai & T. Harada. J. Jap. ceram. Soc., 1953, 61, (686), 379.

[74] Calloy Ltd., G. N. Kirsebon. Brit. Pat. 490421 (1937).

[75] T. W. Parker. Proc. 3rd Internat. Symposium on the Chem. of Cement, London 1952, 485.

[76] M. B. Rane, V. S. Dube & M. K. Ratnam. Curr. Sci., 1936, 4, (11), 814. S. Lupan & R. Bädoi. Revista Chim., Roum., 1957, 8, 88.

[77] Anon., Ferro Concrete 1932, 23, (11), 261. Concr. Constr. Engng, 1956, 530. Cement & Lime Manuf. 1952, 25.

[78] V. F. Krylov & V. K. Pomyan. Tsement 1960, (2), 1. See also L. D. Ershov & O. P. Kashperovskaya. Tsement 1959, 25, (4), 14.

[79] E. Eipeltauer. Berg-u. hüttenm. Mh. 1953, 98, (12), 256 : 1954, 99, (2), 27 : 1955, 100, (3), 117.

CHAPTER 2.—THE CHEMICAL COMPOSITION AND PHYSICAL PROPERTIES OF HIGH-ALUMINA CEMENTS

CONTENTS

CHAPTER TWO

The Chemical Composition and Physical Properties of High-Alumina Cement

In order to simplify the discussion of chemical compounds present in cements, the customary abbreviations will be used for the various oxides e.g. $CaO = C$, $Al_2O_3 = A$, $SiO_2 = S$, $Fe_2O_3 = F$, $FeO = f$, $TiO_2 = T$, $MgO = M$, and $H_2O = H$. Thus CA represents $CaO.Al_2O_3$ or monocalcium aluminate and C_4AF represents $4CaO.Al_2O_3.Fe_2O_3$ or tetracalcium aluminoferrite.

For an understanding of the possible constitution of H.A.C. it is necessary to consider the lime-alumina-silica equilibrium diagram.

1. THE LIME-ALUMINA-SILICA SYSTEM (C-A-S SYSTEM)

This system was first defined in detail by Shepherd and co-workers[1], and is shown, with later amendments[2], in Fig. 3. The areas containing compositions corresponding to Portland cements, ordinary high-alumina cements, and special white high-alumina cements are marked P, HAC, and WHAC respectively.

Naturally, this diagram is strictly applicable only to those high-alumina cements which are free from iron compounds, but it can also give useful information about cements containing a relatively high proportion of iron oxides, provided that suitable empirical assumptions are made in order to " allocate " the iron oxides to the percentages of lime and alumina[3].

Originally the compounds formed by lime and alumina were listed as tricalcium aluminate (C_3A), monocalcium aluminate (CA), and tricalcium penta-aluminate (C_3A_5). It is now believed, as shown in Fig. 3 that C_5A_3 is really $C_{12}A_7$ and that C_3A_5 is CA_2. An additional compounds CA_6 has been discovered[4] since the early work. It can also be seen that the only compounds of silica which are of interest to the composition of H.A.C. are dicalcium silicate (β C_2S) and gehlenite (C_2AS).

B   33

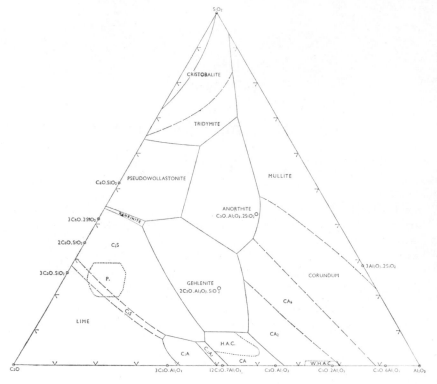

FIG. 3. The Lime-Alumina-Silica System. (After Osborn and Muan. American Ceramic Society and E. Orton Jr. Ceramic Foundation.)

2. THE COMPOUND CONSTITUTION OF COMMERCIAL HIGH-ALUMINA CEMENTS

(1) *The Aluminates and Silicates.*

Of the compounds previously mentioned, tricalcium aluminate (C_3A) does not appear as a normal constituent of H.A.C. although it is, of course, present in Portland cements. Calcium hexa-aluminate (CA_6) also does not exist in H.A.C. but may be formed when concrete made with H.A.C. and corundum aggregate is heated to a high temperature. The presence of calcium dialuminate (CA_2) has been reported[5], particularly in those high-alumina cements which have a relatively high Al_2O_3/CaO ratio, or when complete chemical homogeneity has not been reached during the fusion process. A considerable portion of CA_2 is present in certain of the special white high-alumina cements used for high-duty refractory concretes.

Accordingly, the aluminates and silicates which may be found in commercial H.A.C. are $C_{12}A_7$, CA, CA_2, β C_2S, C_2AS, and these compounds will now be discussed briefly. Excellent descriptions of the structures, optical properties etc. of these compounds have been given elsewhere[6].

(a) $C_{12}A_7$.

This is usually found in small proportions in H.A.C. Other things remaining equal, the amount of $C_{12}A_7$ in the cement rises when the CaO/Al_2O_3 ratio is increased. This compound hydrates very rapidly, and if it is present in any substantial quantity, the cement tends to be quick-setting[7]. There is also evidence that this effect is increased if the cement contains rather more alkali than usual. Consequently $C_{12}A_7$ is not regarded as a very desirable constituent of H.A.C. except in minor amounts.

It was originally described as C_5A_3 by Rankin and Wright but was later thought to be C_3A_2[8] or C_9A_5[9]. Eventually Bussem and Eitel[10] concluded that the correct composition was $C_{12}A_7$ and it would appear that this view has been adequately confirmed[11]. However, references to the old and more familiar C_5A_3 formula must be expected, even in current literature.

(b) CA

Monocalcium aluminate is by far the most important compound present in H.A.C. since it is primarily responsible for the particular cementitious behaviour found in this type of cement. It is slow-setting, particularly if rapidly cooled from the molten condition[12], but it subsequently hardens with great rapidity. It is believed that the maximum hydraulic activity at early ages is obtained by slowly cooling the molten cement composition in order to allow the fullest growth of CA crystals[13]. If molten H.A.C. compositions are very rapidly quenched, so that the product is entirely a glass, the resultant cement will hydrate and harden very slowly, but if kept under water, the ultimate strength appears to be normal.

(c) CA_2

First thought to be C_3A_5, this compound was given the present formula by Tavasci[14] and by Lagerqvist[9].

The pure compound reacts very slowly with water at ordinary temperatures, but hydration and strength development are accelerated by lime-water or solutions of high pH value. Once hydration of pure CA_2 has started, the rate accordingly increases

35

with the growing concentration of hydration products[15]. For the same reason it will hydrate at reasonable speed when mono-calcium aluminate is also present.

(d) β-C_2S

This compound is often detected as small rounded grains or in the eutectic portions of H.A.C. clinkers, particularly in those cements which contain not more than about 5 per cent. SiO_2. In clinkers with higher silica content it is usual to find that gehlenite (C_2AS) becomes increasingly predominant. As in Portland cement, the dicalcium silicate is hydraulic but it hydrates relatively slowly, so that any contribution to concrete strength is not likely to be evident at very early ages.

(e) *C_2AS*

In H.A.C. of higher silica content, gehlenite appears as a regular constituent, often in considerable quantities. It has been shown that pure gehlenite reacts extremely slowly, if at all, with water[16]. However, it seems to have a greater hydraulic activity when present as a glass, and it will hydrate in lime-water. It must be remembered that the gehlenite in H.A.C. is far from pure and it perhaps should be considered more generally as a member of the melilite series, containing magnesia, ferrous oxide and ferric oxide. Activation of gehlenite by modification of the crystal structure has been claimed by Budnikov and Tcherkasova[17] so it is therefore probable that some hydration and strength development will result from its presence in H.A.C. Neverthe-less any hydraulic activity is very slow, and the presence of high proportions of gehlenite in H.A.C. almost inevitably causes a serious reduction in the rapid-hardening properties so characteristic of the normal cement. It is for this reason that the silica content of H.A.C. compositions is kept low.

(2) *The Compounds containing Iron.*

Most high-alumina cements contain a relatively high proportion of iron oxides (up to 18 per cent.) and it is therefore clear that iron compounds must constitute an important part of the composition of these cements. Starting with iron-free cement, Akiyama[18] studied the effect of added ferric oxide and found that up to a concentration of 10 per cent. Fe_2O_3, the hydraulic strength of the cement was actually increased. He suggested that iron-free cements were intrinsically quick-setting and, although this would now be challenged, it is cer-

36

tainly found in practice that cements of high iron content can give strength properties at least the equal of others.

Both ferric and ferrous oxides are normally present in H.A.C. and the exact state of combination of these oxides is still far from clear. Ferric oxide forms calcium ferrite (CF) and dicalcium ferrite (C_2F) and each may be present in H.A.C.[19]. It has been shown that a solid-solution series between C_2F and the hypothetical C_2A extends as far as the composition C_6A_2F[20], and much of the ferric oxide in H.A.C. is combined as calcium alumino-ferrites with compositions between C_6AF_2 and C_6A_2F. Although its existence as a distinct compound has been doubted, C_4AF is a member of this series and a special position can justifiably be assigned to it. The products of hydration at 20°C. of some of these solid-solutions has been described by Mori and Tagai[21]. On the basis of microreflectivity work with polished clinker specimens, Parker and Ryder[22] concluded that, in cements containing a high proportion of CA, the composition of the alumino-ferrites lies between C_4AF and C_6AF_2. Both CA and $C_{12}A_7$ also take ferric oxide into solid solution[23].

The combinations in which ferrous oxide occurs are rather more obscure but it can exist free[24] as Wüstite in certain high-alumina cements and, in association with Fe_2O_3, it often provides the major component of the glass portion of the clinker. The presence of Fe_3O_4 is indicated by the magnetic nature of the glass. Ferrous oxide also enters into the composition of the so-called " fibrous constituent " which is present, to some extent, in many high-alumina cements and which may be produced occasionally in large quantities under certain conditions of manufacture and composition. This compound crystallises readily in long needles, laths, or fibres which exhibit strong pleochroism, and for a long time it was confused with the " unstable C_5A_3 " described by Rankin. There now seems no doubt that this latter compound exists since it may be readily prepared on the hot-wire microscope but Sundius in 1938 gave evidence that the fibrous constituent in H.A.C. contained oxides other than lime and alumina. In 1952 Parker described a compound, believed to be C_6A_4MS, which appeared isomorphous with the fibrous constituent and he therefore suggested that possibly the formula of the latter was C_6A_4fS. However, there were still reasons to doubt the exact nature of this compound and further work, again based on magnesia analogues, suggests that the " fibres " in H.A.C. may be a solid solution of C_7A_5f and C_2AS[25].

Parker and Ryder indicated that the magnesia compound " C_6A_4MS " was slow-setting but possessed quite good hydraulic properties particularly at later ages. Nevertheless, when H.A.C.

37

contains a high proportion of fibrous constituent there is usually a marked reduction in strength development and this compound cannot be regarded as a desirable major component in the cement.

(3) *The Minor Constituents.*

Bauxites used for H.A.C. manufacture contain a small proportion of titania, and consequently 1 - 3 per cent. TiO_2 is always found in the cement. It normally appears as calcium titanate (Perovskite) but it has also been suggested[26] that, when the cement is rich in iron compounds, some of the titania may be combined as a calcium ferro-titanate. Kühl and Omar[27] found that up to 4.5 per cent. TiO_2 had a beneficial effect on cement properties.

Magnesia (MgO) is a constant component of H.A.C. but the proportion is usually below 1 per cent. It may replace ferrous iron in the composition of the pleochroic fibrous constituent, but unless the quantity of magnesia is abnormally high there is little evidence of spinel formation.

The alkali content of ordinary H.A.C. is much lower than that of Portland cement. It consists of both sodium and potassium oxides, but in total they do not often exceed 0.3 per cent. (the corresponding figure for Portland cement is 0.5 - 1.3 per cent.). Typical figures for British and French H.A.C. are 0.05 per cent. K_2O and 0.05 - 0.15 per cent. Na_2O, but special white-alumina cements, originating from alumina instead of bauxite, may have higher alkali contents. Much of the sodium oxide is probably combined as $2\ Na_2O.3CaO.5Al_2O_3$ and it has also been suggested[24] that the compound $3Na_2O.Al_2O_3.3SiO_2$ may enter gehlenite. Certainly not all the alkali is immediately soluble when the cement is gauged with water.

Total sulphur expressed as sulphuric anhydride (SO_3) is usually not greatly in excess of 0.15 per cent. in the case of those high-alumina cements to which no addition of gypsum is made during grinding. H.A.C. made by the blast-furnace method is relatively high in sulphur and may contain 0.5 - 1.0 per cent. sulphur as sulphide, together with an appreciable proportion of SO_3. Such cements often produce a rather unpleasant smell on gauging with water and additives have been patented[28] which are claimed to minimise this effect. H.A.C. made by this method customarily contains up to 1 per cent. of free metallic iron, because of incomplete separation of the metal formed by re-ductive fusion of the raw materials. Cements made by other manu-facturing processes also contain traces of metallic iron, but this is derived from the grinding media, and the quantity is very slight.

The only other minor constituents of H.A.C. consist of traces of compounds of manganese, phosphorus, etc. derived from the raw materials, additives, and the fuel used in manufacture.

(4) *Summary of Constituents.*

It will be seen that the compounds which it is possible to find in commercial high-alumina clinkers are as follows :—$C_{12}A_7$, CA, CA_2, βC_2S, CT, C_2AS or melilites, the fibrous constituent, and FeO as a final crystallization phase. Fe_2O_3 occurs in ferrites of variable analysis but normally having compositions between C_4AF and C_6AF_2. The composition of these ferrites may lie between C_4AF and C_6A_2F in the abnormal cements which contain little CA and a high proportion of the fibrous constituent. Considerable progress has been made towards determining the precise nature of the latter compound but it still cannot be said that information is complete. Solid-solution is frequent, particularly with some of the minor constituents, and free lime is never found.

Not all the above-mentioned compounds will appear in the same clinker and in 1952 Parker[7] gave his view of the phase assemblages considered possible. In practice it is found that the various commercial clinkers can be broadly classified into two predominant types, i.e. $CA-C_2S$ and $CA-C_2AS$. Cements which give the highest early strengths (6 hours onwards) tend to belong to the first type and usually contain less than 5 per cent. SiO_2. Cements made with a higher proportion of silica tend to fall into the second group, and are usually slower in hardening. The properties of the two predominant types can of course be modified according to the amount (if any) of $C_{12}A_7$ or fibrous constituent.

3. COMPARATIVE ANALYSES OF HIGH-ALUMINA CEMENTS

A survey of the analyses of early high-alumina cements (Table I) particularly those made by different methods or from different bauxites, apparently reveals a surprising variability in their chemical nature. This is true even of present-day cements (Table II), and it is not feasible to describe this type of cement within the relatively close chemical limits possible for Portland cement.

Many attempts have been made to define the oxide proportions or ratios in order to produce a quality of cement which is considered satisfactory. For example, Berl and Löblein[13] proposed the following ranges :—SiO_2 0-12 per cent., Al_2O_3, 45-70 per cent., CaO 28-47 per cent. Biehl[29] suggested SiO_2 5-10 per cent., Al_2O_3 35-55 per

TABLE I. ANALYSES OF EARLY HIGH-ALUMINA CEMENTS (up to 1930). (See Reference No. 39)

Type of Manufacture	SiO_2 %	Al_2O_3 %	CaO %	Fe_2O_3 %	FeO %	TiO_2 %
Water-jacket furnace	8.0	39.3	43.9	1.9	4.4	1.8
	6.7	43.3	39.6	1.8	6.4	2.0
	7.1	44.9	35.1	1.7	8.8	1.8
Electric furnace	5.3	41.2	36.8	5.1	9.8	1.5
	4.0	40.6	37.2	6.1	9.2	2.0
	7.0	39.2	35.7	2.9	13.5	1.5
	5.2	39.2	39.3	6.3	7.8	1.7
Sintering	4.0	42.9	35.3	13.6	Trace	2.0
	4.1	41.0	37.6	12.2	Trace	2.0
	5.7	42.1	38.3	9.7	Trace	2.0
	6.0	41.7	38.1	9.8	Trace	1.5

cent., CaO 35-45 per cent., Fe_2O_3 5-15 per cent., TiO_2 1-3 per cent., and Richter[30] concluded that SiO_2 and Fe_2O_3 should not exceed 6 per cent. and 15 per cent. respectively. Endell[31], Agde and Klemm[32], together with many later workers, attempted to locate on the Rankin diagram the area of compositions most likely to give H.A.C. of the highest strength. Possibly the most useful and accurate indication (at least for cements containing little iron compounds) came from Solacolu[33] who sited the most favourable cement compositions on the line from CA to the invariant point of C_2AS, CA and C_2S. When relatively high proportions of iron compounds are present there is still no very exact way of calculating the compound constitution of H.A.C. from its chemical analysis, although methods have been described[7][34] which sometimes give reasonable success. However, much more information about the possible state of combination of the iron compounds is required if the constitution of H.A.C. is to be calculated with an accuracy equivalent to that possible for Portland cement. Manufacturers of H.A.C. proportion their raw materials and control the composition of the product by methods which are based partly on theory and partly on experience.

In practice it is found that the high-alumina cements containing less than 5 per cent. silica may contain about 60 per cent. CA, about 10 per cent. C_2S and a small amount of C_2AS. Cements of higher silica content may contain 15-25 per cent. C_2AS and any C_2S is usually present in the ternary eutectic CA-C_2AS-C_2S. The glass content of the cements varies considerably. In general, the German, American

TABLE II. TYPICAL ANALYSES OF MODERN HIGH-ALUMINA CEMENTS. (See Reference No. 40).

Country of Origin	Type of Manufacture	Colour	SiO_2 %	Al_2O_3 %	CaO %	Fe_2O_3 %	FeO %	TiO_2 %	MgO %	S %	SO_3 %	Metallic Iron %
Germany	Blast-furnace. Reductive Fusion	Very light Grey	5-8	48-51	39-42	0.1	<1.0	1.5	1.0	1.0	0.5	1.0
U.S.A.	Rotary Kiln. Fusion	Light Grey	8-9	40-41	36-37	5-6	5-6	<2.0	1.0	0.2	0.2	Trace
Czechoslovakia (Hungary)	Brick Kiln furnace. Sintering	Light Brown	6-8	40-45	37-42	12-14	Trace	<2.0	1.0	Trace	0.5	Trace
Yugoslavia	Reverberatory furnace. Fusion	Grey	6-8	38-40	36-39	8-10	4-7	<2.0	1.0	Trace	0.1	Trace
Spain	Reverberatory furnace. Fusion	Grey	4-5	36-38	39-42	10-12	4-5	<2.0	1.0	Trace	0.1	Trace
England	Reverberatory furnace. Fusion	Grey	4-5	38-40	36-39	8-10	5-7	<2.0	1.0	Trace	0.1	Trace
France	Reverberatory furnace. Fusion	Grey	3.5-4.5	38-40	36-39	9-11	4-6	<2.0	1.0	Trace	0.1	Trace

and Spanish cements have the highest proportion of glass (up to 20 per cent.) while the Yugoslavian, French and British cements usually contain 5-10 per cent.

The proportions of the various compounds present is determined by X-ray analysis or by microscopic examination of cement or thin sections of clinker, or more usually by examining polished specimens after surface etching with selective reagents[35]. Among the solutions used for revealing CA are boiling water, hot dilute aqueous sodium hydroxide, sodium carbonate, or potassium bromate. Cold aqueous solutions of sodium fluoride colour this compound. Alcoholic nitric acid may be employed for C_2S and it is coloured by hydrofluoric acid vapour. C_2AS is coloured by aqueous sodium fluoride and a boiling aqueous mixture of sodium phosphate and ammonium chloride can be used to render this compound more visible. A boiling solution of borax is helpful in the case of $C_{12}A_7$.

A chemical method in which C_2S is first dissolved by dilute boric acid, and the aluminates in the residue are determined by solution in hot sodium carbonate solution, has also been proposed[36].

4. Physical Properties of High-Alumina Cements

(1) Colour.

A comparison, by photometer, of the colour characteristics of H.A.C., Portland cement, and white or coloured Portland cements was carried out by Dawson and co-workers[37], but the colour of the different high-alumina cements available on the World market varies widely according to the manufacturing process, or to the type of bauxite used as raw material.

The chief factors determining the colour of the cement powder are the amount and state of oxidation of the iron compounds present. Low-iron cements are very light in colour, similar to many Portland cements, but those containing a considerable quantity of iron oxides are very dark coloured when much of the iron is present as ferrous compounds. On the other hand, when nearly all the iron occurs as ferric compounds a brown or rust colour is produced. There is no relation between the colour of H.A.C. and its potential strength properties.

German H.A.C. contains only minor quantities of iron oxides (practically all in the ferrous condition) and therefore has a very light pearly-grey colour. Hohl[26] states that it sometimes has a greenish-yellow tint which he attributes to the small calcium titanate content.

American H.A.C. contains a higher proportion of iron oxides (divided almost equally between ferrous and ferric) and the colour is light-grey. Yugoslav, Spanish, French and British cements have still higher iron contents and in all cases it is normal to find more ferric than ferrous compounds. The usual colour is a very dark grey but sometimes this tends towards a lighter and browner tint when the ferric/ferrous ratio is high. Czechoslovak and Hungarian cements, in contrast to all the foregoing, are not melted but sintered, and substantially all the iron compounds are in the ferric form. This imparts a yellow-brown colour.

(2) *Specific Gravity.*

The specific gravity of the various high-alumina cements varies from just under 3.00 to about 3.25. The iron compounds present have a specific gravity of about 3.70 to 4.00 but the average for the aluminates and silicates is under 3.00, and the specific gravity of any H.A.C. is therefore closely related to the iron oxide content. Calcium titanate also has a high specific gravity (4.05) but the amount in H.A.C. is small and relatively constant and so does not greatly affect the comparison of specific gravities.

German H.A.C. has a specific gravity of 2.98 - 3.00. American cement, with an intermediate iron content, has a value of about 3.10 and Yugoslav, Spanish, French or British cements are usually within the range 3.20 - 3.25. For comparison, the specific gravities of Portland cements lie between 2.95 and 3.20.

(3) *Loose Bulk Density.*

When H.A.C. is loosely filled into a measure, without vibration or tamping, the weight of a cubic foot is 60 - 85 lbs. The cements of higher iron content tend to give the higher unit weights. In practice, however, it is customary to consider that the loose bulk density of H.A.C. is 90 lbs. per cu. ft., i.e. the value which is usually taken for Portland cement when proportioning by volume. When H.A.C. is consolidated into the measure the bulk density may be as high as 118 lbs. per cu. ft.

(4) *Fineness.*

H.A.C. clinker of the fused type is very compact and hard (it scratches glass easily) and requires much more power than Portland clinker to reduce it to cement fineness. As will be seen below, there

43

is some difference in the fineness of various high-alumina cements but, in general, they are not ground as finely as the modern Portland cements.

Sieve tests carried out over several years on all common types of H.A.C. showed the following typical ranges in residues :—

Sieve.	% Retained.
Aperture 0.10 mm.	1 - 5
B.S. No. 170 (0.089 mm.)	2 - 6
European 4900/cm² (0.09 mm.)	2 - 6
A.S.T.M. No. 200 (0.074 mm.)	5 - 10
A.S.T.M. No. 325 (0.044 mm.)	14 - 20

The specific surface area of the cements, determined by the air-permeability method (Lea-Nurse or Blaine) is 2500-4000 sq. cm./g., the most frequent values being about 3000 sq. cm./g. Similar tests with the Wagner turbidimeter give a range of 1250-1900 sq. cm./g. (most common value about 1350 sq. cm./g.).

Roughly 50 per cent. by weight of H.A.C. consists of particles with a diameter less than 30 microns but this fraction in the various cements may vary between 45 per cent. and 60 per cent.

With any individual H.A.C. the effect of finer grinding is to accelerate the set and to increase the mortar and concrete strengths obtained at early ages (particularly at times within the first 24 hours after casting). The effect on ultimate strength is not marked.

(5) *Soundness.*

The soundness of H.A.C. may be confirmed by the Le Chatelier test, by hot or cold pat tests, or by the autoclave expansion test. These tests, designed to indicate the presence in Portland cement of excessive sulphate, or " dead-burned " lime and magnesia, are probably of doubtful utility for H.A.C. since expansion is always absent or negligible. Certainly the occurrence of crystalline calcium or magnesium oxides in any of the fused cements should be impossible. Eipeltauer[38] has reported that experimental sintered cements containing as much as 8 per cent. magnesia showed no expansion even in the autoclave test, and of course the proportion of this oxide in commercial clinkers is maintained at a much lower level, for other reasons. Some types of H.A.C. contain small amounts of added gypsum, and in such cases a soundness test might be considered valid for checking accidental over-dosage. However, analysis would probably be quicker and more informative.

According to British Standard Specification " High Alumina Cement " (B.S. 915), the maximum expansion in the Le Chatelier test is limited to 2 mm. (against 10 mm. for Portland cement). The usual value found is 0 -1 mm. Expansion in the A.S.T.M. autoclave test (C. 150) should rarely exceed 0.05 per cent., (the limit for Portland cement being 0.5 per cent.).

(6) *Storage Properties.*

All hydraulic cements will slowly absorb water and carbon dioxide from air of high humidity and, if left long enough without suitable protection, or if stored under unsatisfactory conditions they become lumpy and " air-set." However, comparative tests show that the storage properties of H.A.C. are generally superior to those of ordinary Portland cements and much superior to those of high-early-strength Portland cements.

Monthly tests on bags of H.A.C. in a cement store indicated little evidence of loss of strength for at least 10 months. In another test[26] a sack of H.A.C. was left for three years in unfavourable storage conditions which rendered ordinary cements useless after a few weeks. At the end of the storage period the H.A.C. contained 14 per cent. by weight of lumps and most of these were still soft enough to be crushed in the fingers. The soft and hard lumps were re-ground separately to cement fineness and it was found that the cement which had passed the sieve gave, at 24 hours, 97 per cent. of its original strength, the re-ground soft lumps gave 97.9 per cent. and the re-ground hard lumps gave 94 per cent.

At the stage when hard lumps begin to appear in stored II.A.C. it may be found that the setting-time of the cement is slowed and the strength at 24 hours is somewhat reduced, but even in this condition the strength after 2-3 days is usually normal. Nevertheless, every precaution should still be taken to store H.A.C. in a dry place, preferably raised from the floor by battens. H.A.C. may be made hydrophobic in the same way as Portland cement, by grinding with a small proportion of oleic acid, stearic acid, etc.

The determination of " loss on ignition " is complicated by the fact that many high-alumina cements contain considerable proportions of ferrous iron compounds. In such cases a net gain on ignition is usually found and a full analysis is necessary before this method can reveal the weight loss due to water and carbon dioxide which may have been present.

LITERATURE REFERENCES

1 E. S. SHEPHERD, G. A. RANKIN & F. E. WRIGHT. Amer. J. Sci. 1909, **28** (4), 293. G. A. RANKIN & F. E. WRIGHT. Amer. J. Sci. 1915, **39**, (4), 1.

[2] N. E. FILONENKO & I. V. LAVROV. Zh. Prikl. Khim. U.R.S.S. 1950, 23, 1040, 1105.

[3] T. D. ROBSON. Proc. 3rd International Symp. on Chemistry of Cement, London 1952. Discussion 521.

[4] N. E. FILONENKO & I. V. LAVROV. C.R. Acad. Sci. U.R.S.S. 1949, 64, (4), 529.

[5] S. SOLACOLU. Zement 1933, 22, (3), 33. C. GORIA & A. BURDESE. Ric. Sci. 1951, 21, 1613.

[6] F. M. LEA " The Chemistry of Cement and Concrete " E. Arnold, London, 1956. R. BOGUE " The Chemistry of Portland Cement " Reinhold, N.Y. 1955. A. BURDESE. Ric. Sci. 1954, 24, (9), 1862. L. G. WISNYI. Dissert. Abstr. 1955, 15, 2498. M. W. DOUGILL. Nature 1957, 180, (4580), 292. H. G. MIDGLEY. Mag. Concr. Res. 1957, 9, (25), 17. W. BÜSSEM. Symp. on Chemistry of Cements, Stockholm 1938, 141. A. HELLER. Thesis Univ. of London 1951.

[7] T. W. PARKER. Proc. 3rd International Symp. on Chemistry of Cement, London 1952, 485.

[8] K. KOYANAGI. Zement 1931, 20, 72.

[9] K. LAGERQVIST, S. WALLMARK & A. WESTGREN. Z. anorg. Chem. 1937, 234, 1.

[10] W. BÜSSEM & A. EITEL. Z. Krystallogr. 1936, 95, 175. Amer. Min. 1937, 24 (156).

[11] T. THORVALDSON & N. S. GRACE. Canad. J. Res. 1929, 1, 36. T. THORVALDSON & W. G. SCHNEIDER. Idem 1941, 19, 109.

[12] C. BLANCHET. Rev. Matér. Constr. 1927, 219, 397.

[13] E. BERL & F. LÖBLEIN. Zement, 1926, 15, (36), 642 : (37), 672 : (38), 696 : (39), 715 : (40), 741 : (41), 759 : (42), 783 : I. Z. VOLCHEK. C. R. Acad. Sci. U.R.S.S. 1953, 90, (3), 437.

[14] B. TRAVASCI, Chim. e Industr. 1935, 17, 461. Tonindustr. Ztg. 1937, 61, 717, 729.

[15] F. G. BUTTLER. Thesis, Univ. of Aberdeen. 1958.

[16] T. YAMAUCHI, R. KONDO & T. TABUCHI. Semento Gijutsu Nenpo 1949, 3, 69. S. NAGAI & R. NAITO. J. Soc. Chem. Ind. Japan Suppl. 1930, 33, (4), 133B, 164B, 316B : 1931, 34, (5), 159B.

[17] P. P. BUDNIKOV & A. F. TCHERKASOVA. C.R. Acad. Sci. U.R.S.S. 1955, 102, (4), 793.

[18] K. AKIYAMA. J. Soc. Chem. Ind. Japan Suppl. 1934, 37, (7), 382B.

[19] S. SOLACOLU. Dissertation. Berlin 1932.

[20] M. A. SWAYZE. Amer. J. Sci. 1946, 244, 1, 65. T. F. NEWKIRK. J. Res. nat. Bur. Stand. 1958, 61, (4), 233. R.P. 2900.

[21] J. MORI & H. TAGAI. Semento Gijutsu Nenpo. 1956, 10, 23.

[22] T. W. PARKER & J. F. RYDER. Proc. 3rd International Symp. on Chemistry of Cement. London 1952, 485.

[23] H. F. MCMURDIE. J. Res. Nat. Bur. Stand. 1937, 18, 475. R.P. 987.

[24] N. SUNDIUS. Symp. on Chemistry of Cements, Stockholm 1938, 395.

[25] R. W. NURSE & J. H. WELCH. Private communication 1960.

[26] O. HÖHL. " Aluminous Cement " 1936. Hochofenwerk Lübeck A.G.

[27] H. KÜHL & M. OMAR. Zement 1925, 14, 37.

[28] A. R. ZEHRLAUT. Zeco Research Corp. U.S. Pat. 2919997 (1960). Soc. d'Etudes Chimiques pour l'Industrie. Brit. Pat. 298637 (1928).

[29] K. BIEHL. Zement 1927, **16**, 115.

[30] H. RICHTER. Zement 1932, **21**, 445.

[31] K. ENDELL. Prot. Ver. dtsch Portl. ZemFabr. 1919, 30.

[32] G. AGDE & R. KLEMM. Z. angew. Chem. 1926, **39**, 175.

[33] S SOLACOLU. Zement 1933, **22**, (3), 33 : (9), 114 : (15), 191 : (19), 250 : (23), 311.

[34] P. TERRIER. Rev. Matér. Constr. C. 1959, (528), 199.

[35] B. TRAVASCI. Symp. on Chemistry of Cements, Stockholm 1938. Discussion p. 422. Cemento armato 1935, **32** (10), 107 : (11), 114.

[36] S. ROJAK, E. J. NAGEROVA & G. G. KORNIENKO. Cement (U.R.S.S.) 1959, **25**, (2), 22.

[37] L. R. DAWSON, R. V. ANDES & T. D. TIEMANN. Industr. Engng. Chem. (Industr.) 1941, **33**, (1), 95.

[38] E. EIPELTAUER. Berg-u. hüttenm. Mh. 1953, **98**, 256 ; 1954, **99**, 27 ; 1955, **100**, 117.

[39] E. RENGADE. " Les Liants Hydrauliques." L. J. ROTHGERY. Bull. Mich. Engng. Exp. Sta. 1926, No. 4. J. L. MINER. Concrete (N.Y.). 1927, **30**, (4), 35. L. S. WELLS & E. T. CARLSON. J. Res. Nat. Bur. Stand. 1956, **57**, (6), 335. R.P. 2723. A. G. FLEMING. Engng. J. Can. 1933, 215. A. V. HUSSEY. J. Soc. Chem. Ind. 1935, **54**, (12), 262. H. J. DAVEY. Instn. Engng. Inspection, London, 1923. C. BLANCHET, Rev. Matér. Constr. 1928, **220**, 8 : **221**, 44. P. H. BATES. Int. Assoc. Test. Mat. Zurich, 1930, 210. D. B. BUTLER. J. Soc. Engrs., 1932, **23**, (4), 206. D. A. SOULE. Concrete 1925, **26**, (2), 71.

[40] A. TRAVERS. Ciment, 1934, **39**, (12), 327 : 1935, **40**, (1), 11. R. SALMONI. Cemento armato, 1934, **31**, (9), 93. J. C. SEAILLES. 15th Congr. Industr. Chem. Brussels, 1935. Comptes-Rendus, **1**, 600. K. AKIYAMA, J. Soc. Chem. Ind. Japan. Suppl. 1937, **40**, (4), 139B. B. TAVASCI, Chim. e Industr. 1938, 469. Tonindustr. Ztg. 1938, **62**, (72/73), 808. T. D. ROBSON, Architect. Science Rev. (Sydney) 1959, **2**, (1), 49. E. HRIBERNIK. Ost. Bau-zeitschr. 1959, (50), 8. L. D. ERSHOV & KASPEROVSKAJA. Cement (U.R.S.S.). 1959, **25**, (4), 14.

CHAPTER 3.—THE HYDRATION OF HIGH-ALUMINA CEMENTS

CONTENTS

49

The Hydration of High-Alumina Cements

1. THE LIME-ALUMINA-WATER SYSTEM. (C-A-H SYSTEM).

In 1951, Steinour reviewed work on this system[1] and investigations after that time have been critically examined by Lhopitallier and by Jones[2]. The equilibrium curves for the various hydrates have now been studied at temperatures ranging from 1°C. to 250°C.[3] but it can be said briefly that the only stable hydrates, at ordinary temperatures, are fully-crystallised Gibbsite or $Al_2O_3.3H_2O$, calcium hydroxide, and the cubic tricalcium aluminate hydrate $3CaO.Al_2O_3.6H_2O$ (C_3AH_6). During hydration, metastable calcium aluminate hydrates appear readily and, once formed, they are extremely persistent except at higher temperatures. The alumina gel hydrate, which is formed initially, tends to " age " slowly towards a well-crystallised condition, with simultaneous reduction of its surface area.

For a long time it was thought that the main hydrate produced by H.A.C. was $2CaO.Al_2O_3.8H_2O$ (C_2AH_8) but it is now believed that, although this hydrate does appear in certain circumstances, the most important product of normal hydration is $CaO.Al_2O_3.10H_2O$ (CAH_{10}). The existence of this compound was first suggested by Assarsson in 1935[4] and its solubility curve at low temperatures has been given by Carlson and by Buttler. Percival and Taylor were able to locate its curve at 21°C. and Wells and Carlson indicated that it was still the main hydrate at 24°C. when working with cement pastes (i.e. at a relatively low water-cement ratio). In the opinion of Jones there is a transition temperature at 22°C. above which C_2AH_8 is stable towards CAH_{10}, but it must be remembered that in practical mixes the water-cement ratio is much lower than in most phase-relation studies and this can have a distinct influence on the hydrates found at certain temperatures. The formation of C_2AH_8 is favoured, not only by temperatures above 20°C., but also by very high dilutions[5].

The more basic hydrate $4CaO.Al_2O_3.13H_2O$ (C_4AH_{13}) may also be found in hydrated H.A.C. compositions and two forms have been described which originate from C_4AH_{19} by partial loss of water due to drying.[6] Farran noted that this hydrate was formed by reaction between the surface of a calcite aggregate and H.A.C.[7]

CAH_{10}, C_2AH_8 and C_4AH_{13} (or C_4AH_{19}) are all metastable " hexagonal " hydrates, and they tend to transform into the cubic hydrate C_3AH_6, which is the only stable aluminate hydrate existing over a wide range of temperatures. Exceptionally however, the latter may possibly be unstable to C_4AH_{13} at 1°C. (Carlson), and at 5°C. Buttler found that, in the absence of well-crystallised alumina hydrate, CAH_{10} can also be stable towards C_3AH_6.

Another " hexagonal " hydrate $3CaO.Al_2O_3.10\text{-}12H_2O$ has been postulated[8] and Brocard[9] claimed its preparation by direct hydration of C_3A. Govoroff also believed it could be obtained in an almost pure condition by heating mixed " hexagonal " hydrates at 80°C.[10] Nevertheless, many other workers have discounted the existence of this tricalcium hydrate[11] and at various times its alleged characteristics have been thought to be due to the presence of mixtures of C_2AH_8 and C_4AH_{13}, C_4AH_{19} and a solid solution of hydrates, C_2AH_8 enriched with lime or even possibly C_2AH_5 — a product of partial dehydration of C_2AH_8. In 1956 Schippa and Turriziani[12] failed to obtain any hydrate corresponding to C_3AH_{12} but pointed out that the X-ray data ascribed to this hydrate were very similar to those given by a carbonato-aluminate hydrate, $C_3A.CaCO_3.aq.$, which had been reported much earlier[13]. Confirmation of this view has since been obtained by several investigators[14]. Lhopitallier found no evidence of a " hexagonal " tricalcium compound if carbon dioxide was rigorously excluded, and there is little doubt that some of the hydration work carried out on the C-A-H system has been vitiated because of failure to prevent carbonation. The balance of opinion now is that no C_3AH_{12} exists but that, in ordinary circumstances, carbonato-aluminate hydrate will occur in any H.A.C. which has been hydrated in contact with air.

Alumina hydrate gel is almost always found as a result of the hydration of H.A.C. and its final form, in presence of water, is Gibbsite (AH_3). However, Buttler considers that there is a tendency for Bayerite (AH) to form in presence of carbon dioxide, and it is probable that the other monohydrate, Boehmite, occurs also during the initial stages of hydration.

Differential thermal analysis work on various hydrates or on hydrated high-alumina cements has been reported by many workers[15] and the infra-red absorption spectrum for C_3AH_6 has been given by Majumdar and Roy[16].

2. Summary of the Hydrates formed from H.A.C.

The hydrates which may be produced by hydration of H.A.C. include the metastable " hexagonal " compounds CAH_{10}, C_2AH_8, C_4AH_{13} (or C_4AH_{19}) and the stable cubic hydrate C_3AH_6. In presence of water, the rate of change of the metastable hydrates to the stable cubic hydrate is still very slow below 25°C. but it is accelerated by higher temperatures or high pH values[17]. When H.A.C. is hydrated in air, in the ordinary way, the presence of carbonato-aluminate $(C_3A.CaCO_3.11\ H_2O)$[18] must be expected and this compound can have an important influence on the characteristics of concrete and mortar surfaces.

C_2S will hydrate in the same way as it does in Portland cement but any calcium hydroxide simultaneously liberated will, in this case, react with alumina gel, and residual " free lime " is not found in hardened H.A.C. It has been indicated earlier that C_2AS in H.A.C. may possibly be slowly hydraulic, especially when the compound occurs as a glass, and Zur Strassen[19] has described a C_2AS hydrate, with possibly eight molecules of water.

According to Brocard, iron hydroxide gel, arising by hydration of the iron compounds, may coat the calcium aluminate crystals and thus modify the rate of their hydration, and the system $CaO-Fe_2O_3-H_2O$ has been considered in more detail by Jones[2]. The presence of a cubic hydrate, C_3FH_6, which is isomorphous with C_3AH_6, was first reported by Eiger, but it is now believed that this compound must contain silicon or aluminium atoms in order to achieve stability, and a series of solid solutions between C_3FH_6 and C_3AH_6 are readily formed.[20]

3. The Setting-Time of High-Alumina Cements

As with Portland cements, the setting-times of H.A.C. are determined by needle penetration tests on neat cement pats, under controlled conditions of temperature and humidity. The results obtained on the same cement, using the Standard Specification methods of different countries, can vary appreciably, and in the U.S.A. the Gillmore test tends to give slower setting-times than the Vicat test on the same specimen. In the British Standard Specification (B.S.915) the water-cement ratio is fixed at 0.22 and the normal consistency, common to most other Specifications, is not employed.

American H.A.C. contains a retarder and, with an average initial setting-time of about 8 hours, it normally sets more slowly than the other high-alumina cements. British H.A.C. by specification must have an initial set between 2 hours and 6 hours after gauging, and the average is about 4 hours. French H.A.C. is perhaps slightly faster and most of the other cements have setting-times of the same order. The usual interval between initial and final set is about 30-45 minutes, but a considerably longer gap (sometimes several hours) is apparent with German H.A.C.

On the average, the setting-times of high-alumina cements are found to be slower than those of most Portland cements, yet the opinion is still widely held that H.A.C. is fast-setting. This feeling is obviously not based on the behaviour of the cement in standard setting-time tests, but usually on observation of mortar and concrete under site conditions. Some confusion between the setting and the hardening properties is also evident.

Very high mix-temperatures or contamination with lime, plaster, Portland cement etc. can, of course, cause genuine quick-setting, but experience shows that many examples of apparently premature set are due to the fact that H.A.C. mortars or concretes do not hold water as well as the corresponding Portland cement mixes, and in some circumstance this greater tendency to " bleed " can produce an apparent stiffening or surface consolidation before the initial set is approached. This phenomenon is particularly marked if the concrete is placed on a dry absorbent surface or when it is transported by barrow etc. before final placing. In the latter case it is only necessary to turn the mix over once or twice with a spade in order to regain the original consistency, but in the case of brick-jointing, for example, the addition of a plasticiser to the mortar is desirable.

There is however a great difference in behaviour between Portland cement and H.A.C. once the initial set has been reached. The development of strength in the Portland cement mix is still very slow after this stage, while the H.A.C. mix develops strength so rapidly that it becomes rigid shortly after setting. There is therefore some justification for saying that the practical " working time " of Portland cement is longer than that of H.A.C., even when the setting-time of the latter cement is slower.

4. EFFECT OF TEMPERATURE ON SETTING-TIME

The effect of lower temperatures, e.g. 1°C.-18°C. has been investigated by many workers in the past with rather contradictory results. Flajard[21] found that early American H.A.C. had a minimum setting-time at 10°C. i.e. the set was delayed not only below but also above this temperature. Other investigators have sometimes confirmed and sometimes contested this finding. Thomas and Davey[22] pointed out, with some relevance, that the consistency of cement paste before setting is affected by its temperature and may be reduced above and below a certain temperature. This may have some effect on the penetration of a needle and therefore, possibly, on the setting-time.

In the case of most of the modern high-alumina cements there is certainly evidence that, in the temperature range between 1°C. and 18°C., the setting-time is somewhat faster at about 10°C. than it is above or below that temperature. This is confirmed to some extent by observations on the rate of heat evolution, which is at a maximum around 10°C.

The setting-time of Portland cement is nearly always accelerated by rising temperature, although it has been noted[23] that above 30°C. this effect may cease or even be reversed. However, in the range 18°C.-30°C., the setting time of most high-alumina cements becomes progressively slower as the temperature rises and only above 30°C. does the rate of set accelerate again. This phenomenon appears to have been first described by Periani[24] who claimed that the effect of temperatures between 20°C. and 30°C. on the setting-time of H.A.C. was generally opposite to the effect on Portland cement. He found that H.A.C. which set in 2 hours 50 minutes at 20°C. required 5 hours to set at 30°C. Haegermann[25] and others found that the development of initial strength of H.A.C. mixes was retarded just below 30°C., and the work of Séailles[26] suggested that the speed of hydration of H.A.C. passes through a minimum value around the same temperature.

The delaying effect on setting-time of rising temperatures (up to 30°C.) has since been confirmed with many high-alumina cements, and also the fact that, over 30°C., the setting-time rapidly becomes faster again[27]. Nevertheless this behaviour is not invariable. In general, high-alumina cements which have a normal slow set (say 4 hours) at 18°C. tend to follow the above pattern but there is evidence that if unduly fast-setting cements are produced they may behave like Portland cement (i.e. the set becomes faster as the temperature rises). Even in such cases the final setting-time is usually delayed at about 30°C.

Methods other than penetrometer tests have been employed for investigating the hydration and setting of H.A.C. but none has been adopted as a standard test for setting-time. Salmoni[28] compared H.A.C. from Italy, France, Hungary and Germany and found that discontinuities in the pH curves of the pastes occurred at completion of set. Changes in the electrical conductivity or resistivity of H.A.C. cement pastes on setting and hardening have also been investigated

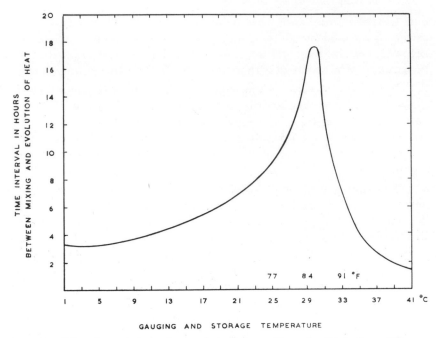

Fig. 4. Time between gauging and evolution of heat for H.A.C. at different temperatures.

by several workers[29] and Calleja noted that the behaviour of H.A.C. under his test conditions was substantially different from that of Portland cement.

The interval of time between gauging H.A.C. and the first sign of heat evolution has given reasonable agreement with the initial setting-time as determined by the Vicat needle. In Fig. 4 the time intervals are given for tests carried out at temperatures between 1°C. and 41°C. It will be seen that this curve supports the view that there is a minimum setting-time between 1°C. and 18°C. and a maximum length of setting-time at about 30°C.

5. HEAT OF HYDRATION

When Portland cement is mixed with water there is usually an immediate but small evolution of heat,[30] followed later by the major release of heat due to the process of normal hydration. High-alumina cements (with the possible exception of those containing gypsum) do not show this initial evolution of heat. The delay before heat is liberated from H.A.C. depends on its origin and setting-time, but in

56

most cases it is about 2-4 hours. Once started, the liberation of heat proceeds very rapidly, so that the maximum temperature rise in H.A.C. concrete is frequently recorded 8-10 hours after placing, and a high proportion of the total heat of hydration is evolved within the first 24 hours.

It is generally agreed that the *total* amount of heat liberated per unit weight of cement (amounting to 100-120 calories/g.) is substantially the same for H.A.C., ordinary Portland cement, and rapid-hardening Portland cement. The basic difference, in this respect, between H.A.C. and the other types is the much more rapid production of heat by H.A.C., once hydration is under way. The approximate amounts of heat liberated at various ages are shown in Table I from data given by Orchard,[31] and it can be seen that, according to this, H.A.C. requires only 1 day, rapid-hardening Portland cement requires 3-7 days, and ordinary Portland cement requires 28-90 days in order to produce the same amount of heat.

TABLE I. COMPARISON OF THE HEATS OF HYDRATION (AT VARIOUS AGES) OF DIFFERENT CEMENTS

Cement	Heat of hydration at stated age, in calories per gram.				
	1 day	3 days	7 days	28 days	90 days
H.A.C.	77-93	78-94	78-95		
Rapid-hardening Portland	35-71	45-89	51-91	70-100	
Ordinary Portland	23-46	42-65	47-75	66-94	80-105

Average values for the maximum rate of heat evolution have been given as follows :—9 calories/g. per hour for H.A.C., 3-5 calories/g. per hour for rapid-hardening Portland cement, and 1.5-3.5 calories/g. for ordinary Portland cement[32]. With low-silica H.A.C. this maximum rate of heat production occurs about 6 hours after placing and thus creates the maximum concrete temperature at 8-10 hours. Again under practical conditions of placing, the temperature rise of an average H.A.C. concrete may be roughly 50 per cent. and 100 per cent. higher than that of similar mixes containing rapid-hardening Portland cement and ordinary Portland cement, respectively[33].

When the curing was adiabatic, so that no dissipation of heat was possible, Davey and Fox found that the temperature rise of

1 : 2 : 4 H.A.C. concrete (W/C = 0.60) was approximately 35°C. at
10 hours, 42°C. at 24 hours, and 45°C. at 3 days[34]. Their comparison of the adiabatic temperature rises of the three types of cement
is given in Fig. 5, and the effect of cement content on the adiabatic
temperature rise of H.A.C. concrete is shown in Table II. When the
H.A.C. concrete was placed at different temperatures, from 15.5°C.

TABLE II. EFFECT OF H.A.C. CONCRETE MIX ON ADIABATIC TEMPERATURE
RISE AT 3 DAYS. (British H.A.C.)

Cement/Aggregate (by weight)	1 : 5¼	1 : 6	1 : 9	1 : 12
Adiabatic temperature rise at 3 days	50°C.	45°C.	33°C.	23°C.
Total heat released during 3 days (calories per g. of cement)	76	77	82	76

to 37°C., there was little effect on the total heat evolved, but the rate
at which the heat was liberated in the early stages was not increased
with rise in placing temperature—as is the case with Portland cement.
A delaying effect on the evolution of heat was noticed as the placing
temperature was raised to 28°C., but the reaction was accelerated above
this temperature. This behaviour closely parallels that of the setting-
time which has already been discussed.

The adiabatic temperature rise at any age can be calculated
from the specific heat of the concrete and the total heat liberated
during that time. The specific heat of a hydrated Portland cement
rises considerably with increasing water-cement ratio and with temperature[35], but a value of 0.20 calorie/g. is often used. There is
reason to believe that the specific heat of hydrated H.A.C. is slightly
higher than that of a similar Portland cement paste, but the specific
heat of H.A.C. concrete is usually taken to be the same as that of
Portland cement concrete, i.e. 0.22-0.25 calorie/g.

6. HYDRATION AND HARDENING AT VERY LOW TEMPERATURES.

The very rapid evolution of heat of hydration, which accompanies
an equally rapid development of strength, makes H.A.C. pre-eminent
for concreting in cold weather, or in industrial situations involving
refrigeration. For such purposes this type of cement is unequalled
and it is greatly superior to rapid-hardening Portland cement even
when the latter is accelerated with calcium chloride. Concreting has

TABLE III. THE EFFECT OF HARDENING AT LOWER TEMPERATURES ON THE FLEXURAL AND COMPRESSIVE STRENGTHS OF CONCRETES MADE WITH DIFFERENT CEMENTS.

7 x 7 x 28 cm. prisms.   Cement Content 590 lbs./cu. yd.   Water/Cement = 0.50.

Temp.	Cement	Flexural Strength (lbs/sq. in.)				Compressive Strength (lbs/sq. in.)			
		6 hr.	16 hr.	1 day	2 days	6 hr.	16 hr.	1 day	2 days
18°C	Portland	0	55	152	237	0	440	1010	2330
	Rapid-Hardening Portland	0	55	189	261	0	510	1720	3250
	H.A.C. (French)	333	442	428	455	3410	5510	5670	6400
12°C	Portland	0	0	55	248	0	171	412	1860
	Rapid-Hardening Portland	0	0	55	248	0	199	483	1950
	H.A.C. (French)	261	406	428	478	3000	5100	5570	6070
6°C	Portland	0	0	0	91	0	57	156	850
	Rapid-Hardening Portland	0	0	0	104	0	85	185	938
	H.A.C. (French)	226	419	442	455	2360	5050	5270	5470
0°C	Portland	0	0	0	31	0	0	28	228
	Rapid-Hardening Portland	0	0	0	31	0	0	43	342
	H.A.C. (French)	67	419	442	469	767	4630	4950	5560

been carried out satisfactorily, and with relative ease, in the coldest temperatures found in the Arctic or Antarctica, or at higher altitudes in mountainous regions. Except in severe conditions, no special measures are usually required beyond ensuring that the mix temperature is reasonably far above 0°C. before the concrete is placed[36].

The ability to concrete with H.A.C. at very low temperatures probably depends on two factors. The first concerns the effect which temperatures between ambient and freezing have on the hydration activity of the cement. This factor can be investigated by casting thin units of concrete within this temperature range, because in these circumstances, the temperature rise in the hardening concrete (whether H.A.C. or Portland) is negligible, and therefore the strengths obtained are dependent almost entirely on the intrinsic rate at which the cement can hydrate at the lower temperatures.

The rate of hydration and hardening of Portland cement concretes is progressively reduced when the temperature falls towards 0°C. This effect is still more obvious with slag or pozzolanic cements and the rate of hardening below 10°C. is extremely slow. On the other hand, the difference between the rates of hardening of H.A.C. at 0°C. and 18°C. is very much less than for any other type of hydraulic cement. This is clearly shown in Table III which is selected from data obtained by Rengade[37] using French H.A.C. The test prisms had a section of only 2.75 x 2.75 in. and, in addition, the aggregates, cement and mixing water were previously cooled to near the temperatures indicated. It can therefore be taken that the concrete temperature remained at, or very close to, the temperature of the storage chamber, and that temperature-rise due to hydration could not play an important part in causing the difference in strengths found between H.A.C. and the Portland cements. Similar results on thin-section specimens have been given by Davey and others[38]. One must conclude that the "negative temperature coefficient of hardening " is much less appreciable in the case of H.A.C.

The first factor has therefore been the ability of H.A.C. to hydrate with reasonable speed at concrete temperatures which seriously delay or almost stop the hydration of Portland cement. Indeed Graf[39] reported that H.A.C. mortar (1 : 6) which has been stored for the first 7 or 14 days at 0°C. gave higher ultimate strength (at 6 months) than the same mortar cured all the time at 15°C.-20°C.

The second factor to be discussed is the more rapid evolution of heat from H.A.C. when hydration starts, because when the concrete section is sufficiently thick to prevent rapid dissipation of heat, a considerable temperature-rise will be produced. We have seen that even thin-section H.A.C. concretes or mortars will harden at temperatures just above their freezing-point, without the benefit of a temperature-rise, but if such sections are cast, without protection, at temperatures well below 0°C., they will quickly freeze throughout and little or no hydration will occur in this condition whatever the type of cement. The formation of ice-crystals in the unset concrete will also prevent the subsequent achievement of full strength, if the concrete is later allowed to mature at normal temperature. Bernhardt[40] who froze concretes quickly at −6°C. and at −18°C. immediately after placing, found that after a subsequent period of normal curing, this gave a reduction in strength of 35 per cent. for Portland cement concretes and 30 per cent. for H.A.C. concretes. Graf also concluded that the damage caused by freezing before the time of initial set was less with H.A.C. than with Portland cement, but it is still clear that every effort should be made to prevent complete freezing before hydration commences.

The position is therefore different if a considerable thickness of H.A.C. concrete is placed, since it takes much longer for the mix-temperature to drop below its freezing point even when ground and air temperatures are far below 0°C., and time is given for hydration to commence in the body of the concrete, thus producing a temperature-rise whose magnitude is dependent on the dimensions of the concrete, on its cement content, and on any formwork or other protection which may be present. A normal H.A.C. concrete mix (1 : 6 by weight) which is laid as a slab in the open air (without water-curing), produces temperature-rises at the centre of 6 in., 8 in., 10 in. and 12 in. thicknesses of about 10°C., 13°C., 16°C. and 18°C. respectively. Units cast in wooden forms, or made with richer mixes, give higher temperature-rises and the adiabatic temperature-rise attainable in the centre of thicker masses is shown in Fig. 5. It can therefore be seen that H.A.C. concrete can protect itself against very low temperatures while hardening, even when the section appears relatively thin by the usual standards of concreting.

The main principles in cold weather concreting with H.A.C. may be summarised as follows :—

(1) The temperature of the mix before placing need only be sufficiently high to allow it to remain at least above 0°C. for about 2-3 hours, i.e. until the hydration and heat production is under way. Obviously, when the ground and air temperatures are not much below 0°C., and when a reasonable thickness of concrete is being placed, satisfactory hardening will take place even when the initial mix-temperature is relatively low (e.g. 5°C.). Under extremely

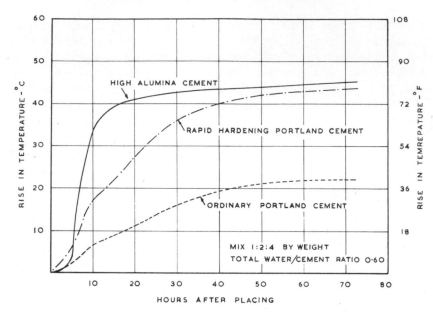

FIG. 5.   Adiabatic temperature rises of neat cements (after Davey and Fox).

severe conditions and with the thinner sections of concrete it may be necessary to ensure an initial mix-temperature of up to 20°C. and to cover the exposed surfaces, at least during the initial stages.   It should never be necessary to have a higher mix-temperature and in any case it may be detrimental to heat the mix above 27°C.   The cement content of the concrete can be increased if very low temperatures are encountered, particularly when thinner sections of concrete have to be placed.

(2) The mix should not be placed if it contains frozen aggregate and ice.   If hot water is used to thaw frozen aggregate or to raise the mix-temperature, it should be added first to the aggregates in the mixer so that, when the cement follows, mixing takes place at a temperature within the limit set in (1).

(3) Longer mixing reduces the interval of time between placing and the start of heat evolution.   It is therefore helpful in preventing freezing of the mix before it starts to set.

(4) Calcium chloride, which is frequently employed with Portland cement in cold conditions, should never be added to H.A.C.

Many practical examples of successful concreting with H.A.C. concrete at remarkably low temperature have been published, e.g. the casting of a rich concrete mix directly onto rock with a temperature of −15°C. when the prevailing air temperature was −30°C. This was in order to provide instrument bases for the Mission Polaire Française in Adelie Land[41]. In Polar regions, H.A.C. concrete is the material of choice for the foundations of weather-masts, huts and tents and for setting triangulation points. In Canadian winters it has been employed for the foundations of iron-ore loading hoppers, etc. and Chapin and Lemire[42] carried out practical comparative tests between H.A.C. concrete and rapid-hardening Portland cement concrete (accelerated with calcium chloride) where the ambient temperature could fall as low as 46°C. below freezing point. Their problem was the construction, at such temperatures, of concrete foundation pads for electricity transmission-lines. The test pads were 3 ft. square by 8 in. thick, cast with a 1 : 2.3 : 3 mix on bedrock, in the open or under canvas. Some were left uncovered and others covered with an insulating blanket, and the development of strength was followed non-destructively with a Soniscope. The pads made with H.A.C. dropped in temperature for about 1 hour but thereafter sufficient heat was generated to overcome losses to the rock and surrounding air, so that forms could be struck and strength determinations started at $3\frac{1}{2}$-$5\frac{1}{2}$ hours after placing. All these pads gave strengths of about 4000 lbs./sq. in. at 16 hours rising later to 6500 lbs./sq. in. In the same conditions, the development of strength of the accelerated rapid-hardening Portland cement was so reduced that forms could not be stripped until after 20 hours, and no Soniscope readings could be obtained on the pads placed in the open air. Accordingly, the use of H.A.C. for this application was approved and it is stated that the resultant lower labour requirements reduced over-all costs by up to 50 per cent. Another interesting use in Canada was the reconstruction of a wharf at Levis, Quebec, where it was necessary for the concrete to gain strength rapidly at low temperatures so that it could resist tidal action[43].

Many accounts have been published of varied construction work with H.A.C. in the less severe conditions of an European winter, or at high altitudes in mountainous regions[44], and the results have confirmed the unique ability of this type of cement to allow concreting to proceed at the lowest temperatures without the necessity for very special precautions.

The effect of freezing and thawing cycles upon the hardened H.A.C. concrete or mortar has also been investigated[45] and it has been claimed that the freeze-thaw resistance is higher than that of similar Portland cement specimens. Lund compared the effect of 25 cycles of freezing and thawing on mortars made with the two types of cement but the Portland cement mortars were initially cured for

29 days (1 day in air, 28 days in water) while the H.A.C. mortars were submitted to the same test cycles after only 2 days (1 day air, 1 day water). The results indicated that the proportional loss in strength due to freezing and thawing was less with H.A.C. than with Portland cement especially in the case of a 1 : 3 mix. As with Portland cement, the resistance to freezing and thawing can be further increased by air-entrainment.

The more rapid hardening of H.A.C. at low temperatures therefore has the additional advantage that the resistance not only to freezing, but also to freezing and thawing, is acquired at an early age. Graf froze H.A.C. specimens for 10 days at − 10°C. when they were only 4 hours old. After subsequent curing at 15°C. until they were 28 days old, he found that the ratio of strength to that of similar specimens cured all the time at 15°C., was 0.86-0.98. Specimens frozen in the same way when 24 hours old gave a strength ratio of 0.98-1.06 and Bernhardt showed that freezing at 8 hours old had also no effect on the strength of H.A.C. gravel concrete. He further concluded that freezing at 4 hours old caused less damage to H.A.C. concrete than to Portland cement concrete.

Although the relatively high rise in temperature produced in appreciable thicknesses of H.A.C. concrete is so useful when concreting at low temperatures, it is a considerable disadvantage when working at high ambient temperatures. Even at ordinary temperatures it is necessary to impose limitations on the depth of lift which may be placed in one operation, in order to prevent " over-heating " of the H.A.C.

The hardening of H.A.C. concretes and mortars at high ambient temperatures (above 25°C.) and the possible effect on physical properties will be considered in detail in Chapter IV after an account has been given of the normal concrete characteristics.

LITERATURE REFERENCES

[1] H. H. STEINOUR. Bull. Portl. Cem. Ass. 1951, No. 34. Cement & Lime Manuf. 1952, 13.

[2] P. LHOPITALLIER. 4th Int. Symp. Chem. of Cements, Washington, 1960. F. E. JONES. Idem.

[3] G. E. BESSEY. Symp. Chem. of Cements, Stockholm, 1938, 178. L. S. WELLS, W. F. CLARKE & H. F. McMURDIE. J. Res. Nat. Bur. Stand. 1943, 30, (5), 367. R.P. 1539. R. B. PEPPLER & L. S. WELLS. Idem 1954, 52, (2), 75. RP. 2476. E. T. CARLSON. Idem 1957, 59, (2), 107. RP. 2777. J. D'ANS & H. EICK. Zement-Kalk-Gips 1953, 6, 197. F. G. BUTTLER. Thesis, Univ. of Aberdeen 1958. F. G. BUTTLER & H. F. W. TAYLOR. J. Chem. Soc. 1958, (433), 2103. J. APPL. Chem. London 1959, 9, (11), 616. A. PERCIVAL & H. F. W. TAYLOR. J. Chem. Soc. 1959, (526), 2629.

[4] G. Assarsson. Z. anorg. Chem. 1935, **222**, (4), 321 Sverig. geol. C. 1936, (399), Arsbok 30.

[5] H. Lafuma. Lecture, Brussels, 1952. J. Farran. 1956, C.E.R.I.L.H. Tech. Publ. 78. L. S. Wells & E. T. Carlson. J. Res. Nat. Bur. Stand. 1956, **57**, 6. RP. 2723.

[6] F. E. Jones & M. H. Roberts. " The System CaO-Al$_2$O$_3$-H$_2$O at 25°C." In publication. M. H. Roberts. J. Appl. Chem. 1957, **7**, (10), 543.

[7] J. Farran. Rev. Mater. Constr. C. 1956, 490/491, 155 : 492, 191.

[8] C. W. Bunn & W. F. Clarke. J. Soc. Chem. Ind. 1938, **57**, 399. T. Thorvaldson, N. Grace & V. A. Vigfusson. Canad. J. Res. 1929, **1**, (3), 201. G. Assarsson. Z. Anorg. Chem. 1931, (200), 385. J. Lefol. C.R. Lab. Bâtim 1933, **197**, 919. A. Travers & J. Sehnoutka. Ann. Chim. (Phys) 1930, **13**, 253. K. Koyanagi. 3rd Int. Symp. Chem. of Cement, London 1952. P. Longuet. Rev. Matér. Constr. C. 1952, 443/444, 227.

[9] J. Brocard. Ann. Inst. Bâtim. 1948, (12), Tech. Publ. No. 3.

[10] A. Govoroff. Rev. Matér. Constr. C. 1956, 490/491, 181.

[11] Peppler & Wells. Ref. No. 3. Wells, Clarke & McMurdie. Ref. No. 3. Lea. Ref. No. 17. R. H. Bogue. " The Chemistry of Portland Cement 1955.

[12] G. Schippa & R. Turriziani. Ric. Sci. 1957, **27**, (12), 3654. G. Schippa. Ric. Sci. 1958, **28**, (10), 2120.

[13] F. E. Jones, Symp. Chem. of Cements, Stockholm 1938. G. E. Bessey. Ref. No. 3. J. Farran. Ref. No. 7.

[14] M. H. Roberts. J. Appl. Chem. 1957, **10**, 543. F. G. Buttler. Thesis, 1958. Percival & Taylor. Private comm. 1958.

[15] M. Rey. Silicates industr. 1957, **22**, (10), 533. S. J. Schneider. J. Amer. Ceram. Soc. 1959, **42**, (4), 184. R. Turriziani & G. Schippa. Industr. Ital. del Cemento. 1956, **26**, (12), 295. R. A. Heindl & Z. A. Post. J. Amer. Ceram. Soc. 1954, **37**, (5), 206. S. Nagai & T. Harada. J. Jap. Ceram. Soc. (Ass.) 1952, **60**, 386 : 1955, **63**, 189.

[16] A. Majumdar & R. Roy. J. Amer. Ceram. Soc. 1956, **39**, (12), 434.

[17] R. Sersale. Ric. Sci. 1957, **27**, 777. F. M. Lea. " The Chemistry of Cement and Concrete," 1956.

[18] E. T. Carlson & H. A. Berman. J. Res. Nat. Bur. Stand. 1960, 64A, (4), 331.

[19] H. Zur Strassen. Zement-Kalk-Gips. 1958, **11**, 137.

[20] J. Pelouze. Ann. Chim. (Phys.) 1851, **33**, 5. H. Hoffmann. Zement. 1936, **25**, 113, 130, 675, 693, 711. G. Malquori & V. Cirilli. Ric. Sci. 1940, **18**, 316.

[21] E. J. Flajard. Ciment 1925, **30**, (6), 329.

[22] W. N. Thomas & N. Davey. D.S.I.R. Building Res. Spec. Report No. 13. 1929.

[23] F. M. Lea. Ref. No. 17.

[24] P. Periani. Ann. Lavori pubbl. 1925 (Oct.). Quoted by J. Bolomey. Bull. tech. Suisse rom. 1926, **52**, (10), 120. Chim. et Industr. 1926, **15**, (5), 795.

[25] G. Haegermann. Tonindustr. Ztg. 1931, **55**, (103), 1430.

C

26 J. C. Séailles. 14th Congrès de Chimie Indust. Paris 1934, 56.

27 J. Brocard. Ann. Inst. Bâtim. 1948, **4**, (54). Tech. Publ. No. 11, 1949. E. Couillaud. C.R. Acad. Sci. Paris, 1952, **234**, 51.

28 R. Salmoni. Cemento armato 1934, **31**, (9), 93. R. Salmoni & H. E. Schwiete. Zement 1933, **22**, (38), 523.

29 H. Kühl, F. Thilo & A. C. Yu. Zement 1934, **23**, (18), 249. S. Michelson. Zement 1933, **22**, 457. S. Koide, M. Kawano & K. Kaiden. Asahi Glass Co. Res. Lab. Rep. 1957, **7**, (1), 44. J. Calleja. J. Amer. Concr. Inst. 1953, **25**, (3), 249.

30 J. C. de Langavent. Rev. Matér. Constr. 1938, (348), 161 : (349), 181 : (350), 208.

31 D. F. Orchard. " Concrete Technology," Vol. I. Contractors Record Ltd., London 1958.

32 A. V. Hussey. J. Soc. Chem. Ind., London. 1936, **55**, (52), 1037. A. V. Hussey & T. D. Robson. Symp. on Matér. Constr. Birmingham 1950. Soc. Chem. Ind. Canad. Chem. Process. 1955, **39**, (6), 54. Orchard. Ref. No. 32.

33 R. Barta. Chim. et Industr. 1936, **35**, (4), 712.

34 N. Davey & E. N. Fox. D.S.I.R. Building Research Tech. Paper No. 15, 1933.

35 R. W. Carlson & L. R. Forbrich. Industr. Engng. Chem. (Anal.) 1938, **10**, 382.

36 Anon. Contract. Rec. 1961, March 8. Min. of Works Advisory Leaflet No. 7. " Concreting in Cold Weather." London.

37 E. Rengade. Int. Ass. Test Mat. London Congress, 1937, 245.

38 N. Davey. Int. Ass. Test Mat. London Congress, 1937, 342. J. Bolomey. Bull. tech. Suisse rom. 1927, **53**, (24), 285. G. Baire. Rev. Matér. Constr. 1923, **166**, 165. W. N. Thomas. Engineering, Lond. 1924, **117**, 464. Bijls & F. Campus. Génie civ. 1937, 110, 229. Anon. Schweitz. Bauztg. 1923, **81**, (23). Anon. Tonindustr. Ztg. 1941, **65**, (37), 358. A. F. Rosher Lund. Zement 1927, **16**, (34), 747.

39 O. Graf. Dtsch. Ausschluss fur Eisenbeton, **57**. Ernst & Sohn, Berlin 1927.

40 C. J. Bernhardt. J. Amer. Concr. Inst. 1956, **27**, (5), 573. Tekn. Ugebl. 1955, **101**, (31), 681. Bauplan. u. Bautech. 1955, **9**, (1), 13.

41 Anon. Bâtim. 1952, (1), 8.

42 C. L. Chapin & W. A. R. Lemire. Ont. Hydro Res. News 1956, **8**, (2), 9, 24.

43 Anon. Rds. Engng Constr. 1951, Sept. 75, 98.

44 Anon. Genie civ. 1935, **107**, (23), 542. Concr. constr. Engng 1936, **31**, (1), 69. Anon. Cement & Lime Manuf. 1940, **13**, (5), 85. M. T. J. Guéritte. Struct. Engr. 1924, **2**, (5), 202. S. Gottlieb. Cement & Lime Manuf. 1940, **13**, (4), 55. H. Eisenbeck. Zement 1926, **15**, (6), 111. Anon. Zement-Kalk-Gips 1957, **8**, 49. S. Kaufman, W. Krol, E. Lebda & T. Wojtan. Materyaly Budowlane (Warsaw). 1957, (11), 321.

45 Anon. Génie civ. Ref. 44. L. J. Rothgery. Bull. Mich. Engng. Exp. Sta. 1926. No. 4 Pt. I. A. F. Rosher Lund. Tekn. Ugebl. 1925, **72**, 324, 335, 350.

CHAPTER 4.—THE PHYSICAL PROPERTIES OF H.A.C. MORTARS AND CONCRETES

CONTENTS

CHAPTER FOUR

The Physical Properties of H.A.C. Mortars and Concretes

The hardening of H.A.C. at very low temperatures has been discussed in Chapter III and the account of the normal physical properties of H.A.C. mortars and concretes, which follows, applies broadly to mixes which are made and cured at temperatures in the range 10°-25°C. (50°-77°F.). Laboratory tests are carried out within a closely-defined temperature range which, in nearly all cases, lies somewhere between 16°C. (61°F.) and 21°C. (70°F.) and the strength data quoted are those obtained at such intermediate temperatures. H.A.C. concretes made at temperatures towards 10°C. may show reduced early strengths but the final strength is as great or greater than at the above laboratory temperatures. Concretes made at temperatures towards 25°C. may give rather lower initial strengths and the difference usually persists at later ages. The effect of still higher temperatures is considered in Section 15.

Although all high-alumina cements are intrinsically rapid-hardening, there are considerable variations in the initial rate of hardening shown by cements from different origins. Previous indication has been given that the cements with silica contents above 5-6 per cent do not harden, within the first day, as rapidly as the lower-silica cements. The latter give mortars or concretes which are often required to give very useful structural strengths at 6-7 hours after placing, even although the setting-times of the cements are slow. Thus, a cement in this category may have an initial setting-time of 3-5 hours and yet give a 1:6 concrete cube strength of 1000-4000 lbs./sq. in. at 6 hours even when the mix consistency is suitable for placing by hand (e.g. W/C = 0.50-0.60). Mixes with a water-content suitable for placing by vibration give higher strengths at the same age. The difference in the strength properties of the lower-silica and the higher-silica cements is naturally most marked at ages of 6-12 hours, and may still be very evident for 1-7 days after casting, but subsequently it progressively diminishes.

Since the lower-silica cements are perhaps used to a greater extent than the higher-silica cements for structural purposes, most of the strength data which follows has been based on the former type. Consequently, the values for certain mechanical properties at early ages may not necessarily apply to all high-alumina cements, but the difference is mainly in the time at which the figures are attained.

1. VISCOSITY OF THE H.A.C. PASTE

The " viscosity " or " flow " of the cement paste is one important factor in determining the lowest water-cement ratio at which a particular concrete mix has sufficient " workability " to be placed. In this respect H.A.C. has very different characteristics from Portland or rapid-hardening Portland cements. Pastes made from most high-alumina cements appear " wetter " than Portland cement pastes of the same water-content, and the difference is greatly accentuated at the lower water-cement ratios. This difference is even more marked when a comparison is made with rapid-hardening Portland cement. The cause may be the distinctive nature of the individual particles of H.A.C. (which are formed by crushing a very hard non-porous clinker), the lower pH value of the H.A.C. paste, or the rather coarser grinding of the H.A.C.

Newman[1] compared the rate of flow, from a simple orifice, of pastes made with the three types of cement and his results are shown in Fig. 6. The same type of comparison was made by Brown[2] between H.A.C. and rapid-hardening Portland cement in connection with an investigation of grouts for steel bars used in prestressed concrete. He measured the paste viscosities by time of flow through a long orifice, and also by noting the areas of the " spread " of pastes on a glass plate, after immediate removal of a cylindrical restraining mould. The fluidity of the H.A.C. pastes was shown by both methods

TABLE I.   COMPARISON OF THE VISCOSITIES OF PASTES OF NEAT H.A.C. AND PLASTICISED RAPID-HARDENING PORTLAND CEMENT

Cement	H.A.C.			Rapid-hardening Portland Cement + 1% of Plasticiser				
W/C	0.36	0.38	0.40	0.43	0.46	0.49	0.52	0.54
Viscosity (Time in secs. to flow through orifice)	100	50	40	370	175	110	60	45

to be much greater than that of similar rapid-hardening Portland cement pastes, with or without the addition of a plasticiser to the latter. It will be seen from Table I that H.A.C. paste with a water-cement ratio of 0.36 had a lower " viscosity " than a plasticised rapid-hardening Portland cement paste with a water-cement ratio of 0.49.

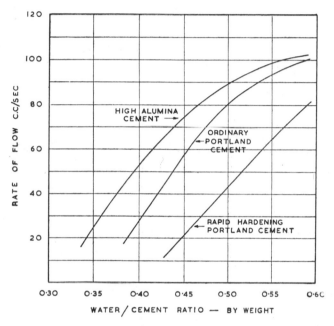

FIG. 6. Fluidities of neat cement pastes.

The result of this intrinsic difference between H.A.C. and Portland cement, or rapid-hardening Portland cement, is that less water is required in an H.A.C. concrete or mortar mix in order to obtain an equivalent placing consistency. For example, with the same aggregates and mix proportions, it may be found that an H.A.C. concrete mix gives the same " wetness " at W/C = 0.55 as a Portland cement concrete mix does at W/C = 0.60. Since this effect is still greater at lower water-cement ratios, it follows that the consistency required for placing H.A.C. mixes by vibration is obtained with a much lower water-cement ratio than is the case for similar Portland cement mixes (particularly rapid-hardening Portland cement mixes). The addition to H.A.C. mixes of more water than is really required to provide the necessary consistency for placing greatly increases the possibility of segregation and also the tendency towards " bleeding."

71

2. THE DEVELOPMENT OF STRENGTH

(1) *Compressive Strength*

The difference in the early strength development of similar concrete mixes made with H.A.C. (low-silica type), ordinary Portland cement, rapid-hardening Portland cement, and accelerated rapid-hardening Portland cement is shown in Fig. 7, and Fig. 8[16] continues the comparison to later ages. The values shown are the compressive strengths of cube specimens and must accordingly be reduced in order to apply to cylindrical specimens. The strength of 12 in. x 6 in. diameter H.A.C. concrete cylinders is about $\frac{2}{3}$-$\frac{3}{4}$ the strength of the corresponding 6 in. cubes.

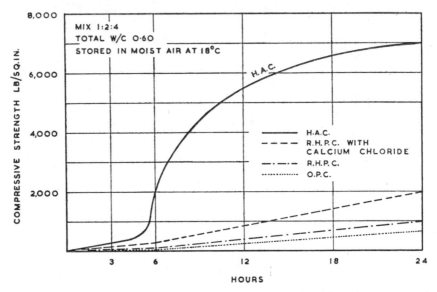

FIG. 7. Early strength development of concretes made with various cements. (Cube specimens).

Other work on the strength development of various high-alumina cements, and strength development comparisons between H.A.C. and various cements have been reported frequently[3]. Formulae relating the hydration and hardening of H.A.C. to the water-cement ratio etc. have also been published[4] and the behaviour of reinforced H.A.C. concrete was studied by several early workers, including Magnel, Leflot and de Tedesco[5].

H.A.C. is used when high concrete strengths are required at early ages and it will be seen that these can be achieved without the use of

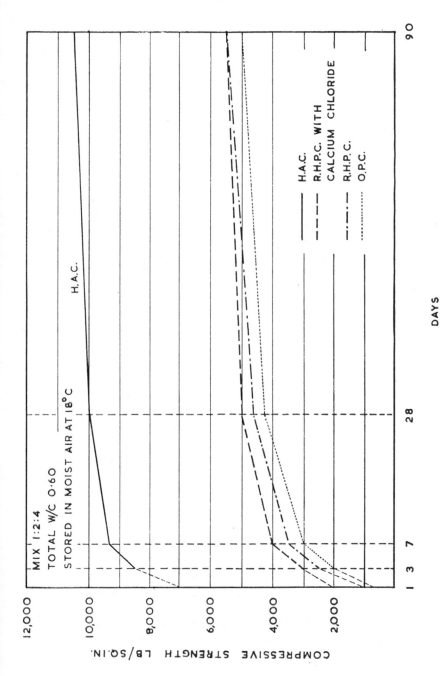

FIG. 8. Later strength development of concretes made with various cements. (Cube specimens)

special or rich mixes[6].   Using the Freyssinet technique of vibration and the application of heavy pressure, it has been claimed that strengths of 14,000 lbs./sq. in. are obtainable within 2-3 hours after the time of initial set[7], but, for all normal purposes, the highest strengths likely to be required can be attained at 12-24 hours by the use of a low water-cement ratio and vibratory compaction, followed by good water-curing.

(2) *Effect of Water-Cement Ratio*

Providing that full compaction of the H.A.C. mix is achieved during placing, a reduction in water-cement ratio gives increased strength and an improvement in other concrete properties.   H.A.C. concrete therefore obeys the same general water-cement ratio " law " which applies to Portland cement concrete.

It is true that H.A.C. combines with a higher percentage of water than does Portland cement, but this should not be construed to mean that higher water-cement ratios must therefore be used, or that there is some minimum figure below which the water-cement ratio of H.A.C. mixes must never be reduced.

We have already noted that it is possible to consolidate H.A.C. mixes with lower water-cement ratios than equivalent Portland cement mixes (particularly by vibrational methods) and this facility should be utilised with advantage, whenever it is feasible.   Strengths which appear more than adequate may be obtained at early ages from H.A.C. concrete mixes of relatively high water content, and consequently there is a greater chance that the use of high water-cement ratios will pass unchecked when concreting on site.   However, other concrete properties, which are frequently more important than strength, are adversely affected and it is just as important with H.A.C. concrete as it is with Portland cement concrete for the mix to be placed with the minimum water-cement ratio which will allow complete compaction. Indeed, as will be seen in Section 16 of this Chapter, there are circumstances in which a low water-cement ratio for H.A.C. can be considered more necessary than it is for Portland cement.

Fig. 9 shows the relation between W/C and the cube compressive strength of H.A.C. gravel concrete (1:6) at 1 day and at 7 days.   The strength rises as the W/C falls but the slope tends to flatten at ratios below 0.45.   This may be due to the fact that the crushing strength of the aggregate is being approached, since Neville[8] found a straight-line relationship between W/C and the cylinder strength of H.A.C. concrete.

74

Many methods of designing Portland cement concrete mixes have been published and Newman[1] has provided information and graphs relating to H.A.C. concrete (made with one aggregate size and type) which allow at least one of these methods to be followed. Irregular river gravel ($\frac{3}{4}$ in. maximum size) was combined with different proportions of silica sand to give three gradings of aggregate corresponding to Gradings 2, 3 and 4 described in Road Note 4, of the Road Research

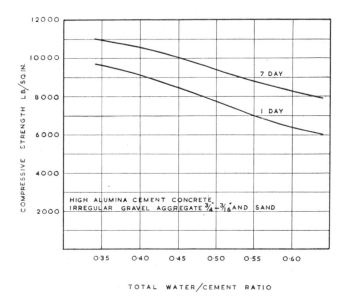

FIG. 9. Effect of water-cement ratio on cube compressive strength of H.A.C. concrete.

Laboratory[9], and the tests covered aggregate-cement ratios from 3.0-7.5 (by weight) and water-cement ratios from 0.30-0.70. It should be understood that these were " effective" water-cement ratios based on the " effective water content " (total water content of the mix minus the water absorbed in 30 minutes by the aggregate) and curves similar to Fig. 9 are given to relate cube crushing strengths with the effective water-cement ratios.

Within the range of H.A.C. mixes tested, Newman did not find that fully compacted lean mixes gave higher strengths than rich mixes, at the same water-cement ratio, and, within the limited range of gradings employed, he found no evidence that an increase in the specific surface of the aggregate reduced the strength of the concrete. The latter point is of some interest since a small increase in the proportion of sand is often recommended for H.A.C. concrete mixes to counteract their greater tendency to " harshness " and segregation.

In the design of H.A.C. concrete mixes the cone slump test is not as useful as it is with Portland cement mixes and it is generally thought that a flow-table or the Vebe consistometer gives more uniform results over a wider range of consistencies. Due to the lower "viscosity" of H.A.C. paste, the compacting factor (employed in Road Note 4) is increased when H.A.C. is substituted for Portland cement in a given mix, and Newman's tests (with British H.A.C.) indicate that this increase in compacting factor value is about 5 per cent. at effective W/C = 0.50, 12 per cent. at effective W/C = 0.40, and 18 per cent. at effective W/C = 0.35, in the case of a 1 : 6 concrete mix.

(3) *Tensile Strength, Bending Strength, etc.*

A tensile briquette test does not appear in the British Standard Specification for H.A.C. since at an early stage it was shown to have a high variability and it did not prove to be an adequate test for the strength properties of the cement[10]. Schuman and Tucker[3] found that the concrete tensile strengths of both Portland cement and H.A.C. regressed after some time in damp air-storage but the effect was much greater for the latter cement. Suenson[11] found that the drop in tensile strength of H.A.C. mortars over a long period was greater in water than in air-storage.

The tensile strength of H.A.C. mortars and concretes develops rapidly like the compressive strength and is much greater than that of similar Portland cement mixes at early ages. However, the tensile strength of Portland cement mortars or concretes continues to increase over a longer period and becomes equal to, or greater than, that of the H.A.C. specimens at later ages. The ratio between the cube compressive strength and the tensile strength of water-stored H.A.C. concretes and mortars is approximately as follows :—

Age	1 day	7 days	28 days
Compressive/Tensile	16-18	18-20	19-22

The strength in bending, flexural strength, or modulus of rupture[12] of H.A.C. concrete tends to be higher than the tensile strength measured in direct tension, but the difference appears to be less than in the case of Portland cement concrete. This may be due to the lower creep of the H.A.C. concrete during the bending test. The modulus of rupture of an orthodox H.A.C. concrete when tested according to B.S.S. 1881 at various ages, is shown in Fig. 10 and it will be seen that the development of bending strength also occurs

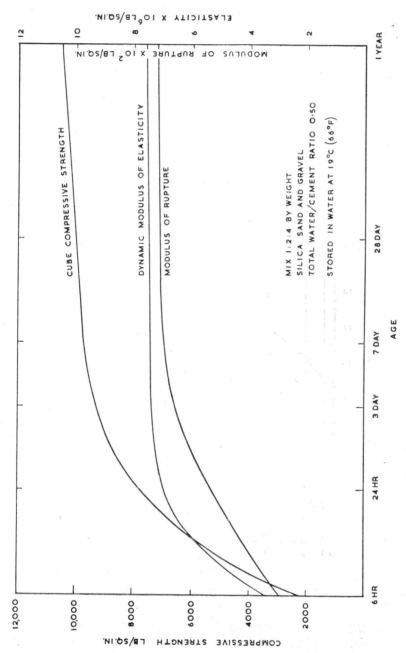

FIG. 10.   Some physical properties of H.A.C. concrete.

rapidly and there is not a great increase at later ages. The value for normal H.A.C. concrete mixes is usually 500-1000 lbs./sq. in. at an age of 1 day or more.

3. IMPACT RESISTANCE OF H.A.C. CONCRETE

The impact resistance of H.A.C. concrete (1 : 6) made with irregular river gravel and silica sand has been tested[13] by determining the average number of blows required to break, or visibly crack, 4 in. cube specimens. The cubes were cast with a steel plate on top, and the impacts were produced by a 50 lb. tup falling through a standard height to contact a hemispherical protuberance in the middle of the top surface of the steel plate. A direct comparison, at various ages, was made between similar concrete mixes containing British H.A.C. or rapid-hardening Portland cement, and the results of one series are shown in Fig. 11.

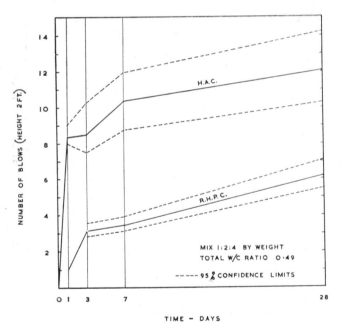

FIG. 11.   Impact resistance of concretes.

Although the variability was quite high, it appeared that the impact resistance of the H.A.C. concrete at 1 day was at least as high as that of the rapid-hardening Portland cement concrete at 28 days. When tests were continued up to the age of 6 months, it was found

78

that the impact resistance of the H.A.C. concrete continued to increase after 28 days but at a very much slower rate than that of the rapid-hardening Portland cement concrete. At 6 months the average impact resistance of the Portland cement concrete was rather higher than that of the H.A.C. concrete, although the latter gave the highest individual result.

4. Modulus of Elasticity

The dynamic modulus of elasticity (E_D) of H.A.C. mortar or concrete may be obtained in the same way as for Portland cement concrete, i.e. by determining the resonant frequency of beam or prism specimens. The development of the modulus with age follows the same general curve as the development of compressive strength, but the effect of variations in water-cement ratio is proportionately less except at very early ages. Fig. 12 shows the customary range in values obtained, at W/C = 0.45-0.60, from 1 : 2 : 4 concretes made with British H.A.C., silica sand and gravel[13].

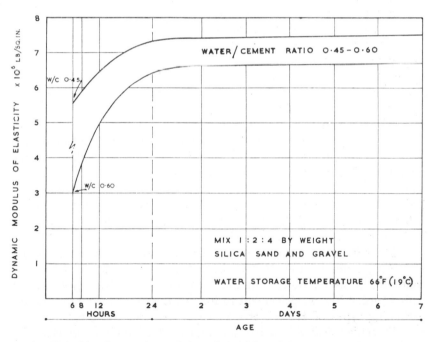

FIG. 12. Dynamic modulus of elasticity of H.A.C. concretes.

Since the modulus of the aggregates is generally higher than that of the cement paste, the value of E_D (obtained at any age for a particular concrete mix) will vary with the type of aggregate and with the aggregate/cement ratio. Accordingly, although there is a good linear relationship between E_D and the compressive or flexural strength for a given H.A.C. mix[14], it is not independent of the richness of mix or the type of aggregate. In addition, the dynamic modulus is reduced by allowing the concrete to dry, while the compressive strength may simultaneously increase. The extent by which E_D is reduced depends on the nature of the concrete and on the amount of water lost but, as an indication, a 20 in. x 4 in. x 4 in. beam of H.A.C. concrete (Mix 1 : 6. W/C = 0.55) had a dynamic modulus of 7.4 x 10^6 lbs./sq. in. after 150 days under water, but the E_D dropped to 6.5 x 10^6 lbs./sq. in. when the concrete was allowed to dry in air for a further 30 days.

Calibration curves relating E_D to compressive strength are therefore particularly useful for water-stored concrete, but, if a period of air-drying intervenes, a suitable correction must be made to allow for the effect on E_D of the change in concrete humidity. All these factors affecting dynamic modulus apply in the same sense to H.A.C. concrete and to Portland cement concrete.

The tangent or secant static modulus of elasticity (E_s) of H.A.C. concrete, as determined by extensometer or strain gauge, is consistently lower than the value of E_D. For example, a typical H.A.C. concrete may give a static modulus of about 5.0 x 10^6 lbs./sq. in. when the dynamic modulus is 6.0 x 10^6 lbs./sq. in. As with Portland cement, any difference between the dynamic and static moduli will be affected by the age of the concrete, by the water-cement ratio, and by the rate of loading in the static determination.

When the static modulus is derived from the load-deflection curve of beams, the value of E_s is usually closer to that of the dynamic modulus. Tests carried out in this way on a large number of pre-stressed concrete beams made with British H.A.C. showed moduli at 1 day of 5.0 - 7.0 x 10^6 lbs./sq. in. with an average value of nearly 6.0 x 10^6 lbs./sq. in.[15]. The corresponding concrete cube strength at 1 day was over 9000 lbs./sq. in.

There is not a great increase in either the static or dynamic moduli of H.A.C. concrete after 28 days, even when the specimens are stored continuously under water, but the subsequent gain is slightly greater with a mix of low water-cement ratio. In the case of the more rapid-hardening types of H.A.C. about 80 per cent. of the ultimate value may be achieved at the end of 24 hours. The modulus of elasticity in compression and tension is approximately the same.

5. Poisson's Ratio

For most concretes, including H.A.C. concretes, a figure of $\frac{1}{5}$-$\frac{1}{10}$ is taken, depending on the cement content of the mix. However, the values obtained with normal H.A.C. concretes (1 : 6) vary between $\frac{1}{4}$-$\frac{1}{5}$ when Poisson's Ratio is calculated from the ultrasonic pulse velocity and the dynamic modulus of elasticity. The following figures obtained in this way are representative of water-stored 1 : 2 : 4 gravel concretes (540 lbs. cement/cu. yd.).

Age.	6 hr.	1 day	7 days	28 days	6 months
Poisson's Ratio	0.30	0.25	0.23	0.23	0.21

6. Ultrasonic Pulse Velocity and its Relation to Compressive Strength

Determination of the time of passage of pulses of ultrasonic waves through a known thickness of concrete has been the basis of a non-destructive method of estimating the quality of site or laboratory concrete. For any given mix, the pulse velocity normally increases with the compressive strength of the concrete, but loss of water (e.g. on drying the concrete in air after water-curing) reduces the velocity although the compressive strength is not similarly affected. As in the case of Portland cement concrete, the velocity obtained is also dependent on the nature of the aggregate and on the aggregate/paste ratio.

H.A.C. concrete mixes (540 lbs. cement/cu. yd.) containing siliceous aggregates and made with water-cement ratios of 0.60-0.45 give pulse velocities of 14,500-16,500 ft./sec. at 1 day. Corresponding cube compressive strengths are in the range 6000-8500 lbs./sq. in.

Jones[17] found that Portland cement concretes and H.A.C. concretes (both stored in water) gave a common curve correlating pulse velocity and compressive strength.

7. Relation between Pulse Velocity and Dynamic Modulus

Observations on the ultrasonic pulse velocity through 24 in. x 4 in. x 4 in. beams of H.A.C. concrete or mortar, and the dynamic modulus of elasticity of the same specimens (derived from the resonant frequency of longitudinal vibration) show that there is a linear relationship between these properties.

The experimentally determined curve for British H.A.C.[13] is very close to a straight line over the range of values tested and this is given in Fig. 13. If the value of one property is known it is there-fore possible to calculate the other with reasonable accuracy. The tests were all performed with the same type of aggregate (flint gravel and sand) but they included mortars and concretes of very varied mix proportions. The relationship was thus found to be independent of the mix, age and water-cement ratio of the specimens.

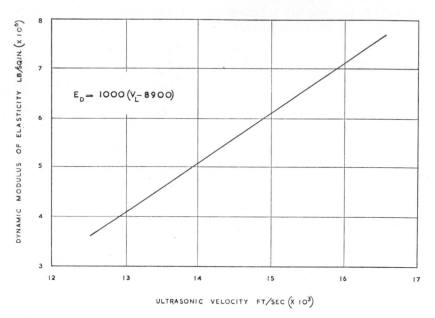

FIG. 13. Dynamic modulus of elasticity vs. ultrasonic pulse velocity for H.A.C. concretes and mortars.

Klieger[18], working with Portland cement concretes, has also found an excellent relation between these properties and reported that it was independent of paste/aggregate ratio, age, amount of air entrained, and type of Portland cement used. However, his graph is quantitatively somewhat different from Fig. 13 and this is probably due to differences in the experimental conditions. It does not seem likely that the substitution of H.A.C. for Portland cement could, in itself, alter the relationship obtained.

8. EXPANSION IN WATER-STORAGE AND SHRINKAGE IN AIR

Appreciable volume changes can take place in any plastic concrete mix before it hardens. These changes are due to settlement of the concrete constituents under gravity, to the action of capillary forces and to " bleeding " of water from the mix. All these effects apply to H.A.C. concrete mixes as well as to Portland cement mixes, the only factor likely to cause any difference at this stage is the tendency to greater " bleeding " of an H.A.C. mix.

(1) *Expansion in Water-Storage*

In considering expansion in water-storage or shrinkage on drying, we are concerned only with volume or length changes which take place after the mix is no longer plastic, that is, after some time corresponding in most cases to the initial set.

When any hydraulic cement hydrates under water, the absolute volume of the hydrates formed is always less than the sum of the volumes of water and anhydrous cement, so that a shrinkage in the volume of the paste should occur as a result of the reaction between cement and water. In practice, it is found that this effect tends to be counteracted by an increase in the apparent volume of the paste, caused by continued production of hydrates and the formation of voids.

It is known[19] that the reduction in the absolute volume of the paste of H.A.C. is much greater and occurs more rapidly than is the case for Portland or rapid-hardening Portland cements. Gessner gives the following percentage diminutions in volume, calculated on the original volume of 100 g. cement and 33 g. water.

Age	1 day	7 days	28 days	100 days
Portland cement (1)	2.8	4.8	6.0	6.9
(2)	1.7	4.4	—	6.3
H.A.C.	11.1	13.8	15.2	16.3

Dutron[20] found that the volume diminution at 3 days was 3.5 cc. per 100 g. cement for Portland cement and 11.5 cc. for 100 g. H.A.C. At 30 days the corresponding figures were 4.25 cc. and 12.10 cc.

This leads to a fundamental difference in the behaviour of neat H.A.C. paste or H.A.C. mortar and concrete mixes when the hydration takes place in the presence of excess water. In the first 24 hours the comparatively large reduction in absolute volume of the H.A.C. paste exceeds the tendency towards apparent volume expansion, so that appreciable shrinkage takes place within this period even when the specimen is well water-cured. The extent of this shrinkage, in the first day or so, is greatest in the case of neat cement, less for mortars and still less for concretes. On the other hand, Portland cement pastes or mixes usually show little volume change or a slight expansion at the end of 24 hours under water, because, in this case, the expansive factor is sufficient to counterbalance the less marked reduction in absolute volume of paste. If the mixes remain continuously under water after 1 day the expansion continues slowly for Portland cement and now starts, at approximately the same rate, for H.A.C. In general, it can therefore be said that the expansion in water-storage shown by neat Portland cement pastes, or Portland cement mortars and concretes, is nearly the same as that of similar H.A.C. mixes when both are measured from the age of 1 day. The difference is that the H.A.C. specimens have already undergone an initial shrinkage before expansion forces gain the upper hand. It may therefore require some period in water-storage before H.A.C. specimens regain their original volume as cast, and begin to show any net expansion. This effect is shown for H.A.C. concretes in Table II which is based on data obtained by Neville[21].

TABLE II. THE LINEAR EXPANSION IN CONTINUOUS WATER STORAGE OF VARIOUS H.A.C. CONCRETES

Time and Measurement start when Concrete is 16 hours old.

Mix	W/C	Shrinkage (S) or Expansion (E) at time of				
		1 day	10 days	20 days	40 days	100 days
1 : 4	0.35	0.002% (S)	0.002% (S)	Nil	0.004% (E)	0.009% (E)
1 : 4	0.55	0.002% (S)	0.002% (E)	0.006% (E)	0.012% (E)	0.022% (E)
1 : 6	0.55	0.002% (S)	0.002% (S)	0.005% (E)	0.023% (E)	0.025% (E)

The average expansion between 1 day and 1 year of Portland cement pastes, mortars, and concretes when stored under water are respectively 0.2 per cent., 0.02-0.04 per cent., and 0.01-0.02 per cent. linear. The figures can vary quite widely about these values according to the batch of cement, the thickness of the specimen, the water-cement ratio, and the nature of the aggregate, if any. However, in the same conditions, they may be applied, as average values, to H.A.C. specimens also.

(2) *Shrinkage in Air*

If water-cured concrete, mortar or cement specimens are allowed

84

to dry in air there is a drying shrinkage, the magnitude of which at any time depends on factors such as :—

(a) the relative humidity of the storage atmosphere.

(b) the size of the specimen.

(c) the presence or absence of reinforcement.

(d) the type of aggregate, if any.

(e) the cement-paste content of the mortar or concrete.

If we consider specimens containing Portland cement or H.A.C. and assume that they are allowed to dry in air after water-curing for 1 day, it will be remembered that some shrinkage has already occurred in the H.A.C. specimen, and this will continue in the air-storage. The Portland cement specimen has undergone no shrinkage at the end of the water-curing but shrinkage will now start in air-storage and will continue at about the same rate as for the corresponding H.A.C. specimen. Therefore, if shrinkage in air is measured in each case from the age of about 1 day, the total figure is very similar for specimens made with either cement. It will be appreciated, however, that several different values can be given for the shrinkage of the H.A.C. specimens if the initial measurement of length is done, not at 24 hours, but at 6 hours, 8 hours, or 18 hours, since varying amounts of the early shrinkage will thereby be included.

TABLE III. PRACTICAL VALUES FOR LONG-TERM DRYING SHRINKAGE OF H.A.C. CONCRETES

Mix by weight	1 : 6	1 : 4	1 : 6	1 : 9	1 : 6
Water-cement ratio	0.35	0.50	0.50	0.50	0.75
Shrinkage % linear	0.03	0.05	0.04	0.03	0.05

Possibly for this reason there are many conflicting statements about the relative shrinkages of Portland cement and H.A.C. For example, Graf[3] compared concretes made with high-strength Portland cement or German H.A.C. and concluded that, although the shrinkage of the H.A.C. units was initially greater, it eventually became less than that of the Portland cement units. The linear shrinkages, after 18 months air storage, of 1 : 6 concretes (W/C = 0.75) have also been quoted as :—Portland cement concrete 0.048 per cent., rapid-hardening Portland cement concrete 0.55 per cent., and H.A.C. concrete 0.037 per cent.[22] Other investigators have stated that the shrinkage of H.A.C. is the same or somewhat greater than that of Portland cement[23]. However, the following points appear to be certain.

(a) During the initial water-curing some shrinkage occurs in H.A.C. specimens. Under the same conditions there is no shrinkage, but often a very slight expansion, in similar Portland cement specimens.

(b) The shrinkage of H.A.C. is greater at early ages than is the case with Portland cement, but it tends to reach similar total values at later ages.

(c) The actual shrinkage value obtained from H.A.C. specimens depends on the time when the initial measurement is made. If made at ages less than 24 hours, allowance may also be required for dimensional change caused by any appreciable temperature-rise.

For practical purposes it has been found quite satisfactory to apply the average shrinkage values given in Table III to normal H.A.C. concretes made with dense non-porous aggregates, and it will be seen that they do not differ from those employed for Portland cement concrete. In view of the very large number of variables and the difficulty of obtaining reproducible results, any quoted figures for shrinkage must be used as general guides, and not as precise values which can be accurately applied in specific cases. Lafuma[24] has summarised the situation well by saying " In general, one can say that the absolute shrinkage is of the same order for all the cements, or at least that it is possible to have the same difference between two cements of the same type as there is between two cements of different types."

(3) Shrinkage Stresses in Fully Restrained Members

When mortars or concretes are completely restrained while drying out in air, the normal shrinkage strains are translated into tensile stresses in the specimen, and when the extensibility of the material is exceeded a crack appears. Fully restrained H.A.C. concretes and mortars will crack under the influence of these shrinkage stresses at a much earlier age than similarly treated Portland cement specimens[25]. This occurs partly because the shrinkage stress develops quickly but mainly because the modulus of elasticity of H.A.C. reaches a relatively higher value at an early age and the internal stress cannot be reduced by creep to the same extent as in a Portland cement mix of the same age.

(4) *Effect of Carbon Dioxide on Shrinkage*

Carbonation of mortars and concretes increases the observed drying shrinkage of both Portland cement and H.A.C. specimens particularly if they are relatively thin. According to tests carried out on 1 : 3 mortars at a relative humidity of 63.5 per cent., the shrinkage at ages up to 100 days of H.A.C. specimens was considerably less than that of Portland cement specimens when both were stored in air completely free from carbon dioxide. In a carbon dioxide atmosphere the shrinkage of all specimens was greatly increased but that of the H.A.C. still remained lower than the Portland cement[26]. The loss in weight on air-drying and the gain in weight in carbon dioxide were also much lower in the case of the H.A.C. specimens.

(5) *Moisture Movement*

The " moisture movement " from the dry to the saturated condition appears to be similar to that of an equivalent Portland cement mix, i.e. for an average H.A.C. concrete (1 : 6) made with a dense aggregate of low absorption value, it is about 0.03 per cent. linear.

9. THE CREEP OF H.A.C. CONCRETES

The early work of Glanville[27] extended later by Glanville and Thomas[28], dealt with concrete (1 : 2 : 4 by weight) made with Portland cement, rapid-hardening Portland cement, or H.A.C. The water-cement ratio was high (0.70) and the load applied amounted to 600 lbs./sq. in.

In the first place, it was found that the initial creep on loading the Portland cement concretes at 28 days was greater than that occurring with H.A.C. specimens loaded at the same age or even at 1 day. After 6 months under load in air, the creep of H.A.C. concrete loaded at 28 days was much less than that of both Portland cement concretes loaded also at 28 days. The creep of H.A.C. concrete when loaded at 1 day was again less than that of the 28-day ordinary Portland cement concrete but it was now higher than that of the 28-day rapid-hardening Portland cement concrete.

After 1 year the creeps of the concretes (all loaded at 28 days) were approximately

1 : 2 : 4 H.A.C. concrete, W/C $= 0.7$ 0.25×10^{-6} per unit length

per lb. per sq. in.

,,   R.H. Portland ,,   ,, 0.39×10^{-6} ,,

,,   Portland   ,,   ,, 1.02×10^{-6} ,,

Between 3 years and 8 years the shape of the creep/time curve for H.A.C. concrete became different from that of the Portland cement concretes and, after 8 years, the creeps were in the ascending order 1. Rapid-hardening Portland. 2. H.A.C. 3. Ordinary Portland. Hummel[29] has also found a similar change at later ages in the creep characteristics of H.A.C. concrete.

Ross[30] determined the relative creeps of concretes made with different cements and stored in a controlled atmosphere. In this case the load was 1040 lbs./sq. in. and he concluded that the creeps after 1 year were in the ascending order 1. H.A.C. 2. Rapid-hardening Portland. 3. Ordinary Portland. 4. Portland/Blast-furnace. The relative movements of the concretes at this age were in the ratios of $1 : 1\frac{1}{2} : 4 : 8$ respectively.

Both Glanville and Ross noted that H.A.C. concrete appeared to give a lower creep value in air than in water-storage, which is opposite to the behaviour of Portland cement concretes, and this has since been accepted as an anomaly peculiar to H.A.C. However, Neville[31] believes that the creep of concretes made with either cement is largely determined by the stress/strength ratio at loading. As this ratio decreases, so does the subsequent creep (and probably the ultimate creep). On this theory, the greater creep in water-storage which Glanville found for H.A.C. concrete can be partially explained by the fact that the concrete used for this test undoubtedly had, for some reason, a lower initial strength than the equivalent mix used for air-storage. Neville's results indicate that the creep of H.A.C. concrete when drying is higher than when the concrete is maintained at 95 per cent. relative humidity — which is the same as for Portland cement concrete. Further investigation is therefore required before this question can be considered as settled.

Due to the very rapid strength development of H.A.C. concrete within the first 24 hours, considerable loads can be applied at early ages without raising the stress/strength ratio above the values obtained when Portland cement concrete is loaded at 28 days or when rapid-hardening Portland cement concrete is similarly loaded at 7 days. In the commercial manufacture of bonded-wire prestressed beams, the wires are cut and the load transferred to the necessarily high-quality H.A.C. concrete at the age of 18-24 hours. The subsequent concrete creep appears to be similar to that obtained from a much later application of the same load to a Portland cement concrete, and this is no doubt due to the low stress/strength ratios which are given, even at early ages, by H.A.C. concretes made with low water-cement ratios.

Neville measured the creep of $9\frac{1}{4}$ in. x 2 in. diameter cylinders of H.A.C. concrete under a constant stress of 2150 lbs. /sq. in. which was applied at ages from 18 hours to 11 days. He found that the creep, after loading-periods extending to 100 days, decreased considerably when the time at which loading occurred was increased from 18 hours to 2 days. When the concrete was more than 2 days old the age at loading had a comparatively small effect on the subsequent creep. As with Portland cement concrete, the H.A.C. concrete exhibited the same pattern of instantaneous elastic recovery upon removal of load, followed by a more gradual creep recovery.

Other factors affecting the magnitude of creep, e.g. the type of aggregate, act in the same way on both Portland and H.A.C. concretes.

10. Bond to Steel

There appears to be little if any difference between the bond strength to steel of H.A.C. or Portland cement[2], or in the resistance to slip of wires in pre-tensioned prestressed concrete[32], and, in this respect, no change in concreting methods is required to satisfy the usual requirements. The only difference again lies in the rate of bond development, and when working with similar mixes, it may be assumed that the bond strength of H.A.C. mortars or concretes at 1 day is at least equivalent to that of rapid-hardening Portland cement at 7 days, or to that of ordinary Portland cement at 28 days. In the case of the lower-silica type of H.A.C., practical experience shows that adequately high bond strengths for any duty are developed well within 24 hours.

11. Porosity and Permeability

The total porosity is the percentage of voids, the latter being defined as any space in the concrete or mortar which is occupied by air or by water which is not combined as a hydrate.

In order to determine apparent porosity in the customary way, it is necessary to know the weight of a known volume of concrete or mortar (a) when in a surface-dry saturated condition (i.e. when the voids are filled with water) and (b) when all the uncombined water has been removed. Unfortunately, it is almost impossible to know when the concrete is in the second condition. It may be heated in an oven at 105°C. or dried at low humidities and pressures, but each method gives a somewhat different result since the milder drying conditions may leave some free water and more severe drying conditions may eliminate part of the combined water. Perhaps this is not of great consequence when comparing the porosities of concretes made with the same type of cement, but the problem becomes more acute if concretes made with different types of cement are tested. Even under the milder drying conditions, hydrated H.A.C. tends to lose part of the combined water more readily than does Portland cement, and therefore a good comparison of the porosities of concretes made with the two types of cement is difficult to achieve by this experimental method.

The theoretical porosities of equivalent H.A.C. and Portland cement concretes, assuming complete compaction, may be calculated if the specific gravities of the cements, aggregates and hydrates are known and if the degree of hydration can be ascertained. Fig. 20 shows the porosities calculated in this way. No great accuracy is claimed for the individual figures but the relative values are believed to be similar to those found in practice. The porosity of the normal H.A.C. concrete is lower than that of the equivalent Portland cement concrete over the usual range of water-cement ratios, and the reason is that H.A.C. combines with a higher proportion of the gauging water and so reduces the amount of free water which forms voids.

Permeability is measured by the rate of flow, under pressure, of a fluid (usually water) through a concrete or mortar. A highly porous concrete is usually very permeable but much depends on the nature and distribution of the pores. A series of connected open pores is necessary to allow flow through the body of a concrete, and the discrete bubbles produced by an air-entraining agent will increase porosity but not necessarily the permeability.

Glanville[33] investigated the permeability, after a period of air or water storage, of 1 : 2 : 4 mixes of concretes made with H.A.C., rapid-hardening Portland cement and ordinary Portland cement and his results are shown in Table IV. After 1 month under water the permeabilities of all the concretes were low and not greatly different, but in air storage the permeability of ordinary Portland cement concrete remained at a high value while the permeabilities of H.A.C. concrete and rapid-hardening Portland cement concrete decreased rapidly with age.

If water continues to flow through the body of an unduly permeable concrete or mortar it will, in the course of time, leach away any hydraulic cement. Due to cement solution and hydrolysis, the water in contact with Portland cement or H.A.C. contains lime and either silica or alumina. So long as the water is in contact only with a concrete surface the action is not usually significant, but *percolating* water can gradually transport out of the concrete most of the lime formerly combined as calcium silicate or calcium aluminate. In this sense the

TABLE IV. PERMEABILITIES OF 1 : 2 : 4 CONCRETES MADE WITH VARIOUS CEMENTS

(Rates of flow of water at 100 lbs./sq. in. pressure in cc/ft^2./hr)

Type of Cement	Permeability after curing					
	2 days in		14 days in		28 days in	
	Air	Water	Air	Water	Air	Water
H.A.C.	110	—	16	10	12	8
Rapid-hardening Portland cement	—	—	17	6	10	5
Portland cement	—	—	510	39	490	12

" solubility " of H.A.C. in the percolating water is greater than that of Portland cement and although all normal H.A.C. concretes should be very impermeable, it is therefore particularly important to eliminate any factor which may accidentally cause excessive permeability. Thus the use of a high proportion of a fine sand (in which the particles are nearly all the same size) should be avoided in H.A.C. concrete designed to resist a high differential water pressure.

12. THERMAL EXPANSION, THERMAL CONDUCTIVITY, ETC.

The thermal expansion of any concrete or mortar is chiefly dependent on the nature of the aggregate. Siliceous aggregates have a higher coefficient of thermal expansion than igneous rock aggregates, and limestone has one of the lowest.

Neat hydrated cements have a higher thermal expansion than any of the common concrete aggregates, and therefore rich mixes tend to give mortars or concretes with higher thermal expansions than those of lean mixes. The expansion of a partially dry mortar or concrete is greater than that of either dry or saturated specimens[34].

Within the atmospheric temperature range it has been found[35] that the coefficient of thermal expansion of neat H.A.C. is considerably lower than that of neat Portland cement, in either the dry or wet condition. However, the thermal expansion of an air-dry siliceous gravel concrete (1 : 6) is almost the same when made with either type of cement, although the H.A.C. concrete still has a rather lower coefficient than the Portland cement concrete when both are saturated. The summary given in Table V is based on the work of Bonnell and Harper.

91

It is believed that the thermal conductivity of H.A.C. concretes and mortars is substantially the same as that of similar Portland cement mixes, and published figures for the latter[36] can probably be used for H.A.C. concretes without introducing any great error. For Portland cement concretes made with gravel aggregate Davey & Fox[37] have quoted values of 0.004 - 0.005 c.g.s. units. The thermal conductivity of a concrete also varies with the type of aggregate, with

TABLE V. AVERAGE COEFFICIENTS OF LINEAR THERMAL EXPANSION 0°C.-40°C.
(x 10⁻⁶ per °C. or °F.)

Type of Specimen	Cement	Air Stored		Water Stored	
		Per °F	Per °C.	Per °F.	Per °C.
Neat Cements	Portland	12.6	22.7	8.2	14.8
	Portland/ Blast-furnace	12.9	23.2	10.1	18.2
	H.A.C.	7.9	14.2	6.7	12.1
1 : 6 Gravel Concretes	Portland	7.3	13.1	6.8	12.2
	Portland/ Blast-furnace	7.9	14.2	6.9	12.4
	H.A.C.	7.5	13.5	5.9	10.6

water-cement ratio, and with the moisture content when tested.[38] Concretes made with silica gravel, limestone, or granite aggregates have thermal conductivities which decrease in that order.

The heat capacity per unit volume of an average concrete may be taken as 0.5 calorie per cc., thus giving a figure for thermal diffusivity of 0.008 - 0.01 sq. cm. per sec.

13. ELECTRICAL RESISTIVITY, CAPACITANCE, AND DIELECTRIC STRENGTH

The electrical resistivity of several types of neat cement was examined by Dorsch[39] who found that it varied in the reverse order to the lime contents of cements tested. Specimens made with lower water-cement ratios had higher resistivities. Data on the electrical resistance of Portland cement concretes have been given by several investigators[40].

The pH value of the water within hardening H.A.C. pastes, mortars, or concretes is much lower than is the case with Portland cement specimens. In addition H.A.C. combines, during hydration, with a greater percentage of the gauging water, and the reaction occurs more rapidly. It is therefore understandable that the resistivity of H.A.C. pastes, mortars, or concretes is greater than that of similar Portland cement mixes at all ages, but particularly so at early ages.

A comparison of the electrical properties of Portland cement, rapid-hardening Portland cement, and British H.A.C. has been carried out by Hammond and Robson[41] who worked with neat cements and also with 1 : 6 siliceous gravel concrete. During curing, and for periods of air-drying up to 150 days, they found that the surface resistance of the cements and concretes was much greater than the corresponding volume resistance. However, with oven-dried mature specimens the reverse was true.

The development of volume resistivity during the first 24 hours, and during a subsequent period of drying in air at ordinary temperatures, is shown in Figs. 14 and 15. Briefly, it may be noted that the ratio of the resistivities of H.A.C. and Portland cements, whether as

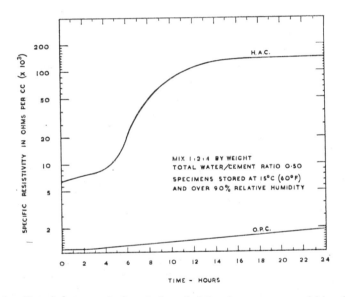

FIG. 14. Development of electrical resistivity in concretes within the first day.

neat cement or concrete, is approximately 10 : 1 up to the setting-time. At 24 hours the ratio is about 100 : 1 and after a period of air-drying it is back to 10 : 1. Whatever the type of cement, the resistivity of concrete (1 : 6 mix) was 3-5 times as great as that of the corresponding neat cement during the first 24 hours, and about 10 times as great after drying out in air. The resistivity of H.A.C. concrete, dried in an oven at 105°C. was very high (about 10^6 megohms-cm.) and it was again considerably greater than that of similar Portland cement con-cretes, although the ratio varied with the applied voltage.

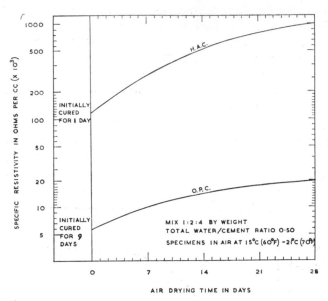

FIG. 15. Development of electrical resistivity of concretes on drying in air.

In all specimens allowed to mature and dry for a period in air, the d.c. resistance was approximately equal to the a.c. impedance and consequently the power factor was near to unity. The capacitancies of the H.A.C. cubes were less than those of the Portland cement cubes, particularly at higher frequencies and the capacitancies of all the neat cements were much greater than those of the corresponding concretes at the same age.

The dielectric strength of oven-dried and air-dried concretes was tested with d.c. and a.c. current, and in all cases it was found that the humidity of the concretes had surprisingly little effect on the break-down values. The dielectric strength of the H.A.C. concrete (16-18 kilovolts per cm.) was rather higher than that of the Portland cement concretes (14-16 kilovolts per cm.), at least for the first break-down.

Practical interest has been shown in the employment of H.A.C. mortars or concretes as insulators or dielectric media. For example,

Lambert[42] and Ferrier[43] described the use of concrete (made with H.A.C. and gravel aggregate, gauged with bituminous emulsion) for casting third-rail insulators for French railways, or for making cap-and-pin insulators on 500-volt transmission lines. The resistivity of this special concrete, after heat-treatment and varnishing, was 10^6 megohms-cm. and it had a dielectric strength of about 10 kilovolts per cm.

14. STANDARD SPECIFICATIONS FOR HIGH-ALUMINA CEMENTS

Standard specifications for this type of cement have been drawn up in Czechoslovakia (CSN), Finland (Govt. Decree No. 460), Italy, Netherlands (N.482), Spain, Britain (B.S. 915), and the U.S.S.R. (GOST. 969). There is no uniformity in the chemical characteristics required by these Specifications and the strength properties are judged by tests which differ greatly in their conditions[44]. The requirements for chemical composition, fineness and setting times are shown in Table VI.

TABLE VI. SUMMARY OF CHEMICAL REQUIREMENTS, ETC., IN STANDARD SPECIFICATIONS FOR H.A.C.

Country	Chemical Requirements	Setting-times (minutes)	Fineness
Czecho-slovakia	$Al_2O_3 \not< 40\%$. $SiO_2 \not> 10\%$ Insol. Residue $\not> 3.5\%$. May not contain water-sol. carbides, sulphides, phosphides	Init. $\not< 60$ Final $\not> 600$	$\not> 1\%$ on 200μ $\not> 10\%$ on 90μ
Finland	No requirements	Init. 180-480	No requiremnts.
Italy	$Al_2O_3 \not< 35\%$. $MgO \not> 3\%$. $SO_3 \not> 2.5\%$. Insol. Residue $\not> 1.5\%$. Loss $\not> 5\%$. No inert material may be added.	Init. $\not< 60$ Final $\not> 240$	$\not> 2\%$ on 200μ
Nether-lands	$MgO \not> 5\%$. $SO_2 \not> 2.5\%$. Insol. Residue $\not> 3\%$.	Init. $\not< 60$	$\not> 14\%$ on 90μ
Spain	Aluminates $> 30\%$. Iron Oxide $< 20\%$.	Init. $\not< 30$ Final $\not> 420$	$\not> 0.5\%$ on 200μ $\not> 6\%$ on 90μ
United Kingdom	$Al_2O_3 \not< 32\%$. $Al_2O_3/CaO \not< 0.85\%$ and $\not> 1.3$. No material except water may be added during grinding.	Init.120-360 Final $\not> 120$ after init. set	$\not> 8\%$ on 89μ or Spec. Surface $\not< 2250$ cm²/g.
U.S.S.R.	$\not> 2\%$ special additives.	Init. $\not< 30$ Final $\not> 720$	$\not> 10\%$ on 90μ

In all cases the aggregate used for the compressive strength of mortars is a " standard " sand, but the specification for this varies from country to country. A mortar tensile test is included, except in the case of Britain, Spain (which substitutes a compressive strength test for concrete) and Finland (which substitutes a flexural test on prism specimens).

British H.A.C. tested according to BS. 915 gives the following average compressive strengths in 1 : 3 standard sand vibrated mortars (W/C = 0.40)

Age.	Compressive Strength (lb./sq. in.)	Required by BS. 915 (lb./sq. in.)
1 day	9,500	≮ 6,000
3 days	10,500	≮ 7,000
7 days	12,000	—
28 days	13,000	—

There is no Standard Specification for H.A.C. in the U.S.A. or in Germany and therefore in these countries standard mortar tests are often made according to the corresponding Portland cement Specifications ASTM. C 109 and DIN. 1164.

(a) American H.A.C. tested according to ASTM. C 109

Standard Mortars	1 day	7 days	28 days
Compressive Strength (lb./sq. in.)	5,100	6,200	7,100

(b) British H.A.C. tested according to DIN. 1164

Standard Mortars	1 day	3 days	7 days	28 days
Compressive Strength (lb./sq. in.)	9,500	11,600	12,500	14,000
Flexural Strength (lb./sq. in.)	950	1,110	1,200	1,250

The apparent disparity in compressive strengths is almost entirely due to the very different nature of the test specimens and conditions in the two tests.

15. EFFECTS OF HOT, WET CONDITIONS AND HARDENING AT HIGH TEMPERATURES

Probably the first major construction in which it was noticed that anomalies occurred in the hardening of H.A.C. concrete at high temperatures was the building of the Plougastel bridge over the Elorn estuary in N.W. France. H.A.C. concrete (670 lb. cement per cu. yd.) was used for work up to the tidal level[45] and it was seen that a portion of the foundation of one of the piers on the access viaduct failed to harden normally ; also the test cubes taken at the same time gave sub-normal strengths. The matter was investigated by Frey-ssinet & Coyne[46] who found that this part of the work had been done in August 1925 when the weather was extremely hot and they attributed the low concrete strength in this section to the high mix temperature and high ambient temperature while the concrete was hardening. Sea-water had been used for gauging (a practice now condemned for H.A.C.) and their explanation was not accepted by everyone at that time[47] but other investigators soon confirmed that when H.A.C. concrete or mortar was allowed to set and harden for some time at high temperatures, lower strengths were obtained[48]. For example, Bates tested high-alumina cements from six countries and found that concretes maintained at 38°C. (100°F.) for the first 24 hours gave lower strengths than those cured for the same time at 21°C. (70°F.). The loss in strength of the hot-cured concretes also appeared to continue during subsequent curing at 21°C. Davey[49] cured H.A.C. concretes adiabatically and confirmed that the strengths obtained were much lower than when the concretes hardened at normal temperatures, thus demonstrating that, unless the self-generated heat was allowed to dissipate quickly, it might be sufficient to cause permanent damage to the concrete properties.

Thus the adverse effect on H.A.C. mixes of high temperatures, maintained during the hardening period, was realised at an early stage but it took some time to appreciate that normally cured and mature concretes could also suffer the same loss in strength if sub-sequently kept for long enough in hot wet conditions. Possibly the earliest statement of this second possibility was due to Bolomey[50] in 1927, although this work appears to have been overlooked by most investigators until it was re-published, in largely the same form[51] during 1935. Dealing first with the hardening of various concretes at different temperatures Bolomey showed that the later strengths of concretes made with Portland cement, rapid-hardening Portland cement, or H.A.C., were all reduced when the specimens were main-tained at 30°C. (86°F.) or 75°C. (167°F.) after gauging. The effect was more noticeable at the higher temperature, and it was not great in the case of ordinary Portland cement. It was more marked with rapid-hardening Portland cement but was obviously very important with H.A.C. He then made the further observation that a mature H.A.C. concrete (cured at 15°C. or 59°F. for 21 days) lost a proportion of its strength when subsequently maintained under water at 75°C.

Bolomey concluded " Not only does an aluminous cement concrete hardening under water at 75°C. give a strength much inferior to that normally expected, but even those concretes initially hardened under good conditions lose 40-80 per cent. of their acquired strengths after some days (under water) at a temperature above 50°C. This drop in strength, accompanied sometimes by a change in colour from grey-black to yellow-brown, must be attributed to a change in the chemical combinations, or in the crystal structures. The loss in strength is permanent and does not tend to diminish when the temperature again becomes normal." It will be seen below that these early remarks give an admirable summary of some of the conclusions reached later by other investigators.

Davey[52] also cured H.A.C. concretes normally at 18°C. (64°F.) for periods ranging from 1-90 days and then stored them under water at 38°C. (100°F.). He found that in all cases the strengths were eventually reduced in the hot water to a uniform value, irrespective of the concrete maturity. Still further storage in the hot wet conditions, after the drop in strength had occurred, sometimes produced a partial recovery in strength.

(1) *Theories accounting for Loss in Strength in hot, wet conditions*

Investigation of the relative stability of the calcium aluminate hydrates present in the system lime-alumina-water revealed that the hexagonal hydrates formed at ordinary temperatures were metastable (see Chapter Three), and although normally very persistent they could change or convert into the stable cubic hydrate $3 \text{ Cao.Al}_2\text{O}_3.6\text{H}_2\text{O}$[53]. The speed of conversion of the normal hydrates was known to be very slow below about 25°C. (77°F.) but it increased as the temperature was raised so long as water was present. It was therefore reasonable to conclude that there might be a connection between the anomalies observed in the setting and hardening of H.A.C. at higher temperatures, and the change in structure of the hydrates which was known to occur more rapidly at those temperatures. By 1933 it was possible to say with some confidence that the loss in strength of H.A.C. concretes, hardened at high temperatures, should be attributed, at least in part, to the conversion of the normal form of hydrates into the stable cubic hydrate[54]. If accepted, this theory was able to explain not only the loss in strength of H.A.C. concretes which were allowed to harden at high temperatures, but also the loss in strength of concretes initially cured at normal temperature and then stored in hot water, because conversion of the hydrates could obviously occur at any time in the life of the concrete when the conditions were sufficiently hot and wet to accelerate greatly the rate of change.

Confirmation of the role played by conversion of hydrates was obtained by several investigators including Couillaud[55] who followed the change by X-ray examination of H.A.C. after varying periods under hot water. She found that the appearance and continued formation of the cubic hydrate, C_3AH_6, was closely associated with the loss in strength. SÉAILLES[48] had pointed out in 1934 that iron-free H.A.C. also gave lower strengths when hardened under hot conditions, thus disposing of a rival theory which suggested that the presence of iron compounds was responsible, and in 1940 Lea[56] showed that pure monocalcium aluminate (the main cementing agent in H.A.C.) behaved in the same way. Evidence obtained from dehydration tests and density determinations supported the hypotheses that the fall in strength should be ascribed to conversion of the hydrates under hot wet conditions.

More recently it has been suggested that such lower strengths are not due to formation of the cubic hydrate but to " ageing " of the alumina gel which is formed during the hydration of H.A.C.[57] It seems probable that both processes may have an effect on H.A.C. in hot wet conditions although many observers are satisfied that conversion of the hydrates is the more important. However, all the factors (described below) which accelerate the conversion of hydrates equally favour the transformation of alumina gel to the stable crystalline state[58], and it will therefore be difficult to separate effects due to conversion of hydrates from the possible effects due to alumina gel. In discussing the practical results of hot wet conditions upon H.A.C. mixes, it is thus unnecessary to distinguish between the two effects and the phenomenon will be described by the general term " conversion."

(2) Principles governing Conversion

(a) Conversion under water or in saturated conditions.

It has already been noted that the rate of conversion increases with rising temperature and that the presence of water is necessary. Travers and Leduc[59] thought that there was a definite transition temperature at 25°C. (77°F.), above which the normal hydrates would convert to cubic hydrate and below which the reverse change would take place. However, there are fundamental reasons for rejecting the idea of a transition temperature. Instead it is believed that below some such temperature level the rate of conversion, even in water storage, is so slow that it is usually of no practical consequence but at higher temperatures the rate increases rapidly and therefore the effects of conversion can be detected within a reasonable period of time in concretes stored under water at about 30°C. (85°F.) and above.

99

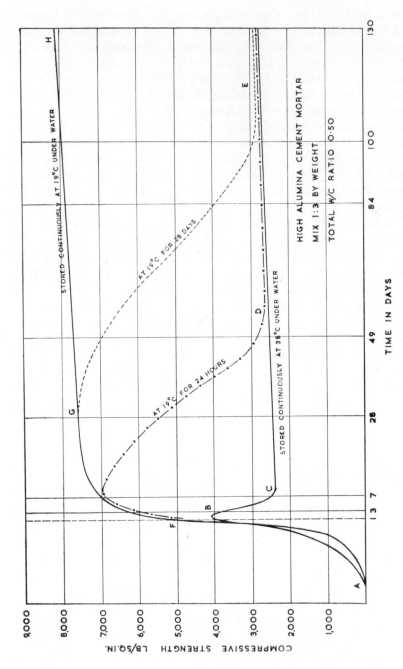

Fig. 16. Development of strength of H.A.C. concrete in hot water. (Cube specimens).

Curve AFGH (Fig. 16) shows the normal strength development of H.A.C. mortar or concrete hardening under water at 19°C. (66°F.), but if the same mix is maintained, after gauging, under water at 38°C. (100°F.), the strength development is similar to curve ABCE, i.e. when the mix hardens under hot wet conditions the strength rises to a maximum at B before falling to the general level CE, which (for convenience only) we may call the residual or " fully converted " strength of this particular mix. However prolonged the storage in hot water, the strength never subsequently drops below this level, since the effects of conversion are practically finished at this stage. The time required to complete the cycle and to reach the stable lower strength depends on the temperature of the water, the process being faster at higher temperatures. At any fixed temperature the conversion cycle occurs with maximum speed when (as in this case) the specimen is always under water and is submitted to the hot wet conditions immediately after gauging.

A mix allowed to harden, even for a short period, at normal temperatures before being placed in the hot water, takes longer to reach the fully converted strength level. Thus at 38°C. it requires 5-7 days when the mortar or concrete is immersed immediately (curve ABC), but for specimens cured normally for 6 hours, 1 day or 28 days it requires roughly 20-30 days, 50 days and 100 days respectively. For example, the course of strength reduction in water at 38°C. of specimens cured normally for 1 day and 28 days is given by curves FD and GE[13].

A given mix eventually reaches the same level of residual strength whether it is submitted to the hot wet conditions immediately, or after any period of curing at normal temperatures, i.e. the conversion has the same ultimate effect on strength no matter what time it occurs in the life of the concrete. Some investigators have indicated that the converted strength level is lower when the concrete is well matured at ordinary temperature before being placed in hot wet conditions[60], but this has not been confirmed by later work[61].

The residual strength after conversion of any particular mix therefore appears to be very characteristic and consistent, being independent of the maturity of the mortar or concrete and of the temperature of the water. Higher temperatures merely hasten the completion of conversion without materially changing the converted strength. Apparent anomalies[62] are usually due to tests whose duration is too short to ensure that the true residual strength is always reached.

From time to time various figures have been published for the compressive strength which may be expected from H.A.C. concretes or mortars after complete conversion in hot wet conditions, most values being in the region of 2000-2500 lb./sq. in., but some lower results have also been quoted[63]. For long it was assumed that all H.A.C. mixes inevitably gave this low level of strength if allowed to convert fully, but later studies[64] showed that the converted strength and quality of H.A.C. concretes or mortars can vary within wide limits, the controlling factor being the original water-cement ratio of the mix. If this is sufficiently low the concrete can have a very high strength and satisfactory quality even after full conversion has been brought about.

The effect of water-cement ratio upon the residual or fully converted strength is clearly shown in Fig. 17. In this case it should be noted that the water-cement ratios are based on the total amount of water added to air-dry aggregates of low absorption value, but

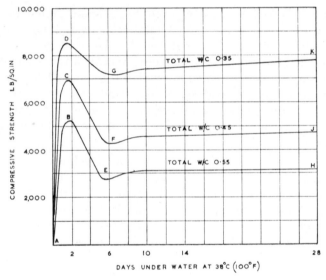

FIG. 17. Effect of water-cement ratio on converted strengths of H.A.C. concrete. Conversion effected by maintaining concrete cubes under hot water from time of gauging.

Newman[1] has given similar curves relating to " effective " water-cement ratios. The substantial increase in the level of converted strength at the lower water-cement ratios will be evident, and a further point is the increasing upward slope of the lines EH, FJ, and GK which represent the converted strengths. At W/C = 0.60 - 0.50 it is found that there is only a very slow gain in strength on continued storage in hot water once the residual strength level has been reached, and therefore the line EH, for example, is practically level. However at W/C = 0.35 there is a considerable and sustained gain after the basic strength has been achieved at G. Although Fig. 17 only gives results up to 28 days' storage, the strength of this mix had exceeded 9000 lbs./sq. in. after 1 year in the hot water. It is probable that the slow gain in strength on continued storage in hot wet conditions is due to secondary hydration. Mixes of lower water-cement ratio contain a higher proportion of unhydrated cement nuclei, and, during the conversion process, the latter become available for subsequent hydration to the cubic hydrate. Curves drawn from A through EH, FJ and GK might be regarded as the strength development due to the cubic hydrate at different water-cement ratios, and therefore this hydrate appears capable of giving concrete strengths of the same order as the normal hydrates but, to do so, it requires much lower water-cement ratios.

A curve relating converted strengths (e.g. points E, F, G etc.) to water-cement ratio is given in Fig. 18. A comparison with the strengths of the same mixes cured at ordinary temperature (19°C.) for 1 day, shows that the effect of conversion upon compressive strength diminishes rapidly as the water-cement ratio is reduced. It is also clear that quite high structural strengths are obtained after complete conversion providing that the water-cement ratio is below 0.45-0.40. Of course the curve AB for the 1-day strengths of normally cured H.A.C. mixes should really be a rather broad family of curves to include variations caused by different cement contents and aggregate gradings, etc. On the other hand, it has been found that the converted strengths are dependent almost uniquely on the water-cement ratio and they therefore fall within a very much narrower band represented by CD. In fact, this latter curve seems to be valid, within experimental error, for mortars or concretes and for mixes ranging from 1 : 1 to 1 : 9. With the usual types of concrete aggregate the strength which any H.A.C. mix will give after full conversion can therefore be predicted with sufficient accuracy if the water-cement ratio is known. Similar curves have been published by Newman (for " effective " water-cement ratios) and by Masterman[65] who shows that several previously quoted values for converted strengths fit this relationship.

(b) Conversion in air

At any particular temperature the time required for complete conversion increases greatly as the humidity of the concrete is reduced. Even a small reduction in humidity to below the saturation point diminishes the rate of conversion and there is, for example, a noticeable

103

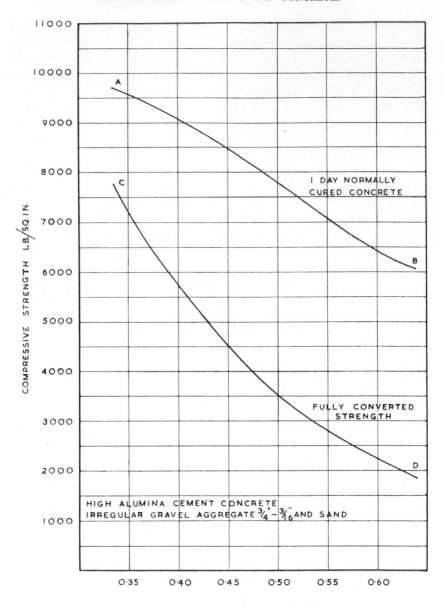

FIG. 18. Cube compressive strengths vs. water-cement ratios.

difference between storage in air at 95 per cent. relative humidity and storage under water at the same temperature. Air-dried concrete submitted to the normal wide fluctuations of atmospheric humidity

104

has an extremely slow rate of conversion at the highest atmospheric temperatures, and Newman has shown that H.A.C. concrete placed in an oven at 52°C. (125°F.) immediately after gauging exhibits an initial drop in strength while wet but after drying there is no further effect of conversion upon strength. Mortar specimens cured normally for 7 days and kept for seven years in an oven at 38°C. (100°F.) also maintained their strength[13]. Schneider[66] found that the hexagonal hydrate CAH_{10} does not convert to the cubic hydrate at high temperatures when the water is free to escape, and X-ray examination[67] of hydrated specimens of neat H.A.C. stored in completely dry air revealed no sign of the cubic hydrate after 6 years at 37°C. (99°F.) or after 3 years at 50°C. (122°F.). The presence of water is essential for the conversion process which therefore may not occur in dry concrete even at high temperatures[38].

(c) Factors accelerating conversion

The accelerating effect of increasing humidities and temperatures has already been mentioned. We have also noted that any condition causing conversion has its most rapid effect when the concrete is setting and hardening. The effect of hot wet conditions is also accelerated if the liquid in the concrete has an unusually high pH value. For example, Brocard[68], following up an earlier indication by Dorsch, stored neat H.A.C. prisms in strong sodium or potassium hydroxide solutions at room temperature and detected the appearance of cubic hydrate within 28 days. This, of course, was rather drastic treatment. Storage of H.A.C. concrete in warm saturated potassium carbonate gives faster conversion than storage in tap-water at the same temperature, but the effect of saturated sodium carbonate or saturated lime-water is very much less. Certain aggregates can liberate alkalis into the concrete and an excessive proportion of dust from some igneous rock aggregates should be avoided in H.A.C. concrete.

(d) Measures proposed for retarding conversion or minimising its effects

Under given conditions of high temperature and humidity the rate of conversion is constant and predictable unless some of the unusual features mentioned above are present, and there are few agencies which appear to affect the basic pattern of strength development and reduction, or to alter its natural speed.

It has been claimed that the addition of normal hydrates (separately prepared at low temperatures) to the mix during gauging, will prevent or retard the formation of cubic hydrate, but this has yet to be con-

D* 105

firmed. Equally, there is no evidence that the presence of pre-formed cubic hydrate has any accelerating effect on the subsequent rate of formation of this hydrate in hot wet conditions.

Lafuma[69] has suggested that pozzolanas may modify the hydration and hardening of calcium aluminates. The addition of a proportion of various pozzolanic materials to H.A.C. mortar mixes has been found[13] to have little effect on the reduction in strength in hot water, or on the time to reach the fully converted strength but the gain in strength during continued storage in hot wet conditions was noticeably increased, i.e. the upward slope of the lines EH, FJ, etc. (Fig. 17) was greater. Noto la Diega[70] studied the hydration at ordinary temperature of monocalcium aluminate mixed with an active form of silica and detected the presence of a calcium silicate hydrate within 28 days. It is therefore possible that the addition of some pozzolanic material may have a favourable effect, at least on the later converted strength of H.A.C. mixes which are maintained for considerable periods in hot wet conditions.

If the H.A.C. contains a considerable amount of calcium di-aluminate, CA_2, this may modify the shape of the strength evolution curve of mortars and concretes stored in hot water. This compound hydrates only slowly at ordinary temperatures, but the hydration is accelerated in hot wet conditions and, although the end products in these circumstances are again the cubic hydrate and alumina hydrate, a useful contribution to the fully converted strength may result.

Budnikov[71] has reported that the strength of H.A.C., hardening at high temperatures, is improved by the addition of calcium sulphate to the mix. In this case, however, it would seem that any improvement is due to a change in the hydraulic bond from calcium aluminate hydrates to the calcium sulphoaluminate hydrate, and patents for such an addition to H.A.C. were taken out by the French Lafarge Company as early as 1928[72].

More recently, patents have been granted[73] which claim that the addition to H.A.C. mixes of certain classes of compounds has the effect of reducing the loss of strength during hardening at high temperatures. Among such compounds are some inorganic salts (e.g. aluminium sulphate, ammonium chloride and sodium phosphate), polysaccharides or polyhydric alcohols, and anionic, cationic or non-ionic surface active agents. The effect of the latter class of compounds upon the hydration of calcium aluminates has also been studied by other investigators[74].

So far it cannot be said that any reliable and effective method has been discovered which will greatly retard or prevent the conversion process when the conditions for the latter are specially favourable. When there is any probability of rapid conversion the best procedure is to use a sufficiently low water-cement ratio. This does not appreciably affect the rate of conversion but it does ensure that even the fully converted concrete will have greatly improved properties.

(3) *Effects of Conversion on Physical Properties*

The effect of conversion on compressive strength and the decisive influence of water-cement ratio upon converted strength has been described. The influence of conversion on tensile and flexural strength is proportionately much less and this is illustrated in Fig. 19 which compares the development of H.A.C. mortar tensile strength in hot water with the behaviour in cold water.

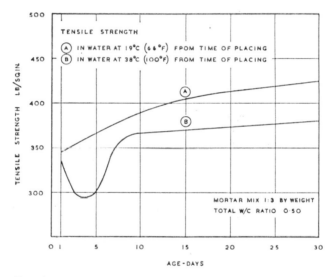

FIG. 19. Development of tensile strength during (A) Normal curing and (B) Conversion in hot water.

The cubic hydrate has a much lower density than the hexagonal hydrates from which it is formed, and therefore some shrinkage of a specimen undergoing conversion might be anticipated. In practice this does not occur and, indeed, the usual small expansion of a concrete or mortar stored continuously in cold water is somewhat increased when a similar specimen is converted by storage under hot water. The result of the hydrate conversion and of the simultaneous "ageing" of the alumina gel hydrate, is revealed by an increase in the porosity and permeability of the mortar or concrete. A comparison is made in Fig. 20 of the calculated porosities of H.A.C. concretes in the normal condition and after full conversion. It will be seen that, in order to obtain a concrete giving a satisfactorily low porosity *after* conversion, it is necessary to use a water-cement ratio below about 0.40. Mixes of relatively high water-cement ratio (e.g. 0.60) have a high strength and low porosity when cured and hardened normally, but if they are then allowed to convert fully, the porosity may be too high and the strength too low for many structural or chemical resistance applications.

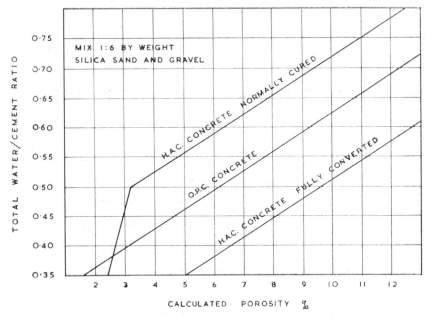

Fig. 20. Porosity of H.A.C. concrete (normally cured and fully converted) compared with that of ordinary Portland cement concrete.

When mixes of ordinary or high water-cement ratios are converted in hot wet conditions the grey-black type of H.A.C. changes to a reddish-chocolate colour. The increase in porosity produced by conversion is sufficient to allow hydrolysis and oxidation of the ferrous-iron compounds and to this the change in colour is probably due. Mixes made with a low water-cement ratio (e.g. 0.35) do not change colour during conversion under hot water since, in this case, no doubt, the porosity and permeability of the fully converted concrete is still adequately low.

The evolution of dynamic modulus of elasticity during conversion follows closely the changes in compressive strength, the maximum and minimum values occurring at the same times in each case. The ability to follow changes in dynamic modulus by a non-destructive method accordingly provides a useful way of noting the progress and velocity of conversion when the latter occurs under saturated conditions. The effect of conversion on dynamic modulus is shown in Fig. 21 for concretes of high and low water-cement ratios, and once more the great influence of a low water-cement ratio is demonstrated. It is of interest to note that when the specimen with $W/C = 0.35$ was examined after 6 months' continuous storage under hot water the colour was still black, although complete conversion has taken place, and the compressive strength, flexural strength and modulus of elasticity were higher than those values for the specimen with $W/C = 0.55$ which had been stored for the same time in cold water. The porosities of these two specimens were comparable at the end of the 6 month period. The concrete with $W/C = 0.55$ which had been stored in the hot water was chocolate brown and had a relatively low strength and high porosity[13].

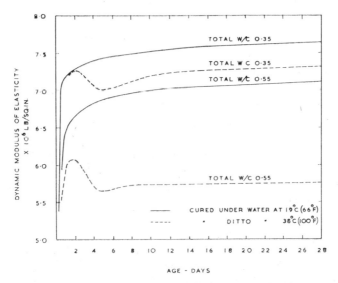

FIG. 21. Effect of hot wet curing on the dynamic modulus of H.A.C. concretes made with high and with low water-cement ratios.

16. THE CURING OF H.A.C. MORTARS AND CONCRETES

The importance of the proper curing of H.A.C. mortar or concrete cannot be sufficiently stressed. H.A.C. concretes, particularly when made with the lower-silica cements, should be ready for any desired structural or chemical resistance duty within 1 day and therefore a high proportion of the total hydration must take place in this time. The quality of the concrete can be made or marred in this period and, if certain curing measures are recommended, it is important that they should be carried out with care and at the right time, especially since attention is rarely needed after the first 24 hours. The recommended curing procedure for Portland cement concrete lasts much longer but it is frequently curtailed and sometimes ignored. Although this is extremely bad practice, the loss in concrete quality may not always be apparent. However, in the case of H.A.C. mixes the same degree of neglect can mean that, in some cases, the concrete is not fit for its intended duty.

H.A.C. mortars and concretes harden under ideal conditions when they are kept WET and relatively COOL and this usually necessitates the use of water for curing. According to circumstances, the chief function of the water may be either to keep the concrete wet or to keep it cool during the hardening period, and the most suitable curing method for any particular concreting job depends on the relative importance of these two functions.

(a) When the concrete need only be kept wet.

Thin sections of mortar and concrete, such as floor topping panels, renderings, etc., having a large surface area in relation to volume are very prone to excessive evaporation of mix water during hardening unless the exposed surface is kept thoroughly wet or is sealed at an early stage, e.g. by application of a membrane-curing compound. Final trowelling should be done at a time when it requires fairly heavy pressure to bring back the necessary small amount of moisture to the surface, and very shortly after this, steps should be taken to see that no further evaporation is possible. Otherwise a dusty top surface is likely, particularly if the mix is rich. In this type of application there is little or no temperature rise because of the thin section and therefore, when curing water is used its function is to prevent the surface of the mortar or concrete from drying out and carbonating during the first 24 hours. If the surface of an H.A.C. floor or floor-topping is found to be unsatisfactory, the almost invariable reason is inadequate curing or lack of curing. Applications in this class are cured by " ponding " the area, by fog-sprays or by sprinklers starting just as soon as the surface is sufficiently hard to remain undamaged and continuing for the remainder of 24 hours. Alternatively, wet hessian may be used for covering but some provision should be made to keep it saturated. Polythene sheets or a continuous coat of curing compound are also effective and wet sacking placed on top gives additional security.

When small H.A.C. concrete units (less than 6 in. thick) are cast in steel moulds so that there is only a small area of concrete left exposed it is often not necessary to take any curing precautions beyond covering or sealing the concrete surface. Again, there will be little temperature rise and the conditions for hardening within the mould are satisfactory. This applies to thin section beams and small precast units. When the moulds are required quickly for re-use, the concrete units when stripped should be kept in a cool, wet condition or immersed in cold water where this is convenient.

(b) When the concrete must be cooled

As the thickness of the concrete increases so does the temperature rise caused by cement hydration and then the chief function of the curing water is to control the maximum temperature and to dissipate the heat as rapidly as possible. In the case of slabs, beams, foundations, machine bases, precast piles and any other concrete units where the thickness is above 6-9 in. all wooden side-forms and non-supporting shuttering should be stripped or eased away just as soon as the concrete is sufficiently hard, in order to expose the maximum concrete surface to the immediate cooling action of water. For cooling purposes the water is best applied as a continuous light spray or by intermittent sprinkling or hosing, care being taken to see that the concrete never dries out. The layer of stagnant water produced by " ponding " is not very effective and hessian or damp sand are not recommended since they act as insulation if inadvertently allowed to dry. It will be clear that membrane curing-compounds, polythene sheet, etc., are in themselves quite useless when cooling is the predominant need. It is not so important to strip steel formwork since water running over the outside of this is reasonably effective in cooling the concrete, and steel does not have the heat insulating capacity of thick wooden forms. However, when cooling is necessary it is always best to remove steel forms also if this can be done without too much inconvenience.

The aim in cooling the concrete is to reduce the maximum temperature therein to below about 25°C. (77°F.) within the first 24 hours. If the concrete is too thick or is placed in too great a depth of " lift " this cannot be achieved even when forms are quickly stripped and cooling water applied. In practice it is found that normal mixes (about 550 lb. cement per cu. yd.) should not be placed in a " lift " deeper than 18 in. This applies directly to flat slabs, etc. and if successive lifts are required they should be cast at 24 hour intervals, each one being thoroughly cured with water. A more general statement

111

is that no part of the concrete being placed should be more than 12-18 in. away from a surface which can be cooled with water. Thus a column or wall 2 ft. 6 in. thick could be cast with any desired depth of lift so long as the side-forms were quickly stripped and all or both sides of the structure could be cooled with water. It is preferable to maintain 18 in. as the maximum figure for lean mixes also although a somewhat greater depth of " lift " is perhaps acceptable in this case. With mixes richer than normal the maximum " lift " must be reduced to 12 in. In all cases in which the concrete thickness approaches the maximum it is particularly important to strip or ease away the forms as soon as possible (at perhaps 2-6 hours after placing), to spray with cold water immediately and to continue to keep the concrete thoroughly wet for 1 day at least. Water sprayed on any reinforcing steel emerging from the concrete also has a cooling effect. If for any reason it is considered essential to place H.A.C. concrete in one operation to a thickness greater than normally recommended, provision for internal cooling should be made. Metal pipes arranged at not more than 1 ft. centres in the construction are connected to a water supply and cooling water is passed through while the concrete is hardening.

In Fig. 22 lack of proper curing is contrasted with efficient curing by the effect on temperature rise at the centre of 18 in. cubes of H.A.C. concrete cast in wooden moulds. It will be seen that when the mould was stripped early and water applied the temperature rise was quickly dissipated. On the other hand, the insulating effect of the mould, if not removed, resulted in the maintenance of much higher temperatures for longer than 24 hours.

In order to prevent appreciable conversion and hence to produce a normal concrete it is therefore probably necessary to ensure (i) that the maximum temperature in the hardening concrete never exceeds about 59°C. (122°F.), (ii) that temperatures above 38°C. (100°F.) are reduced as quickly as possible, and (iii) that the concrete temperature is below 25°C. (77°F.) by the end of 24 hours. In temperate climates all these criteria will be automatically fulfilled if the curing and cooling precautions given above are observed. It is therefore quite common for temperatures well above 38°C. (100°F.) to be reached in relatively thick sections of H.A.C. concrete (even when well cured) but, providing the proper procedure has been followed there is not sufficient time for any considerable conversion to take place, and the concrete can be considered normal.

The slower-hardening types of H.A.C. give temperature rises somewhat lower than those of the lower-silica type but when the former cements are used for structural or chemical resistance purposes the same curing procedure is necessary. According to Budnikov[75]

112

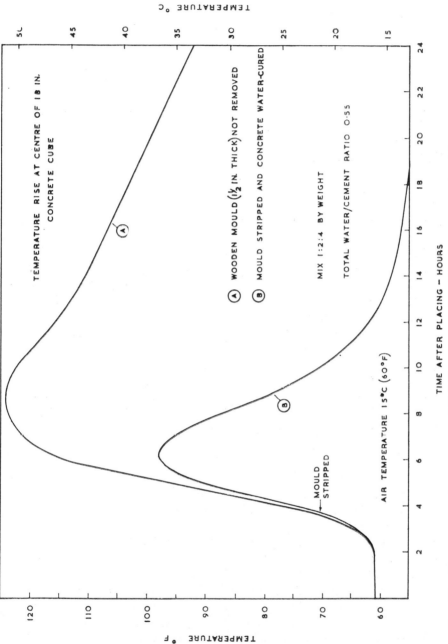

FIG. 22. Temperature rises at centre of H.A.C. concrete cubes (A) when not cured and (B) when properly cured.

the addition of a silicic acid sol to H.A.C. mixes reduces the heat evolved but it is not known whether this has been of practical use. Some retarders of set (see Chapter Five) tend to " spread out " the heat evolution curve and may be helpful when concreting in hotter weather.

Any temperature rise produced by hydration is added to the original mix temperature, and therefore the latter should be kept as low as possible in warm or hot weather. Gauging water must not be allowed to stand in the sun before use, aggregates may require spraying with water, and " lift " depths should be further reduced. There is no doubt that the production of normal high-quality H.A.C. concrete is much more difficult to achieve in hot climates and in some conditions it may be practically impossible. If the temperature of the concrete remains continuously above 30°C. (86°F.) for the first 3 or 4 days there will be sufficient time for a considerable amount of conversion and the concrete is said to be over-heated. The same result is produced in the first 24 hours if a temperature of 38°C. (100°F.) persists in the concrete for most of this period. For this reason many authorities consider that the casting of structural H.A.C. concrete should cease when the ambient temperature is above 30°C. and is likely to remain so.

Not infrequently H.A.C. structural concrete units, which have been well and successfully cured, are immediately stocked in the yard exposed to a very hot sun. Although the units will probably be about 24 hours old, and therefore less susceptible to conversion, they may then become very hot in the sun, particularly if made with grey-black H.A.C. In very hot weather it is therefore best to shade them from the direct sun for a time, either by storing indoors or by screening with a light-coloured sheet until they have matured and dried out for a day or two at least.

Steam-curing of H.A.C. mortars or concretes at atmospheric or higher pressures must cause full conversion of the hydrates and therefore it should not be used[76], at least with mixes having water-cement ratios above 0.40. With such mixes, steam-curing will reduce the strength to a relatively low value and will also impair the other concrete properties.

Although full investigations have not been made, there is every reason to believe that H.A.C. mixes with a sufficiently low water-cement ratio could give very high strengths when steam-cured. In these conditions nearly complete hydration of all the cement can be quickly achieved and the full potentialities of the cubic hydrate as a binder might be revealed. Budnikov contended that this hydrate can give higher strengths than those obtained from the normal hydrates and, with Kravchenko,[77] he claimed that a monocalcium aluminate paste (W/C = 0.50), maintained under water at 45°C. (113°F.) gave higher ultimate strengths than similar specimens kept at 15°C. This is not in accordance with the views of many investigators but further Russian work[78] indicates that H.A.C. concrete steam-cured at 174°C. (345°F.) gave a strength at 1 day which was three times normal. However, there is very strong evidence that H.A.C. concretes with permanently favourable properties will be obtained by steam-curing only when the lowest water-cement ratios are used. In connection with steam-curing it is interesting to note that the cubic hydrate is stable up to 215°C. (419°F.) and therefore would still remain even under high pressure curing[79]. The alumina hydrate Gibbsite (AH_3) is stable only to 150°C. (302°F.) and above that temperature Boehmite (AH) would appear.

17. PRACTICAL ASSESSMENT OF H.A.C. FOR STRUCTURAL CONCRETE

An orthodox H.A.C. concrete (1 : 6), with a consistency suitable for consolidation by hand, will usually require total water-cement ratios of 0.55-0.60. If well-cured it will readily give high strength, high chemical resistance, low porosity and low permeability. It is therefore eminently suitable for structural work as long as it is not submitted to conditions causing relatively quick conversion. Full conversion has a very deleterious effect upon this " ordinary " type of H.A.C. concrete, resulting in low strength and higher porosity. Other properties such as chemical resistance and freeze-thaw resistance may also be affected. Therefore, in general, such H.A.C. concrete should be used for high-load-bearing structural purposes only when it is evident that no considerable conversion will necessarily take place either during hardening or in subsequent use.

Any reduction in water-cement ratio below the above level (whether obtained by the use of a richer mix or by vibratory compaction) will improve the quality of the converted product and it has been shown that even fully converted H.A.C. concrete has very satisfactory properties if the water-cement ratio is sufficiently low (e.g. below 0.40). In selected cases, H.A.C. concrete made with a low water-cement ratio can thus be suitable for use in situations known to produce full conversion, and certainly no other quality should even be considered for structural purposes in these conditions. However, it is best to utilise the advantages gained from lower water-cement ratios merely as additional security even when no appreciable conversion is anticipated, or more necessarily, when conditions at times may lead to an increased risk of conversion.

The important conclusion is that, in all circumstances, no more water should be used than is required to allow thorough consolidation. The overall advantages of using lower water-cement ratios are even greater than those obtained with Portland cement and they become more valuable with increasing possibility of conversion. The combination of lean mixes and high water-cement ratios must be proscribed for all H.A.C. structural concrete even if the compressive strength thereby obtained appears adequate.

The following summary is a guide to the behaviour of structural H.A.C. concrete in various conditions.

(a) Conditions during hardening.

In temperate countries there should be no undue conversion while the concrete is hardening providing that placing and curing recommendations are followed. In very hot climates it is much more difficult to prevent appreciable conversion[63] and H.A.C. can be considered for making structural concrete only if mixes of low water-cement ratio can be used.

(b) Conditions subsequent to hardening.

1. Even when the concrete is maintained continuously under water, conversion is not of practical consequence when the water temperature is below about 25°C. (77°F.). Miller and Manson[80] found that 7 day old H.A.C. concrete specimens made with three different brands of cement showed little loss, no loss or a gain in strength after 20 years in Medicine Lake, S. Dakota, although the water is highly sulphated and quickly disintegrated similar specimens made with ordinary Portland cement. Specimens buried in the ground for the same length of time had strengths which exceeded the initial value. Lea[38] quotes tests on H.A.C. concrete in water at 18°C. (64°F.) which indicate a strength loss of 3-6 per cent. between 5 years and 10 years but the 10 year strengths were greatly superior to the original 7 day strengths.

Full conversion must eventually take place when even well-cured H.A.C. concrete is subsequently maintained under water or in saturated conditions at temperatures over 25°C.-30°C. (77°-86°F.) and therefore the final strength and quality of the concrete will be very dependent on the water-cement ratio. The results of Miller and Manson on specimens stored in water in the laboratory for 20 years reveal the effects of some conversion due, no doubt, to high water temperatures. For this reason H.A.C. it not normally recommended for high-load-bearing structural purposes in tropical seas or in certain industrial situations where

116

it will be immersed in hot water. Of course, H.A.C. concrete is used quite extensively for chemical resistance purposes in industrial conditions causing conversion (e.g. for hot-liquor tanks, blow-down sumps, gas-washing plants)[84] but such uses do not require a great load-bearing capacity. Nevertheless, low water-cement ratios (often obtained by using richer mixes) are strongly recommended for these applications.

2. Long-term tests on large numbers of H.A.C. concrete specimens exposed to the elements in temperate climates (e.g. in Great Britain) show that any subsequent conversion can be of little practical consequence in the case of well-made and properly cured concrete[13].

3. Long periods of exposure to the elements, in countries where high temperatures and humidities prevail, must increase conversion and the use of low water-cement ratios should be a primary requisite in any consideration of H.A.C. concrete for structural purposes.

4. Temperatures exceeding the highest found in nature, do not cause conversion when the concrete is dry[1, 13].

There have been a number of cases of structures built with H.A.C. concrete which later proved to be in an unsatisfactory condition[81] and this has usually been attributed to conversion after hardening. Bearing in mind the actual climatic conditions it is probable that, in many of these instances, the greater part of any conversion took place while the concrete was hardening and in others the use of a high water-cement ratio has accentuated the effect of any conversion which occurred. The satisfactory quality of other H.A.C. structures, of equal or greater age and subject to substantially the same conditions, is undoubtedly due to proper curing and/or the use of lower water-cement ratios.

Nevertheless the discovery of fully converted concrete has led to restrictions on the use of H.A.C. concrete for permanent structural purposes in some countries[82], although climatic conditions do not always appear to provide justification. With increasing knowledge of the conversion process and of the dominating influence of water-cement ratio upon its effects, there is every indication that unfavourable results can be avoided. The advantages of H.A.C. for structural use can be very great, but they should be utilised only for suitable applications, and with attention to water-content and curing. A canal bridge recently constructed by the Ponts et Chaussées in S. France was completed in 36 hours and it was opened to heavy traffic only

117

7 hours after the H.A.C. concrete portion had been placed[83]. In the opinion of Duriez who described this work, H.A.C. concrete, properly made and used, is suitable for permanent structural work.

LITERATURE REFERENCES

1 K. NEWMAN.   Reinf. Concr. Rev., 1960, **5**, (5), 269.

2 K. J. BROWN.   Civ. Engng. Lond., 1958, **53**, (623), 539.

3 E. RENGADE.   Int. Assn. Test Mater. Congress London, 1937, 245.   J. BOLOMEY.   Bull. tech. Suisse rom.   1927, **53**, (22), 262 :   (24), 285. Travaux, 1935, **33**, 384. O. GRAF. Beton u. Eisen, 1934, **33**, (10), 156. B. TAVASCI. Chim. e Industr., 1938, 469. Tonindustr. Ztg., 1938, **62**, (72/73), 808. L. SCHUMAN & J. TUCKER JR. J. Res. nat. Bur. Stand. 1943, **31**, RP. 1552. L. S. KOGAN & GOL'DSHTEJN. Cement, U.R.S.S., 1960, **26**, (2), 7. M. PROT. Ann. Inst. Bâtim. 1950, (156).

4 J. BOLOMEY. Ref. No. 3. M. DZULYNSKY. Bull. Cent. Rech. Constr. 1953, **6**, 99. W. E. ABBOTT. Cement & Lime Manuf. 1948, **21**, (4), 69.

5 ANON. Génie civ. 1939, **114**, (19), 399. G. LEFLOT. Génie civ. 1923, Aug. 11, 18, 25. G. MAGNEL. Ann. Ass. Ing. Ec. Gand. 1923, **13**, (2). N. DE TEDESCO. Constr. Cim. armé. 1922, Jan-July.

6 A. R. COLLINS. Civ. Engng. Lond., 1950, **45**, (524), 110. Contract. J. 1949, 1884, 1970.

7 E. FREYSSINET. Soc. Ing. Civ. France Mém. 1935, **88**, (8/10), 643. Struct. Eng. 1936, **14**, (5), 242.

8 A. M. NEVILLE. I. L. HOLMES. Test Reports Nos. 1200, 1507, 1954. Canterbury Univ. Coll. Christchurch, N. Zealand.

9 ROAD RES. LAB. Road Res. Note 4, 2nd Edn., H.M.S.O. J. D. McINTOSH & H. C. ERNTROY. Res. Report 2. Cement & Concrete Assn., 1955. H. C. ERNTROY & B. W. SHACKLOCK. Proc. Symp. on Mix Design 1954. Cement & Concrete Assn., 1955, 53.

10 W. H. GLANVILLE. Int. Assn. Test Mater. Congress London, 1937, 249.

11 E. SUENSON. Ingenioren, 1924, 261.

12 R. H. EVANS. Struct. Engr., 1946, **24**, (12), 636. RENGADE. Ref. No. 3.

13 LAFARGE ALUMINOUS CEMENT CO. LTD. LABS. West Thurrock, England.

14 S. KOIDE, K. KAIDEN & M. KAWANO. Asahi Glass Co. Res Lab. Rep. 1958, **8**, (2), 83.

15 O. J. MASTERMAN. Mag. Concr. Res. 1958, **10**, (29), 57.

16 LAFARGE ALUMINOUS CEMENT CO. LTD., London. From data supplied by permission of the Director, Building Research Station, England.

17 R. JONES & E. N. GATFIELD. D.S.I.R. Road Res. Tech. Paper No. 34, 1955, H.M.S.O.

18 P. KLIEGER. J. Amer. Concr. Inst., 1957, **29**, (6), 481. See also R. JONES. Struct. Eng. 1957, 190 (Discussion by R. H. Elvery).

19 H. GESSNER. Kolloidzschr. 1928, **46**, 207 : 1929, **47**, 65, 160.

[20] R. DUTRON. Bull. tech. res. controle Group. fabric. Ciment Belgique No. 28, 1934. Bruxelles.

[21] A. M. NEVILLE. Private communic. 1960.

[22] W. H. GLANVILLE. D.S.I.R. Build. Res. Tech. Paper No. 11, 1930, H.M.S.O.

[23] P. L'HERMITE. Inst. Tech. Bâtim. Circ. Ser. F. No. 37, 1947. 4th Int. Symp. Chem. Cements, Washington, 1960. M. LUCAS. Ann. Ponts Chauss., 1937, **107,** (2), 223. Doctorate Thesis, 1937. M. VENUAT. Rev. Matér. Constr. 1960, (538/9), 169 ; (540), 215 ; (541), 251.

[24] H. LAFUMA " Liants Hydrauliques " Dunod, 1952.

[25] F. G. THOMAS. Struct. Engr. 1936, **14,** (7), 298. A. DE SOUSA COUTINHO. R.I.L.E.M. Bull. No. 5, 26. W. CZERNIN. 3rd Int. Congr. Precast Concr. Industr., Stockholm, 1960. Gen. Report.

[26] F. M. LEA & C. R. LEE. Symp. on Shrinking and Cracking, London, 1946. Soc. Chem. Industry, 1947. F. E. JONES 3rd Int. Symp. Chem., Cement, London, 1952, 368. F. L. BRADY. Ann. Report, Build. Res. Station, England, 1931.

[27] W. H. GLANVILLE. D.S.I.R. Build. Res. Tech. Paper No. 12, 1930. Ist Int. Congr. on Concrete, Liége. 1930, **1,** 511.

[28] W. H. GLANVILLE & F. G. THOMAS. D.S.I.R. Build. Res. Tech. Paper No. 21, 1939.

[29] A. HUMMEL. Zement Kalk Gips, 1959, **12,** (5), 187.

[30] A. D. ROSS. Mun. Eng., 1936, **48,** (2451), 626.

[31] A. M. NEVILLE & H. W. KENINGTON. 4th Inst. Symp. Chem. Cement, Washington 1960.

[32] W. EASTWOOD & R. D. MILNE. Civ. Engng. Lond. 1953, **48,** (566), 741. G. MARSHALL. Mag. Concr. Res. 1949, (3), 123.

[33] W. H. GLANVILLE. D.S.I.R. Build. Res. Tech. Paper No. 3, 1926. H.M.S.O.

[34] S. WALKER, D. L. BLOEM & W. G. Mullen. J. Amer. Concr. Inst. 1952, **23,** 661.

[35] D. R. G. BONNELL & F. C. HARPER. J. Instn. civ. Engrs., 1950, **33,** (4), 320. NATIONAL BUILDING STUDIES. Tech. Paper No. 7, 1951. H.M.S.O.

[36] O. GRAF. Dtsch. Auss. für Eisenbeton 1933, No. 74 (W. Ernst & Sohn). WALKER et al. Ref. No. 34.

[37] N. DAVEY & E. N. FOX. D.S.I.R. Build. Res. Tech. Paper No. 15, 1933. H.M.S.O.

[38] F. M. LEA. " The Chemistry of Cement and Concrete." E. Arnold, London, 1956.

[39] K. E. DORSCH. " The Hardening and Corrosion of Cements " Springer, Berlin, 1932. Cement & Cement Manuf., 1933, **22,** 131.

[40] E. H. WATERS. J. Amer. Concr. Inst., 1952, 24, 536. D. MAGUIRE & M. OLEN. Trans. S. Afr. Inst. elect. Engrs., 1940, **31,** 301. R. DECOUX & J. BARRÉE. Ann. Inst. Bâtim. Circ. Sér. F, No. 3, 1941. R. W. SPENCER. J. Amer. Concr. Inst., 1937, **34,** 45.

[41] E. HAMMOND & T. D. ROBSON. Engineer, Lond., 1955, **199,** 78, 114. See also S. KOIDE, M. KAWANO & K. KAIDEN. Asahi Glass Co. Res. Lab. Rep. 1957, **7,** (1), 44.

42 E. Lambert. Bull. Soc. franc. Elect. 1940, **10**, 257. U.S. Pat. 2038367, 1936.

43 P. Ferrier. Rev. gen. Elect. 1933, **33**, 731.

44 Review of Standards for Cements other than Portland. Cembureau 1958. Malmo, Sweden.

45 Génie civ. 1924, 84, (10), 221.

46 E. Freyssinet & A. Coyne. Génie civ. 1927, **90**, (11), 266.

47 H. Vierheller. Zement 1927, 16, (28), 602 : (29), 649. A. F. Rosher Lund, Zement, 1927, **16**, (34), 747 : 1929, **18**, (23), 718 : (24), 748 : 1931, **20**, (8), 164.

48 R. Féret. Rev. Matér. Constr. 1928, (223), 135 ; (224), 166. W. N. Thomas & N. Davey. D.S.I.R. Building Res. Spec. Report No. 13, 1929. P. H. Bates. Inter. Ass. Test Mater. Zurich, 1930, 211. G. Haegermann. Tonindustr. Ztg. 1931, **55**, (103), 1430. J. Séailles. 14th Congrés Chim. Industr. Paris, 1934. S. Mirnov. Nov. Tekhn. 1936, (57), 20.

49 N. Davey. D.S.I.R. Building Res. Tech. Paper No. 14, 1933. Concr. constr. Engng. 1933, **28**, (12), 717.

50 J. Bolomey. Bull. tech. Suisse rom. 1927, **53**, (24), 285.

51 J. Bolomey. Travaux. 1935, **33**, 384.

52 N. Davey. Inter. Ass. Test Mater. London, 1937, 342.

53 Ann. Report Building Res. Board, England 1928. H.M.S.O. J. Séailles. C.R. Acad. Sci. Paris 1932, **195**, (16), 662. H. Lafuma. C.R. Acad. Sci. Paris, 1933, **196**, (22), 1671. E. P. von Polheim. Zement 1935, 609, 643, 659, 677.

54 Ann. Report Building Res. Board, England 1933. H.M.S.O. J. Séailles. Ref. No. 48. N. Iltchenko & H. Lafuma. Chim. et Industr. 1937, **38**, (3), 438.

55 E. Couillaud. C.R. Inst. Bâtim. 1939, **209**, (8), 397. Thesis, Paris. 1947. Ann. Inst. Bâtim. Circ. Sér. F. 1947, No. 31.

56 F. M. Lea. J. Soc. Chem. Industr. 1940, **59**, 18.

57 L. S. Wells & E. T. Carlson. J. Res. nat. Bur. Stand. 1956, **57**, (6), 335. RP. 2723. E. E. Segalova, Z. D. Tulovskaya, E. A. Amelia & P. A. Rebinder. C.R. Akad. Sci. U.R.S.S. 1959, **124**, 876.

58 R. Fricke. Z. anorg. Chem. 1928, **175**, 249. H. B. Weiser & W. O. Milligan. J. Phys. Chem. 1934, **38**, 1175. K. Funacki & Y. Shimizu. J. chem. Soc. Japan 1952, **35**, 194. S. Suzuki. Kolloidzschr. 1958, **156**, (1), 67. D. Papée, R. Tertiau & R. Biais. Bull. Soc. chim. Fr. 1959, 11-12, 1301. T. Sato. J. Appl. Chem. London. 1961, **2**, (6), 207.

59 A. Travers & P. Leduc. C.R. 1933, **197**, (3), 252 : 1934, **198** (9), 828.

60 Iltchenko & Lafuma. Ref. No. 54. Couillaud. Ref. No. 55.

61 Lafarge Aluminous Cement Co. Ltd. Davey. Ref. No. 52. Building Res. Station Digest No. 27. 1951, H.M.S.O.

62 S. Gottlieb. Cement & Lime Manuf. 1940, **13**, (4), 55. A. M. Neville, Proc. Instn. civ. Engrs. 1958, **10**, 185.

63 G. C. Hagger. J. Instn. civ. Engrs., 1945, **25**, 142. Concr. constr. Engng. 1946, **41**, (8), 210.

[64] T. D. ROBSON. Architect. Science Rev. Sydney, 1959, **2**, (1), 49. NEWMAN. Ref. No. 1.

[65] O. J. MASTERMAN. Civ. Engng. & Publ. Works Rev. 1961, **56**, (657), 483.

[66] S. J. SCHNEIDER. J. Amer. ceram. Soc. 1959, **42**, (4), 184.

[67] CIMENTS LAFARGE. Paris.

[68] J. BROCARD. C.R. Acad. Sci. Paris, 1951, **232**, (5), 413.

[69] H. LAFUMA. Ann. Chim. appl. Roma. 1954, **44**, 719.

[70] G. NOTO LA DIEGA. Il Cemento, 1959, **7**, 23.

[71] P. P. BUDNIKOV & I. G. GOL'DENBERG. Dopovidi Akad Nauk U.R.S.S. Phys. Chem. 1942, (3-4), 73. J. Appl. Chem. Moscow, 1945, **18**, 15 : 1959, **32**, 21.

[72] SOC. ANON DES Chaux et Cim. LAFARGE. Brit. Pat. 317783, 1929.

[73] ASAHI GLASS CO. LTD. S. KOIDE, K. AMATO & K. NISHIDA. Japan Pats. 5431, 5432, 5433. 1959. S. KOIDE, K. KOMATA & M. KAWANO Asahi Glass Co. Res. Lab. Rep., 1956, **6**, 133.

[74] R. SERSALE. Ric. sci. 1957, **27**, 777. A. A. ADAMOVICH. Dokl. Akad. Nauk U.S.S.R. 1955, **103**, 853. N. G. ZAITSEVA & A. M. SMIRNOVA. Kolloid Zhur. 1958, **30**, 636.

[75] P. P. BUDNIKOV. Russian Pat. 57563, 1940. See also Russ. Pats. 127602, 127603, 127607.

[76] P. CLARKSON. Engng. London. 1951, 345. A. R. COLLINS, Ref. No. 6.

[77] P. P. BUDNIKOV & I. V. KRAVCHENKO. Kolloid Zhur. 1959, **21**, (1), 9.

[78] " The Technology and Properties of Heavy Concrete." Edited by A. E. Desov, 1959. In Russian. State Publishing Office for Literature on Building, etc.

[79] R. B. PEPPLER & L. S. WELLS. J. Res. nat. Bur. Stand. 1954, **52**, (2), 75. RP. 2476.

[80] D. G. MILLER & P. W. MANSON. Tech. Bull. U.S. Dept. Agric. 1933, No. 358. Publ. Rds. Wash. 1931, **12**, (3), 64.

[81] F. CAMPUS. Inter. Assn. Bridge & Struct. Engng. 4th Congr. Cambridge & London, 1952. R. CAVENEL, Ann. Ponts Chauss. 1944, **114**, (6), 109. D.S.I.R. Nat. Build. Studies Spec. Rep. 25, 1956. F. M. LEA & N. DAVEY. J. Instn. Civ. Engrs. 1948-49, **32**, (7), 248.

[82] J. DREYFUS. " La Chimie des Ciments " Ed. Eyrolles, Paris, 1950, 279. E. BOLCSKEI & K. SZALAI. Magyar Epitöpar 1958, **7**, (10/12), 474. P. BRZAKOVIC. Nase Gradevinarstro (Belgrade), 1955, **9**, (9), 191 : (10), 220 : (11), 252. V. MATIC. R.I.L.E.M. Bull. 6, 1960.

[83] M. DURIEZ. Rev. Gén. Routes & Aerodr. 1960, **347**, 93.

[84] ANON. Concr. constr. Engng. 1935, **30**, (2), 104.

CHAPTER 5.—ADDITIVES, LATEX/CEMENT COMPOSITIONS AND EXPANSIVE CEMENTS

CONTENTS

123

CHAPTER FIVE

Additives, Latex/Cement Compositions, and Expansive Cements

A very small proportion of certain substances is frequently added to Portland cements, either during grinding or more often at the mixer, in order to accelerate or retard the set, entrain air, reduce permeability, increase workability and otherwise modify some of the concrete properties[1]. The same possibilities are open to users of H.A.C. and some of the agents used with Portland cement are similarly effective when used in approximately the same concentration. Some must be employed in a different proportion, others are of little value or even deleterious, and the various types of H.A.C. do not necessarily give the same reaction. It is therefore recommended that no such addition should be made at the mixer on the basis of satisfactory results with Portland cement, but only after technical advice has been sought and preliminary trials with the specific cement have been made.

1. ACCELERATORS AND RETARDERS

In general, alkalis and alkaline compounds accelerate the set of H.A.C. while acids and acidic compounds retard. This statement is subject to numerous exceptions and there are many compounds which retard the set when present in very low concentrations but which act as accelerators at higher concentrations[2].

(a) Accelerators

Dilute solutions of sodium, potassium and calcium hydroxides and organic bases such as triethanolamine are active accelerators of set but magnesium and barium hydroxides may cause retardation possibly due to buffer action[3]. Sodium or potassium carbonates and silicates also reduce the setting-time of H.A.C. and many H.A.C. mixes designed for special purposes involve gauging with sodium silicate[4]. Highly diluted sulphuric acid is said to produce quick-setting but similar concentrations of hydrochloric and acetic acids retard. Most of the common sulphates and nitrates retard the set if the concentration does not exceed 0.25 per cent. by weight of cement, but at concentrations above 0.5-1.0 per cent. they may produce a rapid set (e.g. calcium and sodium sulphates). A slurry made from H.A.C. together with 1-5 per cent. of salts such as the sulphates of calcium, magnesium, iron and aluminium, calcium chloride or alkali carbonates has been patented as a protective coating for metals. Casein was also added to reduce evaporation and control shrinkage[5]. Various other patents in which H.A.C. is mixed with relatively high proportions of sulphates include one for a quick setting " plaster " consisting of H.A.C., aluminium sulphate, calcium carbonate and a major amount of hydrated lime[6]. H.A.C. itself is sometimes added to plaster-of-Paris or anhydrite plasters in order to give stronger moulds or castings.

Lithium salts have been suggested as accelerators for H.A.C.[7] and it has been shown that if grains of pre-hydrated cement are added to the mix this produces a marked reduction in setting-time[8]. In this respect H.A.C. behaves in the same way as Portland cement which is accelerated in set and early strength development by the addition of about 2 per cent. by weight of previously hydrated cement[9].

If some H.A.C. is fully hydrated, dried, re-ground to cement fineness, and then added to the original cement, the effect on setting-time is shown by the example below[10].

	Setting-times	
	Initial	Final
H.A.C. without addition	4 hrs. 40 mins.	5 hrs. 30 mins.
H.A.C. + 5 per cent. hydrated H.A.C.	3 hrs. 25 mins.	4 hrs. 5 mins.
H.A.C. + 10 per cent. hydrated H.A.C.	2 hrs. 25 mins.	3 hrs. 15 mins.
H.A.C. + 25 per cent. hydrated H.A.C.	10 mins.	40 mins.

Portland cement acts as an accelerator of set for H.A.C. and vice-versa. Indeed, any setting-time between the normal set of the original cement and a practically instantaneous set can be obtained by judicious addition of the other cement. The quick-setting nature of mixes of Portland cement and H.A.C. was noticed at an early stage in the history of H.A.C.[11] and this property has been put to practical use on quite a wide scale. The characteristics and applications of such mixtures have been quite fully described[12] and the main principles are as follows.

126

When Portland cement is added in increasing quantities to H.A.C., the setting-times of the various mixtures rapidly become quicker until a practically instantaneous set is obtained with a certain proportion of the two cements. A mixture of these proportions may also be reached by adding H.A.C. to Portland cement and, in the same way. the set of the mixtures becomes more rapid with increasing quantities of H.A.C. The exact proportion at which the most rapid set is obtained varies with the particular batches of H.A.C. and Portland cement but it frequently lies between equal quantities and 70 per cent. H.A.C./30 per cent. Portland cement. The setting-times observed also depend on other factors such as water-cement ratio, temperature etc., and therefore Fig. 23, which gives the setting-times of all mixtures of the two cements, should be used only as a guide to the general behaviour[13]. Uusually, much less Portland cement can be added to H.A.C. before a very fast or " flash " set is produced than vice-versa, and the set of mixes rich in H.A.C. therefore tends to be more sensitive to small changes in the proportion of Portland cement. In practice, the mixes most commonly used contain a major proportion of Portland cement and the desired setting-time can frequently be obtained with

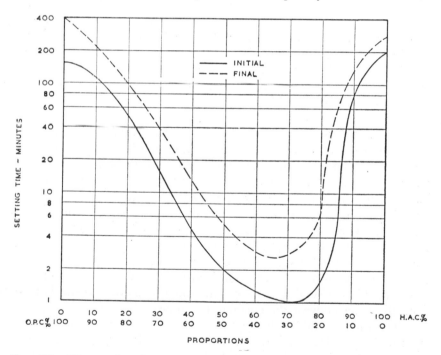

FIG. 23. The setting-times of mixtures of H.A.C. and ordinary Portland cement.

one or other of the following mixes :—Portland cement/H.A.C. 3 : 1, 2 : 1, 1½ : 1. All the setting-times are faster than that of the original Portland cement and the accelerating effect increases in the order given. A preliminary trial is necessary on site to fix the proportions required and if the set at first obtained is too slow, a higher proportion of the minor constituent is needed. The two cements should preferably be mixed in the dry form but if they are blended as slurries, the minor constituent should always be stirred into the major constituent, since the reverse procedure results in a flash-setting composition before addition is complete. Mixes with fast setting times must be gauged in small quantities only, since it is necessary to place and consolidate them before setting starts ; otherwise the set may be " killed " and little or no strength will result. Placing by cement-gun is very suitable.

Mixes of this type are used neat, or as mortars and concretes (but not reinforced concretes), for applications requiring a quick set and the development of reasonable structural strength at a very early age. A mix consisting of 1½ parts of ordinary Portland cement to 1 part of H.A.C. may set in 5-15 minutes and give a mortar or concrete strength of about 1000 lb./sq. in. within the hour[12]. In several countries these mixtures are therefore widely used for repairs to exterior mouldings, for castings[14], for sealing leaks (e.g. in ships, walls[15] and caissons), or for preventing the ingress of water to excavations, for fixing temporary formwork, for cementation of ground or rock, for cold-weather work[16], and for grouting posts, bolts, metal frames, etc. They have also been found particularly useful by plumbers and electricians.

The faster the set obtained the lower the ultimate strength, and the mixed cements should not be used when the highest load-bearing capacity is required. Although much of the work is of a temporary nature there are many cases where concretes made with the mixtures have given long and satisfactory service[17], even in sea-defence constructions. It must be remembered, however, that the addition of H.A.C. to Portland cement can give mixes with a lower sulphate resistance than the original cement[18]. When Portland cement concrete is placed between tides and is subject to early wave-action, H.A.C. may be sprinkled on the unset surface and the reaction between the cements quickly gives a hard skin which helps to prevent damage until the main body of the concrete has time to harden.

The early strengths obtained from the mixed cements are further improved by using mixtures of quick-setting Portland cement and H.A.C., and Féret and Venuat[19] have discussed several of their properties, including setting-time, strength, shrinkage and expansion.

Mixtures of Portland blast-furnace cement and H.A.C. also give faster sets[20] and those containing a major proportion of the slag cement can be gauged with sea-water if necessary.

(b) Retarders

Chlorides of sodium, potassium, barium, magnesium, and calcium in small concentrations usually slow the set of H.A.C. and calcium chloride, which is often added to Portland cement with favourable effects on early strength, should be regarded as a deleterious ingredient in structural H.A.C. concrete[21]. In some special applications such as the soil stabilisation of beaches for military purposes, H.A.C. together with a small amount of calcium chloride gave the best results[22], but for ordinary concreting, calcium chloride should never be added, and proprietary additives designed for Portland cement must be checked before use with H.A.C. in order to determine whether it is present.

Similarly sea-water should not be used for gauging H.A.C.[23] and when placing H.A.C. concrete by trémie special care should be taken to prevent sea-water re-entering the pipe and severely contaminating the mix. Gauging water must be cool and of drinking quality. The deleterious effect of sea-water on the normal hardening of H.A.C. concrete appears to be accentuated as the mix temperature rises, and although it has been used with reasonable satisfaction for unreinforced concrete in regions where fresh water was difficult to obtain, this should be regarded as an emergency procedure and high-quality concrete cannot generally be expected.

Salts of hydroxy-carboxylic acids such as citric, tartaric, gluconic, and also carbohydrate salts, have a retarding action on the set of H.A.C.[24] but, as will be seen below, they may occasionally be used as water-reducing agents since they increase the fluidity of the paste at low water-cement ratios. Other organic compounds, even when present in relatively small proportions may delay the set for long periods or even suppress it, i.e. glycols, glycerine, sugars, flour, casein, starch and cellulose products. Accordingly, when H.A.C. concretes or mortars are being placed in bakeries, flour mills, confectionery works, etc., care is necessary to ensure that one or other of these substances does not contaminate aggregates, tools, and ultimately the mix. The use of old sugar or flour bags for covering the concrete during curing or for storing surplus cement has sometimes been the reason for apparently mysterious results. Many inorganic compounds such as borax, lead salts, phosphates, etc., can have a severe retarding action on H.A.C.

E

129

Accelerators of set may increase the strength obtained at very early ages but later strengths are nearly always affected adversely. In contrast, there are several retarders whose use results in a higher final strength for H.A.C. concretes and mortars. In some cases, although the initial set is delayed for several hours, even the 24 hour strength may be higher than it is in absence of the retarder. Aluminium chloride hydrate is an example and Table I shows the effect of various proportions of this compound on the setting-time of British H.A.C. and on the strength of 1 : 3 mortars. The effect of a proprietary ligno-sulphonate retarder upon the setting-time of another batch of H.A.C. is also given. In this case the higher concentrations reduced the 24 hour strength but the 7 day strength was normal.

TABLE I. EFFECT OF CERTAIN RETARDERS ON SETTING TIME OR STRENGTH.
1. Aluminium Chloride Hydrate (expressed as $AlCl_3$ by wt. of cement)

% Addition	Setting-Times		1 : 6 Concretes W/C = 0.55 Compressive Strength lb/in²			1 : 3 Mortars W/C = 0.50 Compressive Strength lb/in²			
	Initial	Final	1 day	3 days	7 days	1 day	3 days	7 days	28 days
Nil	4 hr.	4 hr. 10 m.	7200	8700	9000	6200	6750	7700	8700
0.1	6 hr. 10 m.	6 hr. 35 m.	8200	9200	10000	7900	8000	8900	10500
0.2	16 hr. 30 m.	17 hr. 10 m.	—	—	—	7950	8400	9800	11000
0.3	22 hr. 15 m.	24 hr. 55 m.	—	—	—	—	—	—	—

2. Lignosulphonate Plasticiser/Retarder (by wt. of cement)

% Addition	Nil	0.1%	0.22%	0.45%	0.67%
Initial Set	5 hr. 40 m.	8 hr.	12 hr.	15 hr. 25 m.	19 hr. 20 m.
Final Set	5 hr. 55 m.	8 hr. 30 m.	13 hr. 20 m.	16 hr. 10 m.	20 hr. 5 m.

Most of the proprietary retarding liquids used for applying to the interior of formwork (in order to obtain exposed-aggregate surfaces) are also effective with H.A.C. since they are frequently based on sugar or carbohydrate derivatives. However, with H.A.C. mixes it is often necessary to strip the forms as early as possible and to brush or wash away the surface cement before hardening of the concrete has progressed too far. A more drastic and deeper action can sometimes be achieved by mixing the retarding fluid with an inert fine powder and applying it as a paste.

2. WORKABILITY AIDS OR PLASTICISERS

Most high-alumina cements give mixes which are " harsher," more difficult to float or trowel, which " bleed " more easily, and which have lower water-retention properties than equivalent Portland cement mixes. Therefore, an increase in the proportion of sand to coarse aggregate is frequently suggested, but although this can have a helpful effect it should not be carried too far. In practice " over-sanded " mixes may require much extra water in order to give the required plasticity and the advantages of lower water-cement ratios have already been mentioned more than once.

The addition of very small quantities of surface-active agents improves the plasticity of H.A.C. mixes (lean mixes especially) usually because some air is entrained. With larger quantities of agent, more than 3-4 per cent. of air may be incorporated and a considerable reduction in strength must then be expected. The effect of the surface-active agent on plasticity frequently diminishes the longer the mix is allowed to stand before being placed. Among such agents are alkyl aryl sulphonates, secondary alkyl sulphates or the sodium salts thereof, and non-ionic compounds. Calcium lignosulphonate improves workability and, when used in the low concentrations necessary to avoid undue retardation of set, it does not entrain much air. Other organic compounds with a retarding action such as soya-bean flour, methyl cellulose and other similar colloids, all give a more plastic mix and reduce the tendency to bleed.

In certain applications where maximum plasticity is required but where strength is a secondary consideration (e.g. brick-jointing, pipe-jointing, plastering or rendering, grouting and cementation by injection) the addition of bentonite (2-4 per cent. by weight of cement) or raw fireclay (10-15 per cent.) has been recommended. The mix becomes more suitable for trowelling and the suction of porous surfaces is resisted much better. The favourable effect is increased if a small amount of surface-active agent is also added. Lime cannot be added to H.A.C. to give plastic mixes for rendering or brick jointing but it is possible to use whiting or finely ground chalk. Fly-ash or granulated slag in very finely divided form also give mixes which are more cohesive and less harsh, but the alkali content of these materials should be watched if the cement is to be used for certain structural purposes.

3. AIR-ENTRAINING AGENTS AND FOAMING AGENTS

Tallow, fats, oils and some sulphonated compounds cause air-entrainment if they are ground with the cement or are incorporated in small quantities with the mix. Soluble salts of wood resins are widely used for this purpose, but it has been found that many of the proprietary air-entraining agents, used in the proportions recommended for Portland cement, do not entrain nearly so much air with H.A.C. H.A.C. mixes containing 3-4 per cent. of entrained air in the form of very fine bubbles, are more plastic, bleeding is reduced and water-retention is improved. The usual increase in resistance to freezing and thawing cycles may also be expected, but an ordinary H.A.C. concrete, providing it has been well compacted and cured, is already very resistant to this treatment[25].

By entraining very large volumes of air in the mix it is possible to produce " foamed " cement or H.A.C. mortars with densities of 10 lb./cu. ft. upwards. A neat H.A.C. mix of this type, with a dried density of about 30 lb./cu. ft. still has appreciable strength and is an efficient heat-insulating material. Foaming agents usually consist of a surface-active compound (such as an alkyl aryl sulphonate) together with a colloidal foam-stabiliser. Hydrolysed protein which is commonly used to produce fire-fighting foams is also an effective agent for making foamed cements or mortars. Both these types of foaming agent retard the set of H.A.C. and the minimum proportion should be used.

If agitation in the mixer is vigorous, with a tumbling action, quite large quantities of air can be entrained when a foaming agent is added directly to the mix, but a much better method of producing a foamed cement or mortar is to prepare a stable foam which can readily be stirred into a slurry of cement or cement and aggregate. A dilute solution of foaming agent in water is rapidly stirred or whipped or is forced with compressed air through some form of labyrinth, and a very stable foam, having a volume 40-50 times that of the original solution, is obtained. This can easily be stirred by hand into the cement slurry, or any ordinary type of concrete-mixer may be employed. The final volume of the foamed cement or mortar, and hence the density of the product after hardening, is determined by the amount of foam added, or by the total water-cement ratio of the mix. Fig. 24 gives the air-dried densities of foamed H.A.C. and H.A.C./sand mortars made by this method.

The addition of aluminium powder to H.A.C. mixes in order to produce a cellular product is not very effective. H.A.C. slurry contains less alkali and free lime than Portland cement and, although there is some initial action between the metal and the wet mix, the expansion produced is usually not sufficient.

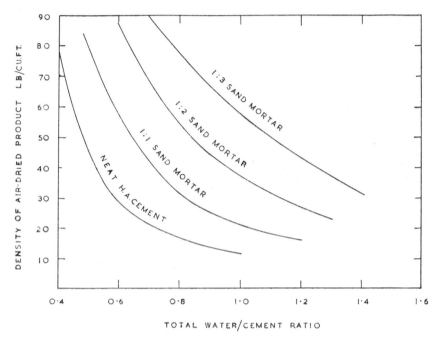

FIG. 24.   Densities of foamed H.A.C. and mortars.

4.   WATER-REDUCING AGENTS

Some substances, notably salts of hydroxy-carboxylic acids have the property of reducing the amount of water required to produce a mix with a given consistency.   They do not reduce bleeding or entrain air and gluconic acid gives a marked effect with H.A.C.   All these substances retard the set of H.A.C. and it is doubtful if their use is often required since, as noted in Chapter Four, high-alumina cement gives, without any addition, a paste which is more fluid than Portland cement at the same water-cement ratio.

5.   WATER-PROOFING AGENTS AND SURFACE HARDENERS

Many of the integral water-proofing agents intended for use with Portland cement contain calcium chloride, lime, or sodium silicate and these should not be incorporated in H.A.C. mortars or concretes designed to give high strengths.   Other agents, such as calcium, ammonium, or butyl stearates could be used, but any favourable action appears to be due as much to an increase in workability as to any specific water-proofing action.   In general, integral water-proofers cannot be recommended with H.A.C., and the best method of ensuring an impermeable concrete is to use a low water-cement ratio, consolidate completely, and cure thoroughly with water.   Surface treatments, e.g. with sodium methyl siliconate, give H.A.C. concretes water-repellant properties.

It is also suggested that chemical " hardeners " should not be added to H.A.C. mixes.   Surface treatment with sodium silicate solution is not very effective in producing a hard skin since there is no free lime with which it can react.   However, a sodium silicate surface treatment is helpful for H.A.C. floors subject to spillage of acids.   A solution of magnesium silicofluoride applied to the surface after the concrete has dried out does increase the hardness and it also improves the resistance to acids and oils.   Surface hardeners of the drying-oil type (e.g. tung oil) are also effective with H.A.C. mortars and concretes, but attention to curing is the first requisite in obtaining a hard dust-free surface.

6.   HYDROPHOBIC CEMENT

When a very small proportion (0.05 per cent. by weight) of commercial grade mixed acids of the oleic, stearic and lauric types is ground with H.A.C. clinker, the resultant cement can be stored for long periods in damp situations without combining with water and forming lumps.   At this concentration the hydrophobic agent has little effect on strength (except the 6-8 hour strength) or on setting-time. When the concentration is higher (0.1 per cent. or 0.25 per cent.) the water-repellant properties are greatly increased but the setting-time is delayed for several hours and the compressive strength of mortars and concretes is reduced at ages up to 7 days.   The hydrophobic coating on the cement grains is removed by the abrasive action of the aggregate when mortars or concretes are thoroughly mixed.

7.   LATEX/CEMENT COMPOSITIONS

These compositions are made by mixing a hydraulic cement with stable latices or water-emulsions of natural rubber, synthetic rubber, synthetic resins or bitumen.   The cement, dry filler or aggregate, and any desired pigment are usually blended together and the resultant powder is mixed on site with a specified proportion of the latex or emulsion, i.e. the latter is used in place of gauging water.   The cement

134

combines with the water in the latex and the mix hardens to a material whose physical properties are, in some degree, intermediate between those of a cement mortar and those of the substance present in the emulsion. In many industrial and marine applications, H.A.C. is the preferred cement[26] because it confers greater resistance to dilute acids, sulphate or other chemicals, it absorbs a higher proportion of the water in the latex and it gives a stronger product especially at early ages. Since H.A.C. has a lower alkali and lime content than Portland cement it also has less tendency to coagulate the latex. A mixture of Portland cement and H.A.C. (2 : 1) is frequently employed as the cement constituent in order to accelerate the hardening and produce a lighter colour[27]. All the latex cement compositions adhere very strongly to a wide variety of materials which must have clean, but not necessarily dry, surfaces. The aggregates or fillers used include sand, crushed granite or other stone, wood chips, asbestos fibre, granulated cork, cork dust, etc.

(a)   Rubber-latex/cement compositions

Early patents date from about 1921[28] but practical interest in these compositions probably started with the publication of Bond's patent of 1930, which proposed that concentrated latex should be combined with H.A.C., fillers, vulcanising ingredients, etc., and the resultant paste used for resilient roadways and floors[29].

Natural rubber-latex/II.A.C. compositions are rather more complex than indicated above since the emulsion as received contains protein and ammonia, and preservatives such as pentachlorophenol together with casein stabiliser and surface-active agents may be added. Many of these ingredients affect the setting-time of the cement[30] and this is usually corrected by the addition of lime or caustic alkalis[31]. The compounding of these mixes is therefore a matter which calls for experience on the part of the manufacturers. In general, however, the rubber amounts to 6-15 per cent. by weight of the mix and the cement content is about 3 times as great[32].

A microscopical study of rubber-latex/H.A.C. has been reported by Wren[33] and it seems clear that rubber is the continuous phase in the hardened material. The compositions therefore have a certain amount of resiliency which increases greatly if the rigid cement matrix is partially broken by traffic or by beating.

A synthetic rubber-latex is used where higher resistance to oils, etc., is required but even the natural rubber-latex/H.A.C. compositions have quite good resistance to grease because the rubber on the surface swells and protects the underlying material. The same applies to dilute acid and alkali attack against which rubber-latex/H.A.C. is more resistant than H.A.C./sand mortars[34]. Broadly speaking, the rubber-latex/H.A.C. mixes can be used where subject to pH values from 4 to 12-14, and for shorter periods they have given good service in contact with 5 per cent. mineral acid solutions up to a temperature of 50°C. They are not resistant to oxidising acids, e.g. nitric acid.

In combination with various fillers or aggregates, rubber-latex/ H.A.C. mixes have been used as adhesives or jointing materials, e.g. for fixing glass or ceramic tiles and slabs, for bedding the lenses in submarine periscopes, for jointing pipes, glass bricks (or engineering bricks in acid-resisting drains, flumes, etc.) and for fixing iron grids in anti-corrosive floors. When materials such as steel, concrete, glass, wood and glazed earthenware are bonded to themselves or each other with latex/H.A.C. the direct pull-off strength is about 550-750 lb./ sq. in.

Such compositions are widely employed for covering the decking or smoothing the hulls of ships and as jointless floors[35] which have considerable acid, alkaline and chemical resistance. They have also been used for linings for tanks such as dye-liquor and brewing-liquor tanks, neutralising pits, and tan pits[36]. Other applications include blocks and pipes[37] or centrifugally spun linings for pipes[38] and resilient linings for fans and pumps[39].

(b) Synthetic-resin/cement compositions

Polyvinyl acetate or chloride emulsions substituted for the rubber-latex give products which are harder and which do not possess the same resilience but which are very useful for corrosion-resistant floor-toppings. Once more H.A.C. is employed when a higher degree of chemical resistance is required. A protective coating for the holds of oil-tankers or for use in shipyards, sewage-treatment plants, oil-refineries, gasworks, etc., has been patented. This consists essentially of polyvinyl acetate/H.A.C. reinforced with a woven fabric and finally coated with an oil and water-resistant varnish[40]. H.A.C. is also used in conjunction with co-polymer resins, with partly con-densed resins, with formaldehyde and urea, with glue and formaldehyde and with drying oil emulsion[41].

(c) Bitumen emulsion/cement compositions

These compositions have a longer history than either of the previous types and the use of H.A.C. or H.A.C./Portland cement as the de-hydrator has been described in many patents[42]. The chief use is for concrete repairs or for flooring, and the incorporation of a vul-canised oil is said to prevent any tendency to dusting.

8. Sulphated H.A.C. and Expansive Cements

When 20-25 per cent. by weight of calcium sulphate is ground or mixed with H.A.C. the product is still capable of giving early strengths not much lower than the original H.A.C. and it does not suffer the same loss in strength when hardening at higher temperatures[43]. The cement bond is now due mainly to a calcium sulpho-aluminate hydrate[44] and is not based on the usual calcium aluminate hydrates—hence the difference in behaviour at elevated curing temperatures.

A sulphated H.A.C. of this type was patented many years ago[45] and since then further work has been published, chiefly in the U.S.S.R. Budnikov[46] reports that the most active form of calcium sulphate for this purpose is an artificial anhydrite prepared by calcining gypsum at 600°-700°C., and this is added in the proportion of about 25 per cent. by weight of the H.A.C. In such concentrations the artificial anhydrite accelerates the set while natural anhydrite retards. Among other advantages claimed for concretes made with this sulphated H.A.C. are lower heat evolution during hardening, high early strengths (increased by elevated curing temperatures) and great impermeability. When stored in water, the concretes showed some expansion, and this was increased when the proportion of anhydrite was raised to 30 per cent. The moderate degree of expansion when in contact with water gave concretes which at 3 days could resist a water pressure of 8 atmospheres and adiabatic curing or external hot wet conditions did not affect the strength adversely. It is further claimed that this cement was stable at 60°-65°C. (145°F.) when subjected to alternate saturation and drying cycles.

Mikhailov[47] has also described a rather similar composition termed waterproof expansion cement or WEC, which he obtained by dry grinding H.A.C., gypsum and the tetracalcium aluminate hydrate C_4AH_{13}. The latter was prepared as a separate operation by hydrating a mixture of H.A.C. and lime and drying the product. The presence of this hydrate in the mix is said to accelerate the formation of the calcium sulpho-aluminate hydrate or Ettringite bond. WEC is a very quick-setting cement whose expansive properties are controlled by regulating the proportions of the ingredients. It is apparently in commercial production in the U.S.S.R. and has been used chiefly to stop leaks or water percolating through porous concrete. It has therefore been employed for sealing dams, tanks, pipes, etc., and is usually applied by guniting. A variant containing a lower proportion of gypsum (75 per cent. H.A.C., 6.25 per cent. gypsum, 18.75 per cent. C_4AH_{13}) is called water-proof non-shrinkage cement and this gives only a very small expansion in wet conditions. However, this is said to be sufficient to give instantaneous water-tightness and the cement is therefore used for caulking cracks and cavities through which water is flowing. All cements of the WEC type appear to be very fast-setting and to give comparatively low strengths, particularly in dry curing conditions.

Russian workers also claim success in the production of a cement which, after hardening, can expand sufficiently to stretch reinforcement and so produce a pre-stressed construction. This self-stressing cement SC is prepared by grinding together H.A.C. clinker and Portland clinker to a fineness of not less than 3500 sq. cm./g. The product is then mixed with gypsum in a vibratory mill to give a composition which may contain 66 per cent. Portland cement, 20 per cent H.A.C., and 14 per cent. gypsum. There are many cement compositions which are capable of producing large expansions but most investigators have experienced difficulty in utilising the expansive forces for general pre-stressing purposes. In the case of SC the claim is made that this can be achieved by a special heat-treatment of the mix (e.g. 6 hours at 100°C.) after it has reached a certain strength. At the end of the heat treatment all the gypsum has reacted and there is no further expansion of the mortar in subsequent water storage. Some of the pre-stress is lost when the mortar or concrete dries but is regained on wetting and this type of cement is therefore recommended chiefly for structures subject to water pressure, e.g. in underground situations and also for pressure pipes. A mortar only 1 in. thick is said to resist a water pressure of 20-25 atmospheres without allowing any percolation. Low water-cement ratios (0.20 - 0.22) increase the self-stressing capabilities and, since the cement is extremely fast-setting, it is best applied by guniting.

European work on " non-shrink " or expansive cements also involves the addition of a calcium sulpho-aluminate composition to Portland cement[48]. Lossier[49] used a " sulpho-aluminate clinker " prepared by burning a mixture of gypsum, bauxite, and calcium carbonate. This expansive cement is therefore a mixture of Portland cement, sulpho-aluminate clinker and blast-furnace slag, the latter being added to absorb excess of calcium sulphate at later ages and thus act as a stabiliser. In the preparation of the " sulpho-aluminate clinker " there was actually no combination to a true sulpho-aluminate, the product being merely a mixture of calcium sulphate and aluminates, ferrites, silicates, etc. Lafuma[50] and others have therefore pointed out that this clinkering process appears to be unnecessary and that a mixture of H.A.C. and calcium sulphate should serve the same purpose

138

as the clinker. More recently, however, a definite anhydrous calcium sulpho-aluminate has been made in the USA[51] and it is claimed that this is very suitable as a component in an expansive self-stressing cement. It is interesting to note also that Kosyreva and Kuznetsova say that the product of burning 40 per cent. bauxite, 40 per cent. chalk and 20 per cent. gypsum at 1100°-1200°C. is, in itself, a good cement with corrosion-resisting properties[52].

Locher[53] has studied the hydraulic properties of lime-alumina-silica glasses, some of which were within the chemical composition range of H.A.C. Good strengths were obtained even from high-silica glasses when they were activated by adding Portland cement, anhydrous calcium sulphate, or lime.

LITERATURE REFERENCES

1   "Admixtures for Concrete." A.C.I. Comm. 212. J. Amer. Concr. Inst. 1954, **26**, (2), 113.

2   F. M. LEA. "The Chemistry of Cement and Concrete." Arnold. Lond. 1956.

3   T. W. PARKER. 3rd Inter. Symp. on Chem. of Cement. Lond. 1952.

4   L. BILLÉ. Brit. Pat. 523312 (1938). A. V. SOMERS, K. SCHWARTZWALDER & GENERAL MOTORS CORP. U.S. Pat. 2906909 (1959).

5   W. V. FRIEDLAENDER & N. C. LUDWIG, Atlas Lumnite Cement Co. U.S. Pat. 2339163 (1944).

6   G. J. FINK, J. A. McCORMICK & C. A. CABELL. Brit. Pat. 239504 (1925). In U.S.A. 1924.

7   ANON. Cemento armato. 1938, **35**, (7), 131.

8   M. DURIEZ & L. LÉZY. Monit. Trav. Publ. 1955, (48), 17. Travaux 1956, (255), 30.

9   H. SCHUNACK. Silikattech. 1959, **10**, (7), 326. G. BALAZS, J. KELEMEN & J. KILIAN. Epitöanyag, Budapest 1958, **10**, (9), 326.

10   CIMENTS LAFARGE, Paris.

11   J. BIED. Recherches Industrielles sur les Chaux, Ciments, et Mortiers. Dunod. Paris 1926. H. LAFUMA, Le Ciment 1925, **30**, 174. W. N. THOMAS, J. Roy. Inst. Brit. Architect. 1924, **31**, (20), 670. M. TOUCHÉ. Le Ciment. 1926, **31**, (7), 240.

12   T. D. ROBSON. Chem. & Industr. 1952, (1), 1.

13   L'Age du Ciment No. 7. Soc. Anon. Lafarge, Paris. K. E. DORSCH. Rev. Matér. Constr. 1935, (304), 13. Cement & Cem. Manuf. 1932, **5**, 337, 426. E. RENGADE, Rev. Matér. Constr. 1934, (300), 255. Concrete 1936, (44), 3, 40. K. KOYANAGI. Zement. 1930, 869. H. KÜHL. Zement. 1930, 795. K. AKIYAMA, NESUGI & KUWABORA. Bull. Was. Appl. Chem. Soc. 1936, **28**, 7 : 1942, 469.

14   J. BROCARD. Ann. Inst. Bâtim. 1956, **9**, (103/104), 710, 725.

15   G. S. LALIN & A/B VALLEVIKENS CEMENTFABRIK. Brit. Pat. 431060 (1933). In Norway 1933.

[16] ANON. Le Bâtiment 1952, (1), 8. D. M. LEVANOW. Nov. Tekhn. Per. Opyt Stroit. (Moscow) 1957, (9), 1.

[17] J. J. MANNING & W. F. WAY. Engng. News Rec. 1927, **98**, (9), 348. H. LOSSIER. Bull. Soc. Encour. Sci. 1924, 738. W. H. GOETZ. Ann. Meeting Highway Res. Bd. Washington, D.C. 1947.

[18] D. G. MILLER & P. W. MANSON. Public Rds. 1931, **12**, (3), 64. U.S. Dept. Agric. Tech. Bull. No. 358. 1933.

[19] L. FÉRET & M. VENUAT. Rev. Matér. Constr. C. 1958, (517), 274 : 1957, (496), 1.

[20] R. VUILLEMIN. Génie civ. 1936, **108**, (18), 416. See also Ann. Inst. tech. Bâtim (Suppl.). 1954, (75/76), 271.

[21] P. F. KONOWALOW & E. J. MOROSOW. Cement U.R.S.S. 1959, **25**, (2), 25. O. GRAF. Zement. 1925, **14**, (10), 213. J. FORET. Doctorate Thesis. 1935. Hermann et Cie., Paris.

[22] F. H. MACLENNAN. Rds. & Rd. Constr. 1955, 147. See also K. E. CLARE & A. E. POLLARD. Mag. Concr. Res. 1951, **8**, (8), 57.

[23] R. FÉRET. Rev. Matér. Constr. 1928, (223), 135 : (224), 166. H. BURCHARTZ. Zement. 1927, **16**, 77. H. LAFUMA, Ass. franc. Essai Matér. 1934. Rev. Matér. Constr. 1935, (304), 7. A. E. FATIN. J. Amer. Concr. Inst. 1950, **21**, (5), 390.

[24] J. M. CURSCHELLES & KASPAR WINKLER. Brit. Pat. 405508 (1933). In Germany 1932.

[25] ANON. Génie civ. 1935, **107**, (23), 542. L. J. ROTHGERY. Bull. Mich. Engng. Exp. Sta. 1926, No. 4, Pt. I. A. F. ROSHER LUND. Tekn. Ugebl. 1925, **72**, 324, 335, 350.

[26] F. H. COTTON. Sands Clays & Minerals. 1938, 244.

[27] SEMTEX LTD. & L. H. GRIFFITHS. Brit. Pat. 558904 (1942).

[28] L. CRESSON. Brit. Pat. 191474 (1921). H. S. WILLS. Brit. Pat. 202652 (1924). V. LEFEBURE. Brit. Pat. 217279 (1923). R. DIMAR. Brit. Pat. 214224 (1923). S. M. KIRKPATRICK. Brit. Pat. 242345, 248033 (1924).

[29] A. E. BOND & R. CRITCHLEY LTD. Brit. Pat. 369561 (1930). W. H. STEVENS. Rubb. Dev. 1948, **1**, (3), 10. H. BARRON. Ind. Rubb. J. 1936, **91**, (6), 167 : (7), 199. F. G. MOTTERSHAW. Rubb. Dev. 1949, **2**, (2), 5. M. TEXIER. Ingén. et Tech. 1950, **21**, 133. Soc. Pneu. Dunlop. French Pat. 939217 (1949). H. W. FRITTS, E. D. VARINK JR. et al. Ind. Engng. Chem. 1951, **43**, (10), 2193.

[30] ANON. Bull. Rubb. Growers Ass. 1936, (18), 337.

[31] W. G. WREN et al., Rubb. Producers Res. Ass. Brit. Pat. 484712 (1936).

[32] L. H. GRIFFITHS. Chem. & Industr. 1947, **66**, 578.

[33] W. G. WREN. Trans. India Rubb. Inst. 1937, **13**, (3), 189.

[34] L. H. GRIFFITHS. India Rubb. J. 1952, **72**, 304, 319.

[35] BRAITHWAITE & Co. Brit. Pat. 525708 (1939). BARRON. Ref. 29. GRIFFITHS. Ref. 32.

[36] P. B. CORMAC. Corr. Techn. 1956, **3**, (2), 43 : (3), 76. Contract. Rec. 1955, **66**, (38), 29. E. G. RAWLINGS. Corr. Engr. 1959, **1**, (2), 2, 7. Corr. Techn. 1955, 278.

[37] SHEPHERD'S INDUSTRIES LTD. & W. H. STEVENS. Brit. Pat. 524227 (1939).

[38] RUBBER CEMENT PRODUCTS LTD. & STANTON IRONWORKS CO. LTD. Brit. Pat. 526931 (1939).

[39] REVERTEX LTD. & E. F. LASCHINGER. Brit. Pat. 567574 (1943).

[40] V. G. (LONDON) LTD. & G. MAY. Brit. Pat. 721510. ANON. Mod. Transp. 1956, **74,** (1919), 6.

[41] SEMTEX LTD. Brit. Pats. 559541 (1942), 562268 (1944). DURASTIC LTD. Brit. Pat. 635485 (1946). PATENT & LICENSING CORP., U.S. Pat. 2742441 (1956).

[42] SEMTEX LTD. Brit. Pat. 584344 (1944). PATENT & LICENSING CORP. U.S. Pat. 2322641 (1943). ALUMINIUMERZ BERGBAU U. INDUSTRIE A.G. Brit. Pat. 357293 (1930).

[43] P. P. BUDNIKOV & I. G. GOL'DENBERG. Dopovidi Akad. Nauk. U.R.S.S. Phys.-Chem. 1942, (3/4), 73. P. P. BUDNIKOV & I. V. KRAVCHENKO. Kolloid Zhur. 1951, **13,** 408.

[44] P. P. BUDNIKOV & I. G. GOL'DENBERG. J. Appl. Chem. U.R.S.S. 1945, (18), 15. P. P. BUDNIKOV & V. S. GORSHKOV. Idem. 1959, **32,** 21.

[45] SOC. ANON. LAFARGE. Brit. Pat. 317783 (1929). In France 1928.

[46] P. P. BUDNIKOV. 4th Inter. Symp. Chem. of Cement. Washington D.C. 1960. BUDNIKOV & GOL'DENBERG. J. Appl. Chem. U.R.S.S. 1947, **20,** 1155.

[47] V. V. MIKHAILOV. 4th Inter. Symp. Chem. of Cement. Wash. D.C. 1960. See also E. LEWICKI. Bauplan u. Bautech. 1956, **10,** (11).

[48] A. HUMMEL & K. CHARISIUS. Zement-Kalk-Gips. 1949, **2,** (7), 127. F. KEIL & F. GILLE. Idem 1949, **2,** (8), 148. C. GORIA & M. APPIANO. Il cemento 1949, **3,** 34 : **4,** 54. Industria cemento 1950 (7), 112. F. FERRARI. Idem. 1949, (5/6), 64.

[49] H. LOSSIER. Génie civ. 1936, **109,** (14), 285 : 1944, **121,** (8), 61. **Zement.** 1937, **26,** (32), 507. Travaux. 1943, **120,** (6), 203. J. Amer. **Concr.** Inst. 1947, **18,** (9), 1074. R. PERRE. Travaux 1943, **120,** (6), 205.

[50] H. LAFUMA. 3rd Inter. Symp. Chem. of Cement. Lond. 1952, 581.

[51] A. KLEIN, T. KARBY & M. POLIVKA. J. Amer. Concr. Inst. 1961, **58,** (1), 59.

[52] Z. S. KOSYREVA & I. P. KUZNETSOVA. Sborn. Nauch. Rabot. Khim. Tekh. Silikatov. 1956, 70.

[53] F. W. LOCHER. 4th Inter. Symp. Chem. of Cement. Wash. D.C. 1960.

CHAPTER 6.—CHEMICAL RESISTANCE PROPERTIES

CONTENTS

CHAPTER SIX

Chemical Resistance Properties

In most concrete mixes the amount of water which has to be added to provide the necessary workability is more than the cement requires for hydration and a proportion of free water is therefore left to evaporate when the concrete hardens. Capillaries and voids connecting with the outside surface of the concrete are thus created and the entry of water, saline solutions, or aggressive agents is possible. Concrete made with an adequate cement content, with clean, well-graded aggregates, and with no more water than is necessary to allow thorough compaction has the minimum permeability, particularly when careful attention is given to curing, and any greater permeability increases the risk of attack either by physical or by chemical means. If an unduly permeable concrete is alternately wetted with saline solution and allowed to dry, the crystallisation of the salt within the pores will alone cause relatively rapid disruption, even when the salt has no chemical action on the cement. Concrete subjected to water pressure from one side is also vulnerable unless it is sufficiently impermeable to prevent percolation and the consequent leaching of the cement constituents.

The effect of these physical actions is greatly enhanced if the water contains any substance which is chemically aggressive to the cement, and the importance of obtaining a dense concrete with minimum permeability is then particularly evident — whatever the type of cement used. The life of a good-quality concrete may be twenty times or more that of indifferent concrete (made with the same materials) when both are subjected to aggressive conditions[1].

Numerous books and technical articles have dealt with the corrosion of concrete subjected to chemical agents[2], and many assess the behaviour of the different types of hydraulic cement. Dogmatic recommendations are especially unwise in the field of chemical resistance since, although much can be learned from laboratory tests, it is usually impossible to duplicate the conditions in nature or in industry. Effluents or trade wastes vary between factories, even when the latter

145

are engaged in the same manufacture, and the effect of complex mixtures is not necessarily the sum of those due to the constituents.

The use of H.A.C. in aggressive situations is mainly based on its resistance to sulphates, to certain hydroxylic substances and to a limited degree of acidity. Apart from the cases where a good quality H.A.C. concrete gives virtual immunity from the chemical agent in question, it is frequently used in industry under conditions where resistance is far from complete. If it gives service over an extended period of time when other materials are rapidly disintegrated, then its use is justified. The rapid-hardening properties are an additional advantage in these situations since replacement or repair can be effected quickly.

1. RESISTANCE TO SULPHATES

H.A.C. was originally developed for its specific resistance to sulphates in the soil, in sea-water, or in industrial liquors. The extensive tests carried out at that time[3] and the knowledge subsequently gained[4] leave little doubt that H.A.C. is pre-eminent in this field. Indeed the conclusion has been reached that " properly made high-alumina cement concrete seems from both practical experience and laboratory tests extending over many years, to be immune from attack by sulphate salts[5].

The resistance of even very lean and porous H.A.C. concretes and mortars to the purely chemical attack of sulphates is very high (e.g. when the specimens are kept fully immersed). However, there are few site conditions where resistance to chemical attack is the sole factor, and H.A.C. concrete of this poor quality would invite deterioration by physical agencies including frost action, percolation, and crystallization of salts within the pores of sections exposed to evaporation. Therefore, when H.A.C. is required to resist sulphates under practical conditions, a dense, well-compacted concrete should always be provided and, for example, the frequent practice of " haunching " pipes in sulphated ground with a very lean mix is not recommended.

If conversion of the H.A.C. hydrates takes place for any reason, the porosity and permeability of the concrete or mortar will be increased, and, unless the water-cement ratio of the mix is sufficiently low, the sulphate resistance may be seriously reduced. Adequate attention should therefore be given to proper curing and cooling when placing any substantial thickness of H.A.C. concrete used for sulphate resistance. In industry H.A.C. is sometimes employed for protection against hot sulphate liquors (e.g. for tank linings, drains, sumps, etc.)

146

and in such cases (where conversion is probable) rich mixes of low water-cement ratio give the best results. For this reason gunited mortar linings have given good service.

(1) *Sea-Water and Saline Lake Water.*

Magnesium sulphate in sea-water can attack Portland cement concrete by reaction with the free calcium hydroxide or tricalcium aluminate and the rate of this chemical attack is probably increased in countries with hot climates. However, deterioration may be more frequently caused or initiated by frost action, by leaching of cement or by crystallization of salts in the body of the concrete. Rusting of reinforcement and the consequent cracking or spalling of the concrete cover is a major source of trouble whenever the concrete quality is insufficient to prevent the penetration of sea-water. The total effects are more evident on concrete which is above the low-water mark, and they are usually greatest just above the high-water level. Many long term comparative tests and observations have therefore been carried out[6] on various concrete specimens or structures exposed to tidal conditions and the results have been summarised by Lea[7].

After exposure for 21 years in a tidal zone in West Norway it was found that satisfactory resistance was obtained only from specimens (1 : 2 : 3 concrete cylinders) containing H.A.C. or a pozzolanic trass cement, and 20 year trials at Ostend showed that concretes made with H.A.C. and with slag-cement gave the outstanding results. Féret reported the satisfactory behaviour of H.A.C. concrete in sea-water in France, and Eckhardt and Kronsbein, as a result of 19 year tests at Wilhelmshaven, concluded that the rapid-hardening and resistance properties of H.A.C. made it the preferable cement for sea-water constructions. The latter investigators found that H.A.C. concretes containing 540 lbs. or 675 lbs. of cement per cubic yard gave excellent long-period durability but concretes containing only 450 lbs. cement/cu. yd. showed some deterioration. Tidal trials at Maine, U.S.A., also showed that H.A.C. concrete containing 500-600 lbs. cement/cu. yd. had excellent durability in conditions which were rendered severe by frost action. Similar Portland cement concretes were affected within 1 year unless air-entrainment was employed. The results of work carried out in England (over a period of about 20 years) using short reinforced piles and concrete cylinders have given additional confirmation of the relatively high resistance of well-made H.A.C. concrete to sea-water conditions[8]. The waters of Medicine Lake, S. Dakota (which contain about 5 per cent. sulphate) provided Miller and Manson with a severe test of the sulphate resistance of different

147

types of cement, and H.A.C. concretes proved to be immune after immersion for 20 years[9].

In tropical or semi-tropical seas there is greater difficulty in preventing conversion of H.A.C. concretes during hardening or in subsequent use. This type of cement is therefore not generally recommended for structural work in these seas, although satisfactory durability has been noted in several cases. Only mixes of low water-cement ratio could be considered for use in such circumstances.

H.A.C. has been quite extensively used for building or repairing sea-defences, and for this work its rapid-hardening nature is often more important than its undoubted resistance to the chemical action of sea-water, since construction between tides is facilitated. The repair of docks, and the provision of jetties, slip-ways and piers[10] are other examples of the use of H.A.C. for marine or estuarine duties.

(2) *Mineral Sulphates in the Ground.*

Calcium sulphate, magnesium sulphate and sodium sulphate are the three most commonly encountered in natural ground. Calcium sulphate in the form of gypsum and anhydrite can occur in massive formations but it is also found disseminated in clays and gravels in many parts of the World. Sodium and magnesium sulphates also occur with calcium sulphate in these situations but the concentration may be higher in the sulphated ground or " alkali soils " of dry and desert regions. Magnesium sulphate and sodium sulphate have a much more aggressive action than calcium sulphate on mortar or concrete made with ordinary Portland cement but resistance to all is greatly increased by the use of Sulphate-Resisting Portland cement or A.S.T.M. Type V Portland cement.

Ground-waters and soils have been classified according to their probable action on different types of concrete and recommendations based on the percentage of sulphur trioxide in the water or soil samples have been published[11]. Water which contains less than 30 parts SO_3 per 100,000, or soils which contain less than 0.2 per cent. SO_3 can generally be regarded as harmless to well-made ordinary Portland cement concrete. Above 100 parts SO_3 per 100,000 in the water or 0.50 per cent. SO_3 in the soil requires the use of cements with high sulphate resistance and H.A.C. is recommended for use in sulphate soils up to and including the most severe conditions, since a well-made and properly cured H.A.C. concrete should be immune from the chemical action of any concentration of these mineral sulphates. Concrete in contact with sodium sulphate solution is particularly susceptible to crystallisation of salts within the pores and adequate concrete density is essential to prevent deterioration by this physical process. It should be noted also that the reaction of calcium hydroxide with sodium sulphate solution releases caustic alkali, to which H.A.C. concrete has poor resistance, but the conditions necessary for this to occur are unlikely in nature and infrequent in industry.

Aggressive sulphate soils are also found in marshy districts close to the sea or estuaries, and here, as in other sulphated ground, acidity is often produced by bacterial action. The weathering of certain shales[12] may also result in acidic ground-waters and the resistance of H.A.C. to dilute acids as well as to sulphates is beneficial.

H.A.C. concrete is therefore recommended for constructional work in sulphated ground and in contact with ground-waters containing high concentrations of sulphates. It is frequently laid as a carpet or surround for ordinary concrete foundations[13] and for the construction of piles[14], pipes, culverts and sewers[15], drain-tiles[16], tunnel segments[17] and other underground structures[18].

(3) *Sulphates in Industry.*

The widest range of sulphate salts may be found in process liquors, or trade effluents and in the ground under or adjacent to certain industrial plants. Undoubtedly the most aggressive to ordinary concrete is ammonium sulphate, which is commonly associated with gas and coke works, and the fertiliser industry[19]. The resistance of suitable H.A.C. concrete to ammonium sulphate is probably unequalled by concrete made with any other type of hydraulic cement and this property has been utilised with advantage in many industries. Excellent resistance is also provided against nickel sulphate, copper sulphate (e.g. in plating works), and most of the other metallic sulphates likely to be encountered.

2. RESISTANCE TO ACIDS

H.A.C. mortars and concretes have a considerably greater resistance to very dilute acidity than similar specimens made with a Portland-type cement, and, among the hydraulic cements, only super-sulphated cement is usually credited with a higher acid resistance. To some extent the behaviour of H.A.C. may be due to the absence of any calcium hydroxide in the set cement, but more probably it results from the presence of alumina gel which, by enrobing the hydrates, exerts a protective action. Alumina gel does not readily dissolve until the pH value of the surrounding liquid is below 4.0[20], and, in practice, the required resistance of H.A.C. mortars and concretes to dilute acids is normally limited to pH values above 3.5-

4.0. Although some attack will occur in stronger acid conditions, the substitution of Portland cement by H.A.C. in mortars and concretes is often beneficial for acid concentrations up to about 0.5 per cent. (or up to 1 per cent. in the case of a few acids). At higher concentrations H.A.C. is frequently attacked more rapidly than Portland cements.

Although the ultimate acid resistance of all hydraulic cements is low, the difference in resistance between the types is of considerable commercial importance, since a wide range of slightly acid aqueous solutions, encountered under natural or industrial conditions, can have a severe corrosive action on ordinary concrete. The resistance of H.A.C. to such dilute acidity is therefore very useful.

H.A.C. is of course used (especially for floors) where it is subject to occasional spillage of acids much stronger than the cement can normally withstand. If the floors are frequently hosed or washed, an economic life may be obtained and the rapid-hardening properties of this cement enable repairs to be effected without materially affecting production. H.A.C. mortars gauged with rubber latex may resist alkalis and up to 5 per cent. mineral acids for extended periods[21], since, although the skin of cement is attacked, the rubber tends to swell and seal the surface.

It is important to recall that once the limit of acid resistance of ordinary H.A.C. mortars and concretes has been exceeded, the attack can be as rapid or, in many cases, more rapid than it is with Portland cement. This explains the apparently anomalous results which have sometimes been obtained when comparing the resistances of various cements to relatively strong acid conditions[22]. No type of hydraulic cement is suitable for continued resistance to even moderately strong acidity, and for such conditions a non-hydraulic " acid-proof " cement of the silicate, resin, or sulphur type will probably be required.

A natural recommendation is that concretes subjected to dilute acids should be made with aggregates which are themselves insoluble in acids. However, Stutterheim[23] has shown that certain physical properties of limestone concretes and mortars are less affected by immersion in dilute acids than those of concretes containing insoluble aggregates. It appears possible that any acid diffusing into the limestone concrete is neutralised by the reactive aggregate and at least the internal attack is thus delayed or prevented.

(1) *Inorganic Acids.*

Liquors produced by condensation of the combustion products of fuels contain sulphurous and sulphuric acids and their corrosive action on Portland cement concrete can be severe. H.A.C. concrete usually shows excellent resistance to this degree of acidity and has therefore been employed for flues, chimneys and stacks[24], boiler plant[25], gas-washing towers[26], etc. H.A.C. has also been preferred for brick-jointing in these situations[27] and in railway tunnels[28]. Acid solutions obtained by quenching coke and ashes are well resisted and ash-sluices, ash-hoppers and wet-coal hoppers are constructed or lined with H.A.C. concrete.

Slag-heaps and chemical refuse dumps contaminate the ground with miscellaneous chemicals, and sulphuric acid is usually present[29]. Very high acid values are sometimes reported and many may be beyond the normal resistance of H.A.C. In difficult cases H.A.C. concrete foundations, coated with an external layer of bitumen, have been employed[30].

Strong inorganic acids which form soluble calcium salts, e.g. hydrochloric and nitric acids, attack all concretes. H.A.C. concrete is rather more resistant than Portland cement concrete to very dilute solutions of such acids but any advantage is usually lost at higher concentrations. Nevertheless, it has been reported that cubes of H.A.C. mortar, immersed for 90 days in 1 per cent. solutions of these acids, retained a fair proportion of the normal strength, while similar Portland cement cubes lost their strength completely.

Excellent resistance to sulphur dioxide and sulphurous acid has been obtained from H.A.C. concretes or mortars, and this type of cement therefore has many uses in sulphuric acid plants, in the paper industry, and in bleaching chambers. H.A.C. concrete storage tanks for chlorine bleach have also given very satisfactory service.

Acids used for pickling metals attack concrete quickly but H.A.C. mortar is used for jointing brickwork on the outside of the baths, and also for laying floors in electric-battery plants. Both uses can be regarded only as examples of the practical utility of H.A.C. even when its resistance is far from complete.

The action of sulphate-reducing bacteria on the sulphates in sewage produces hydrogen sulphide and this is converted into sulphuric acid through the agency of sulphur-oxidising bacteria. Bacterial activity is increased by temperature or lack of sewage flow and in some countries (e.g. S. Africa, Egypt, Malaya, Australia, U.S.A.), extremely high acid concentrations may occur above the sewage-line in sewer pipes. H.A.C. concrete appears to be immune from attack by hydrogen sulphide and has given good resistance to sulphuric acid in sewers where Portland cement concrete has been badly affected[31]. Tests by Hansen and co-workers[32] have indicated that the presence of

151

sulphates in sewers may play an auxiliary part in the attack of sewage on Portland cement concrete but, in situations where the greatest trouble is experienced, sulphuric acid attack is the main factor. Although H.A.C. has been extensively used for sewers, sewage treatment tanks, for jointing the bricks in manholes and for spun-linings in sewer pipes, it must be recognised that, in the worst conditions, this type of concrete can also be badly corroded[33]. Acid values corresponding to pH 1.0 have been reported, and it is doubtful whether any hydraulic cement could satisfactorily resist this environment, although some interest has been shown in the use of H.A.C./latex mixes for brick-jointing or coating structures exposed to this strong acidity.

(2) *Organic Acids.*

H.A.C. concrete appears to give satisfactory service for floors in the vinegar industry, although it cannot be considered immune from attack by strong acetic acid solutions. Up to concentrations of 0.5 per cent. acid the high-alumina type of cement is more resistant than the Portland type. Relatively strong solutions of lactic acid (above 1 per cent.) attack H.A.C. concrete more vigorously than Portland cement concrete but H.A.C. becomes progressively more resistant as the concentration falls[34] and it is often the preferred material of construction for floors, drains and effluent tanks in the dairy industry[35]. According to Harper[36], H.A.C. floors should give a longer life than Portland cement floors, but detergents used for washing must not contain more than 4 per cent. alkali. Excellent results were obtained from H.A.C. concrete in tests against the effluents from milk processing plants[37] and resistance is also shown to butyric acid which occurs in sour milk, sour beer and sour silage[38].

H.A.C. has been employed for floors or for jointing tiles in fruit-juice factories, giving good resistance to the sugar, citric acid, sulphur dioxide and carbon dioxide. Conditions vary considerably, however, and its suitability is open to doubt in some cases. Malic acid is very aggressive to concrete and H.A.C. concrete cannot be recommended for storage vessels for cider. Nevertheless experience in Algeria and in the U.S.A. shows that H.A.C. mortar renderings are very effective in wine-tanks. An initial surface treatment of the rendering with tartaric acid was considered beneficial. Tartaric acid itself behaves towards concrete in a way similar to that of lactic or acetic acid, but oxalic acid has little or no action on H.A.C. or Portland cement.

The use of H.A.C. for tannery floors[39] and storage tanks is generally satisfactory. Vegetable tan liquors do not seem to affect it greatly but chrome-tan is more aggressive. New tanks should be washed out with the tan liquor since some iron compounds may be dissolved from the cement at the first filling and this can otherwise cause staining of the skins.

Higher organic acids such as oleic, stearic, and palmitic acids are found in vegetable and animal oils and fats. Mainly they are combined as glycerides but free acid is present in varying amounts and this may attack concretes directly. The free lime in Portland cement concretes can bring about saponification of the oil or fat and reaction will then occur not only with the fatty acid but also with the glycerol which is released. Free acidity is usually higher in unrefined oils, and the quantity increases if the material becomes rancid ; accordingly an oil which can be safely stored in a closed concrete tank may cause rapid disintegration if spilled on a floor or otherwise exposed to the air.

Animal fats such as tallow, lard, and beef fat have a slow action on ordinary concrete unless the viscosity of the fat is reduced by heating or unless it becomes rancid. H.A.C. concrete has a good resistance and is employed for floors etc. in abattoirs and meat-packing plants. The fish oils (including seal, cod-liver, whale and shark-liver oils) are usually very aggressive in the unrefined condition and H.A.C. concrete is not necessarily immune. Bone-oil and neatsfoot oil usually have little effect on ordinary concrete.

In general H.A.C. gives better resistance than Portland cement concrete to vegetable fats and oils, especially to cotton-seed, coco-nut, mustard and olive oils. Castor, rape-seed and linseed oils can corrode both types of concrete. Paints, especially when based on linseed oil, are attacked by the alkali present in fresh Portland cement concrete but the action of H.A.C. concrete on paint films is much less owing to the lower alkali hydroxide content.

H.A.C. mortars and concretes have been used to combat the corrosion of sour crude-oils in petroleum oil-refineries but refined hydrocarbons have no chemical action on Portland cement concrete. Lubricating oils or cutting-oils, with a vegetable oil component, are better resisted by H.A.C. cements.

Animal and vegetable wastes may affect Portland cement concrete silos, floors, etc. in farm buildings and the increased resistance of H.A.C. to the dilute acidity has led to the use of this cement for containers for silage, cut potatoes, and beets. Pre-stressed H.A.C. concrete for slatted floors in cow-sheds has also attracted attention.

(3) *Acid Salts.*

The hydrolysis of certain salts produces dilute acid solutions.

153

Portland cement concrete is frequently affected by contact with such solutions and although H.A.C. concrete usually gives superior resistance, there are instances in which the limit of acid resistance of H.A.C. may be exceeded. Ammonium salts can also react specifically with the calcium hydroxide present in set Portland cement, hence ammonium chloride, acetate and nitrate solutions are destructive to Portland cement concrete. H.A.C. concrete is little affected by dilute solutions of these salts but can be attacked when their concentration is high[40].

Aluminium acetate and nitrate solutions are quite aggressive to Portland cement and are resisted by H.A.C. but aluminium chloride is said to attack H.A.C. more vigorously than it does Portland cement. Aluminium sulphate and alum solutions can quickly corrode Portland cement concrete and, in concentrations of 5-10 per cent., they have an etching action on H.A.C. mortars and concretes.

H.A.C. concrete appears to be immune to magnesium chloride, although solutions of 5-15 per cent. concentration affect the strength of Portland cement. Lawrence and Vivian[41] found that 30 per cent. calcium chloride solutions caused severe disruption of Portland cement specimens and also attacked porous H.A.C. mortars. Dense H.A.C. concretes and mortars were not appreciably affected.

(4) Carbon Dioxide and Pure Waters.

Carbon dioxide when combined as carbonates or bicarbonates in water has no action on Portland cement concretes but the latter are attacked at least superficially by free carbon dioxide in the water. Certain spring-waters contain a relatively high percentage of aggressive carbon dioxide and the resistance of H.A.C. concretes to these is very high. Grün[42] found no damage after 8 years immersion and he showed that porous H.A.C. mortars increased in strength by 45 per cent (and compact mortars by 15 per cent.) in waters at Bonn containing 125 mg./litre of aggressive carbon dioxide. Decomposing vegetable matter can cause abnormally high concentrations of carbon dioxide in sea-water in estuaries and other sheltered localities, and local attack on ordinary concrete may be quite severe.

Portland cement concrete in contact with very pure " soft " water suffers surface erosion and the action may progress to some depth due to removal of soluble calcium hydroxide. Such waters may result from a catchment area of igneous rock (e.g. Norway, Sweden and Scotland) and, by dissolving carbon dioxide and organic acids from peat, they usually have an acid reaction which accelerates the attack. Halcrow[43] found that H.A.C. concrete resisted this corrosion although in some cases the water had a pH value of 4.0. After many years the marks of form-work still had their original sharpness. Halstead[44], however, found a loss of strength in both H.A.C. and rapid-hardening Portland cement concretes when stored in soft water of low pH value. In comparative tests on different cement, against cold pure water, distilled water and spring water, Rengade[45] claimed superior results for H.A.C. Although compact H.A.C. concretes and mortars have excellent resistance to the solvent action of pure water, the powdered hydrated cement can be leached with water more readily than Portland cement and percolation through unduly porous mortars and concretes must be specially avoided. Bidron[46] compared the resistance of various cement mortars to the erosive action of a jet of pure hot water and established that H.A.C. gave the best results in this type of test.

3. RESISTANCE TO ALKALIS

H.A.C. mortars and concretes cannot be recommended for resistance to solutions of sodium or potassium hydroxide. Portland cement specimens are little affected by strong concentrations of these alkalis but the strength of H.A.C. is often reduced even when the concentration of alkali is not sufficient to cause visible attack. The solvent action of the alkali on the normally protective alumina gel is probably the main reason for this difference in behaviour of the two cements. Alkaline detergents containing less than 4 per cent. alkali can be used for washing H.A.C. floors[36], but caustic soda should never be employed for this purpose. Dilute solutions of sodium carbonate do not appear to cause deterioration of compact H.A.C. concrete but strong solutions of potassium carbonate might be expected to have a deleterious action.

An interesting case of the deterioration of H.A.C. concrete through the intermediary action of alkali has been described[47]. Unduly porous H.A.C. concrete electricity-poles were set in Portland cement concrete blocks in the ground. Alkali carbonate, originating from the alkali present in the Portland cement bases, was drawn up into the porous H.A.C. concrete by capillary action, and reacted with the hydrated aluminates thus releasing alkali hydroxide and alkali aluminate. Atmospheric carbonation completed the cycle and regenerated the alkali carbonate for further attack.

Strong ammonia solutions have no effect on either H.A.C. or Portland cement concretes.

4. RESISTANCE TO MISCELLANEOUS CHEMICALS.

The calcium hydroxide in hydrated Portland cement can react with hydroxylic substances such as glycols, glycerine, sugars and

155

phenols. The absence of free lime in the hardened H.A.C. may be one reason for its generally greater resistance to such materials, and H.A.C. concrete is usefully employed in the sugar-refining, soap and plastics industries. Although H.A.C. concrete gives much better resistance to sugar solutions and molasses, it is sometimes affected, especially by partially refined molasses. The phenolic substances found in tar liquors can attack Portland cement concrete and H.A.C. concrete has therefore been used for resistance in the gas industry.

It has been mentioned that hydrogen sulphide solutions have no effect on H.A.C. concrete and this applies also to sodium sulphide. Storage tanks for 14 per cent. sodium sulphide solution were found to be in perfect condition after 5 years' service. Nelles[48] gave H.A.C. and trass cement the highest durability rating after testing various concretes by immersion for 12 years in flowing water containing sulphides and sulphates. Good resistance is shown to calcium bisulphate, and H.A.C. mortar has been employed for setting the tiles in paper-mill digesters. H.A.C. concrete is used for floors, drains and machine-bases in the same industry. Sodium thiosulphate attacks Portland cement concrete but has little action on H.A.C. which has been successfully used for benches in photographic developing rooms. It resists most photographic chemicals with the exception of caustic alkali.

Cyanides do not affect H.A.C. concrete and according to Eisenbeck[49] it is immune from 5 per cent. potassium hydrogen sulphate solution which has a strong action on Portland cement concrete.

5. Action of Concrete on Certain Metals

Aluminium, certain aluminium alloys, zinc and lead can react with the alkali present in Portland cement. When these metals are embedded in, or placed in contact with, a Portland cement concrete or mortar mix, any reaction normally ceases when the mix hardens and dries out[50]. If the concrete is in damp conditions and is sufficiently permeable to allow the ingress of moisture, additional corrosion may cause it to crack. Due to the lower alkali content of H.A.C. there is no appreciable action between these metals and the cement after setting, and H.A.C. concrete has therefore been used as a protective surround for cables, pipes and fittings. Rengade[51] has noted the employment of H.A.C. concrete in underground cable-ducts for telephones.

6. Surface-treatment for increasing Chemical Resistance

Treatment of the surface of H.A.C. concrete with sodium silicate solution has little beneficial action in ordinary circumstances, since there is no free lime in this type of concrete. However, if the concrete is subsequently required to withstand dilute acids, a previous treatment with sodium silicate does tend to increase the acid resistance. Treatments with magnesium silico-fluoride solutions, or with a drying-oil harden the concrete surface for ordinary use and probably increase the chemical resistance. Coatings of acid-resistant enamels or epoxide-resin compositions are suitable for use on H.A.C. concrete, and adhere equally as well as they do on Portland cement concrete.

In all cases where good chemical resistance is required the quality of the concrete itself should be high. Maximum resistance is obtained if lean mixes are avoided and attention is paid to the thorough compaction and curing of the mix.

LITERATURE REFERENCES

[1] F. M. LEA & N. DAVEY. J. Instn. civ. Engrs. 1948-49, **32**, (7), 248.

[2] K. E. DORSCH. "The Hardening and Corrosion of Cements" (In German), Springer, Berlin, 1932. I. BICZÓK. "Concrete Corrosion and Protection" (In German). Akadémiai Kiadó, Budapest, 1960. F. M. LEA. "The Chemistry of Cement and Concrete." 2nd Edn. 1956. E. Arnold, London. M. DURIEZ. Travaux, 1951, **35**, (202), 449. T. D. ROBSON. Corrosion Technol. 1955, **2**, (3), 66, 96. A. V. HUSSEY & T. D. ROBSON. Symp. on Materials of Construction, Birmingham Univ. 1950. Soc. Chem. Industry. J. H. P. VAN AARDT. S. Afr. Industr. Chem. 1950, **10**, 211. T. SNECK. Nordisk Betong (Stockholm). 1957, **1**, (?), 117.

[3] M. TOUCHÉ. Le Ciment. 1926, **31**, 240. G. R. SHELTON. Industr. Engng. Chem. (Industr.). 1925, **17**, (12), 589, 1267 : 1926, **18**, 854. A. G. FLEMING. Engng. J. (Montreal). 1933, 215, 260. R. FÉRET. Ann. Pnts. Chauss. 1922, (4), 2, 5.

[4] A. ECKHARDT & P. W. KRONSBEIN. "Beton u. Zement im Seewasser." Ernst & Sohn, Berlin. Dtsch. Ausschuss für Stahlbeton. Vol. 102, 1955. Ernst & Sohn. G. GALLO & G. CAMPANA. Pubbl. Scu. Ing. Pisa. 5th Ser. 1934, (230). S. KONDO & T. YAMAUCHI. J. Ceram. Ass. Japan, 1932, (40), 212 : 1936, (44), 316 : 1954, (62), 656. F. M. LEA & C. M. WATKINS. Nat. Building Studies. R.P. 30, 1960. H.M.S.O. London. D. G. MILLER & P. W. MANSON. Minn. agric. Exp. Sta. 1948, Tech. Bull 180 : 1951, Tech. Bull. 194. MILLER & MANSON. U.S. Dept. Agric. 1933, Tech. Bull. 358. Publ. Rds. Wash. 1931, **12**, (3), 64. H. H. MILLER. Petrol Engr. 1942, **13**, (12), 50. R. E. STRADLING. 16th Report Inst. civ. Engrs. 1937, 15. H. LAFUMA. Rev. Matér. Constr. 1929, **243**, 441 : **244**, 4. Zement. 1927, **16**, 1179. Rev. Gén. Sci. Appl. 1952, 1, (3), 66.

[5] F. M. LEA. J. Inst. sanit. Engrs. 1936, **40**, (6), 185.

6   U.S. Bur. Stand. Tech. Papers, 44, 95, 214, 307. A. S. Dawson. J. Engng. Inst. Canada 1920. F. R. McMillan, T. E. Stanton, I. L. Tyler & W. C. Hansen. Amer. concr. Inst. Special Publicn, 1950. Den Norske Ingen. Betongkomité. Meddelelse 3. 1936 (Oslo). Eckhardt & Kronsbein. Ref. No. 4. F. Campus. Ann. Trav. Publ. Belg. Aug. 1947. H. K. Cook. Proc. A.S.T.M. 1952, 52, 1169. T. B. Kennedy & K. Mather. Proc. Amer. concr. Inst. 1954, 50, 141.

7   F. M. Lea. Ref. No. 2, p. 544.

8   F. M. Lea & C. M. Watkins. Ref. No. 4.

9   D. G. Miller & P. W. Manson. Ref. No. 4.

10 Anon. Canad. Engr., 1931, 22.

11 Building Research Station Digest 31. H.M.S.O., London.

12 J. Moum & I. Th. Rosenqvist. J. Amer. concr. Inst. 1953, 31, (3), 257.

13 N. Ahmad. Indian Concr. J. 1950, 24, (2), 82. E. Probst. ForschBer. Inst. für Beton. Karlsruhe, 1933. R. W. C. Smith. Water & Water Engng. 1936, 38, (459), 55. Concr. constr. Engng. 1936, 31, (6), 354.

14 Anon. Con. constr. Engng, 1953, 48, (1), 47. R. V. Allin. Concr. constr. Engng. 1933, 28, (7), 410 : (8), 449 : (9), 509 : (10), 603. L. Grelot & M. Chalos. Genie civ. 1935. July.

15 G. Jerram. J. Instn. munic. Engrs. 1935, 62, (7), 439.

16 D. G. Miller & P. W. Manson. Minn. agric. Exp. Sta. Tech. Bulls. 180 (1948), 194 (1951).

17 Anon. Concr. constr. Engng. 1953, 48, (1), 59.

18 F. C. Ball. Publ. Wks. Rds. & Transport Congress, 1937. Paper No. 5. A. V. Hussey. Ferro-Concrete 1935, Apr. J. Soc. Chem. Industry, Lond. 1934, 53, (41), 838.

19 C. W. Marler. Corrosion Tech. 1955, 2, (4), 121. Proc. Fertiliser Soc. 1955, (31).

20 F. M. Lea. Ref. No. 2. See also K. H. Gayer, L. C. Thompson & O. T. Zajicek. Canad. J. Chem. 1958, 36, (9), 1268.

21 R. Ward. Symp. on Materials of Construction. Birmingham Univ. 1950, 17. Soc. Chem. Industry.

22 D. N. Evans, R. L. Blaine & P. Worksman. 4th Int. Symp. on Chemistry of Cement. Washington, 1960.

23 N. Stutterheim, J. P. A. Lochner & J. F. Burger. Mag. Concr. Res. 1954, 6, (16), 39.

24 Anon. Steel. 1939, 105, 64. G. T. Haddock. Pwr. Plant (Engng.), 1947, Apr. T. D. Robson. Mod. Pwr. Engng. (Canada). 1954, 134. E. J. Stankiewicz. Combustion N.Y. 1955, 26, (8), 51. Coke & Gas. 1955, 495.

25 C. S. Darling. Steam Engr. 1955, 24. A. S. Pearson. Pwr. Plant (Engng.), 1943, Aug.

26 Anon. Concr. constr. Engng. 1935, 30, (2), 104.

27 Anon. Concr. constr. Engng. 1958, 53, (11), 404.

28 S. C. Britton. J. Instn. civ. Engrs. 1940-41, 16, (5), 65. H. E. Robarts. Instn. civ. Engrs, Railway Paper No. 23, 1947.

29 Anon. Concr. constr. Engng. 1950, 45, (5), 168.

30 L. A. Barnes. Concr. constr. Engng. 1958, 53.

[31] ANON. Corrosion Prevention & Control, 1956, July. Contract. Rec. 1959, 23. D.S.I.R. " Notes on Water Pollution " No. 6, 1959. C. C. COLLUM, J. Inst. civ. Engrs., 1951, (8), 418. J. T. CALVERT, E. A. LEES & H. F. FRANKLAND. Proc. Instn. civ. Engrs. 1958-59, **12,** 269. C. HAMMERTON. J. Inst. Sew. Purif. 1944, 150, 164 : 1939, 126. C. HOGG & E. A. DYER. Inter. Civ. Engr. & Contract. 1958, **10,** (5), 32. H. P. KAUFMAN. Civ. Engng. Lond. 1941. K. R. PATTISON. Engng. & Contract Rec. 1933, 91. L. G. SMITH & B. L. SHEPHERD. J. Instn. civ. Engrs. 1950, **33,** (3), 179.

[32] W. C. HANSEN, R. P. VELLINES & W. W. BRANDVOLD. A.S.T.M. Bull. 231, 1958, p. 85.

[33] N. STUTTERHEIM & J. P. VAN AARDT. S. Afric. Industr. Chem. 1953, **7,** (10).

[34] F. M. LEA. Ref. No. 2.

[35] ANON. Dairy Engng. 1957, June. A. E. HAMMOND. Food, 1952, 434. F. C. HARPER. Brit. Chem. Engng. 1956, **1,** (4), 212.

[36] F. C. HARPER. Dairy Ind. 1951, 1159, 1174.

[37] F. M. LEA & G. E. BESSEY. Concr. constr. Engng. 1939, **34,** 610.

[38] ANON. Concr. constr. Engng. 1933, **28,** (7), 435.

[39] G. W. DOUGLAS. J. Soc. Leather Tr. Chem. 1948, **32,** 398.

[40] R. GRÜN. Z. Angew. Chem. 1939, **51,** 879.

[41] M. LAWRENCE & H. E. VIVIAN. Austral. J. Appl. Sci. 1960, **11,** 490.

[42] R. GRÜN. Zement. 1944, **33,** 10. Zbl. Bauverw. 1936, Dec.

[43] W. T. HALCROW, G. B. BROOK & R. PRESTON. J. Instn. Water Eng. 1928, **33,** See also D. WERNER & S. GIERTZ-HEDSTRÖM. Cement & Cement Manuf. 1934, **7,** (7), 211.

[44] P. E. HALSTEAD. Mag. Concr. Res. 1954, **6,** (17), 93.

[45] E. RENGADE. Rev. Mater. Constr. 1927, 165, 361 : 1932, 309 : 1936, 55. Inter. Ass. Test. Matér. London Congress, 1937. See also J. BROCARD. Bâtir. 1950, **4,** 31.

[46] R. BIDRON. Rev. Matér. Constr. C. 1952, (443-444), 224.

[47] E. RENGADE. P. LHOPITALLIER & P. DURAND DE FONTMAGNE. Rev. Matér. Constr. 1936, **318,** 52 : **319,** 78.

[48] J. S. NELLES. J. Amer. concr. Inst. 1941, **12,** (4), 441.

[49] H. EISENBECK. Chem. Zeit. 1926, **50,** 165.

[50] T. E. WRIGHT, H. P. GODARD & I. H. JENKS. Engng. J. (Canada). 1954, **37,** (10), 1250. P. E. HALSTEAD. Chem. & Industry. 1957, (34), 1132. J. SINGLETON-GREEN. Brit. Pwr. Engng. 1960, **1,** (6), 59.

[51] E. RENGADE. Le Ciment. 1928, **23,** 15.

CHAPTER 7.—NON-REFRACTORY APPLICATIONS OF H.A.C.

CONTENTS

CHAPTER SEVEN

Non-Refractory Applications of H.A.C.

The practical applications of H.A.C. which can now be considered are chiefly those in which the cement is used for concretes or mortars designed for load-bearing functions, and those in which its chemical resistance properties are utilised. Refractory or high-temperature applications are discussed in Chapter 8.

Although H.A.C. concrete is often used for purely structural purposes and at other times for chemical resistance applications involving no load-bearing duty, it is probable that in the majority of cases the decision to employ H.A.C. is based partly on the rapid-hardening or strength properties and partly on its chemical resistance capacity. There are several general reviews which deal with methods of use[1] and many relevant applications have already been given when dealing with some of the characteristics of H.A.C. The applications mentioned below are therefore limited to selected uses which are typical or which present unusual points of interest.

1. Neat Cement and Rich Mortars

H.A.C. is not often used in the neat condition since the drying shrinkage in air of the cement paste is high, thus restricting its use to thin sections and small volumes. However, in the assembly of suspension insulators for electric power transmission lines, the metal castings forming the caps and pins of glass or porcelain insulators are sealed in position by a neat H.A.C. paste. The porcelain insulators are usually assembled with a rich mortar made from H.A.C. and ground porcelain as aggregate.

Another extensive use of H.A.C. paste is for cementing the diamond-drill holes which are necessary in mineral or precious metal prospection[2]. One method is to mix the required amount of cement slurry and to pour it through the drill-rods to the area of rock or ground which requires cementing. The rods are then withdrawn until the cement hardens, after which re-drilling can commence. The rapid-hardening of H.A.C. is therefore very useful for this purpose particularly in cold climates, but in some cases accelerators have been added to the slurry. The cement paste may also be lowered down the hole in a cylinder attached to the end of the drill rods and it is blown out by hydraulic pressure when the necessary depth has been reached. Hall considers that the best method is to pump the cement slurry into the hole through the drill-rods with specially treated foam-rubber balls placed ahead and behind the column of cement.

A similar application on a larger scale is the cementing of oil-wells. In the normal type of deep well, special oil-well cements are of course used but H.A.C. (or even a mixture of H.A.C. and Portland cement) has been found satisfactory for shallow wells where the temperatures are not so high and a heavily-retarded cement is therefore not required. Injection of H.A.C. slurries into the ground or fissured rock has been carried out in the same way as for Portland cement[3].

H.A.C. paste or a rich mortar made with fine sand is commonly used in laboratories for capping concrete cylinders before testing the latter for compressive strength. Werner[4] found that cylinders capped in this way gave a higher strength than when capped with any other of the usual materials but Henning[5] could not confirm this and concluded that the same average strength was obtained whether specimens were capped with H.A.C. or sulphur compound.

When a neat H.A.C. paste or a rich mortar is cast against a polished surface e.g. glass, enamelled or burnished metal, plastic, etc., the contact face of the cement, after hardening, has the same degree of gloss as the material against which it has been placed[6]. This property may be due to the large amount of gel substance which is formed when H.A.C. hydrates, and it is utilised in France (and to some extent in other countries) for producing decorative panels, fireplace surrounds, and monuments in " artificial marble " or " artificial granite." Moulds made from polished metal are usually employed but for flat decorative slabs intended for architectural use, the mix may be cast against glass or plastic. In order to obtain a reproduction of natural granites a wet slurry of H.A.C. or a very rich mortar is mixed with pigment to match the lighter areas of the rock, and is then projected onto the surface of the mould in flecks by dipping a broom-head into the slurry and brushing the bristles with the hand. This is repeated all over the surface of the mould with other suitably coloured slurries until a thin continuous coating is obtained. Just as the coating reaches a certain stage of hardening it is backed to the desired thickness with an or-dinary sand/H.A.C. mortar which bonds integrally with the decorative face. When the unit is separated from the polished mould surface after 24 hours the manufacture is complete — no polishing or grinding of the face being required. For outdoor use it is customary to give

164

the glossy surface three light applications of boiled linseed oil. In the production of " artificial marble " a somewhat different technique is used, the " veins " being made by dropping onto the mould surface a hank of flax fibres which has been dipped in a slurry of white or pigmented H.A.C. Other slurries are then spattered against the mould, usually from the fingers until a coating with the desired effect has been achieved. After this point the process is similar to that used for " granite," and the effects obtained by workers skilled in the art are quite remarkable.

The dark-coloured high-alumina cements are favoured for making monument slabs of terrazzo. A mix of H.A.C. and marble chips is cast into a suitable mould (often made with H.A.C. concrete) and after it has hardened, the surfaces of the unit are ground and polished using the customary equipment employed by monumental masons. Apart from the rapid-hardening advantage, the H.A.C. surface is less liable to " blooming " or efflorescence when exposed to the elements. Decorative panels[7] employing the contrasting dark colour of some high-alumina cements are, of course, made by many other techniques.

The use of H.A.C. by sculptors has become very widespread since they readily obtain a variety of surface finishes which are artistically acceptable[8]. In particular it is difficult to distinguish a bronze statuary from one made with dark-coloured H.A.C., and if necessary the patina can be simulated very effectively. The expensive metal-casting process is eliminated and the concrete work of art is also suitable for outdoor exhibition e.g., in parks or as an external feature for schools, office-blocks, theatres, etc. The resistance of H.A.C. to the rather corrosive atmosphere in some urban or industrial districts is naturally very high. In a book on this subject, Mills[9] describes some of the methods and mixes employed and the casting techniques. The aggregates or fillers used in the rich mortar mixes include sand, marble or granite chips and dust, ground firebrick, pumice and fly-ash. The castings may be suitably reinforced with mild steel, expanded metal or fibre-glass, and practically any desired finish and appearance can be obtained by direct casting or by subsequent surface treatment or tooling. The substitution of H.A.C. for lead in jointing the coloured glass segments of modern stained-glass windows is also noted.

2. TILE-SLABBING

This application is confined largely to Great Britain, New Zealand and, to a lesser extent, Australia. Ceramic tile surrounds for open fires or slow-combustion stoves are made in complete units by laying the tiles face down on a flat surface within wooden battens defining the general outlines of the surround. Edge tiles or " return " tiles are similarly laid along the vertical faces of the battens so that a " mould " completely lined with tiles is obtained, and the latter are usually retained in position by small spots of plaster at their corners. The minimum quantity of plaster, or a Portland cement/H.A.C. paste, should be used for this purpose.

The tile " mould " is then filled with a relatively wet mix of H.A.C. mortar or concrete, and after this has hardened the whole unit with tiles adhering, can be lifted from the slabbing table and despatched if necessary. The use of H.A.C. allows the working space to be cleared each day. The maximum size of aggregate does not exceed $\frac{3}{8}$ in. or $\frac{3}{16}$ in. and the ratio of cement to aggregate is usually between 1 : 4 and 1 : 6 by volume. The customary aggregates include sand, shingle, crushed rock or crushed firebrick, tiles, saggars etc. Surrounds of lighter weight are obtained by the use of expanded clay or shale aggregates, or in some cases, by the addition of perlite. To obtain good tile adhesion the mix is worked into the face of tiles and up to the side of the " return " tiles by hand. Preliminary soaking of the tiles is not recommended but they may be sprinkled with water to reduce the suction, particularly in the case of the thicker " return " tiles. Reinforcing rods or mesh are laid in the mortar as it is placed but care should be taken to see that the metal is not too close to the tiles, especially in the hearth units where the fire may cause relatively high surface temperatures. Slate, marble or decorative stone panels may be used instead of ceramic tiles and they are " slabbed " in much the same fashion.

The adhesion of the tiles is not increased by using excessively rich or wet mixes but it has been claimed that greater adhesion resulted when the mix hardened at higher temperatures[10]. Adhesion (at least at ordinary temperatures) is also improved by giving the backs of the tiles a thin wash with an emulsion such as polyvinyl acetate. Very lean mixes are sometimes suggested for tile-slabbing on the grounds that subsequent shrinkage of the mortar is reduced. It must be remembered however that a considerable reserve of strength is required when the units are handled at 16-24 hours after casting, and this may not always be available if the cement content of the mix is reduced too far. When the surround is fixed in place little mechanical strength is necessary and satisfactory service depends mainly on good tile-adhesion.

3. SOME RAPID-HARDENING APPLICATIONS

H.A.C. concretes should be ready for any designed duty 24 hours after placing[11]. The rapid-hardening properties of the lower-silica types of H.A.C. are such that concrete strengths high enough for many structural purposes are obtainable at 6-8 hours, even although the initial setting-time of the cement may be about 5 hours. Heavy trucks or omnibuses have run over ordinary 1 : 6 H.A.C. concrete which was 6-7 hours old[12] and still higher strengths can be obtained at the same age by vibratory compaction of suitable mixes.

H.A.C. therefore offers useful possibilities for bridge repairs, rapid re-instatement of road excavations, installation of traffic signal pads or for concreting at busy road intersections. Entrances to shops, offices, factories and workshops, level-crossing repairs, erection of stands in exhibition halls, and rapid removal of machinery to new bases are examples of the type of application where the use of H.A.C. concrete allows normal service to commence or recommence in the minimum time[13]. If necessary, machinery may be erected on H.A.C. concrete bases when the latter are 6-8 hours old and the machine can be in full operation again within 24 hours. In such cases, where some duty is required from the concrete within the first 12 hours, water-curing should be started as soon as possible and the concrete should be kept wet for 24 hours, although it may already be in use for part of this time.

Economies can often be effected in the amount of formwork required, by using H.A.C. concrete. For example, the 3 in. thick domed reinforced concrete roof of a large prestressed concrete water tank was quickly constructed in H.A.C. concrete by employing only one sectional form[14]. When precast units require complicated or expensive moulds, the greater output from a given number of moulds, or the reduction in number of moulds for a given output, frequently makes the use of H.A.C. very attractive in spite of its higher cost.

The rapid-hardening property of H.A.C. is also utilised for underpinning[15], concreting in mines[16], work between tides[17], construction or repair of sea-defences, repair of canal locks, for preventing the ingress of water in underground work and for sealing the bottom of caissons[18]. Where flowing water is encountered, it must be remembered that H.A.C. is not quick-setting and therefore no structural strength can be expected for a few hours. Longer mixing-times will curtail the period between placing and the hardening of the cement, and the use of quick-setting mixtures of Portland cement and H.A.C. has been described in Chapter V. These mixtures do not give the high strength of H.A.C. and should not be used for reinforced concrete of a permanent nature.

4. H.A.C. CONCRETE PILES

This is an application where H.A.C. is used either for its rapidity of hardening or its chemical resistance but in many cases for both properties.

(1) *Pre-cast or Driven Piles*

A pile made with the more rapid-hardening types of H.A.C. may be cast and driven within 24 hours even in cold weather. H.A.C. is therefore popular for test-piles and pile-caps since information derived from loading trials can be obtained in the shortest time. It is also used for extending driven test-piles[19] or service piles should they prove to be too short for the ground conditions. In a similar fashion it has been used for splicing together sections of Portland cement piles. The first section is driven, the second section erected above it, and the splice of H.A.C. concrete is placed in a box shutter at the junction[20]. By this method very long piles may be driven with a piling rig of normal height. After Portland cement piles or H.A.C. piles have been driven, any re-heading or extension which may be required can usually be done and the driving completed before the pile-hammer has to be moved to another part of the site.

The concrete mix employed for pre-cast H.A.C. concrete piles with the normal square or octagonal cross-section is approximately 1 : 6 by weight (assuming that the maximum size of aggregate is about ¾ in). Mixes much richer or leaner than this are usually undesirable although piles destined for use in sea-water should have a relatively high cement content. The piles may be cast to any length but the diameter is normally less than 2 ft. In the construction of foundations for the Beaujon Hospital at Clichy, Paris, H.A.C. concrete piles with a square section of 2 ft. 6 in. were driven into the highly sulphated ground[21]. A relatively dry mix, consolidated by vibration, was used and this method of compaction is always desirable.

The curing of pre-cast H.A.C. concrete piles should always be carried out with care since piles of thicker section require the cooling effect of water particularly when the weather is hot. The side-forms must be stripped as soon as possible (within a few hours) and the pile should be kept wet for the remainder of the first 24 hours by sprays or by running a perforated plastic hose along the top surface of the concrete. Gang-moulds, with formwork common to adjacent piles, should not be used unless this part of the mould can be removed. Some users believe that there is an optimum age at which to drive H.A.C. concrete piles but opinions differ widely in defining this period. Records show that very large numbers of H.A.C. concrete piles have been successfully driven at ages ranging from 20 hours to several years and it is thought that the above belief is largely caused by instances in which the curing has been inadequate, since the full effect of different degrees of concrete over-heating is revealed at a variable time afterwards. Piles which have been seriously over-heated during hardening will be very liable to breakage at whatever age they are driven.

The speed with which H.A.C. precast concrete piles can be made and driven is responsible for much of their use[22] but in many cases they are specified where the ground is highly sulphated[23], where it is marshy or peaty[24], or contains chemical refuse and acid[25]. They may also be made in order to maintain the piling schedule in very cold weather[26] and they have an excellent durability record in sea-water[27].

A special case is that of " shell " piles in which short pre-cast hollow concrete cylinders or shells are threaded onto a mandrel and pile tip which is then driven into the ground. Any depth of pile can be obtained and the interior of the pile may be inspected before inserting reinforcement and filling with H.A.C. concrete or Portland concrete (according to circumstances). The pre-cast concrete shells are made with H.A.C. concrete either to give resistance to sulphates, acids etc. in the soil or purely because production from a limited number of moulds is accelerated and the shells can be utilised within a short time.

(2) *Bored or Cast-in-Situ Piles*

Cast-in-situ piles up to about 22 in. diameter are made successfully with H.A.C. concrete but it is doubtful whether H.A.C. should be used in piles of substantially greater diameter since no water curing is possible. When the piling system does not involve any mechanical compaction, there is a tendency to employ mixes of very wet consistencies and this should be avoided as far as possible. The use of an immersion vibrator allows thorough compaction of mixes with more suitable water-cement ratios.

In at least one system, an H.A.C. mix with an earth-moist consistency is vigorously tamped into the hole by means of a heavy hammer. In this case mixes much leaner than 1 : 6 are permissible since the concrete is thoroughly consolidated at a low water-cement ratio, and good quality concrete results. However, the use of similar lean mixes with less effective compaction methods must not be allowed since it would inevitably necessitate a high water-cement ratio and produce a relatively porous concrete.

5. Prestressed Concrete

Advantage has been taken of the high early strength obtainable from H.A.C. (particularly the lower-silica type) in the fabrication of prestressed beams, lintels, purlins, etc. This property is naturally of special value in manufacture by the pre-tensioning method in which the concrete is bonded to stressed wires. The mixes are efficiently vibrated into the moulds (preferably steel moulds) and the wires may be cut 18-24 hours after casting. The process therefore competes successfully with the use of rapid-hardening Portland cement which requires steam-curing in order to fulfil the same time-schedule. Other advantages arising from the use of H.A.C., such as a reduction in the percentage of rejects, have been noted by Blackmore[28]. The majority of the pre-tensioned applications are for floor and roof beams in multistorey offices, flats and factories. Such beams usually have a relatively thin section but they are also manufactured in sizes capable of dealing with long spans[29], and several accounts have been given of constructions employing these units[30]. Beams of thicker section are employed for bridges ; and columns, roof purlins, etc. required for the complete framework of a factory have also been made in H.A.C. prestressed concrete[31].

In post-tensioned construction there is usually adequate time for the individual Portland cement precast units to harden before tensioning commences and the rapid-hardening properties of H.A.C. concrete are not utilised so frequently. However if the concrete units are required urgently on site or if there is difficulty in maintaining the delivery programme, the use of H.A.C. provides a convenient solution[32]. The limitation on the depth of lift or thickness of H.A.C. concrete may however restrict its use for some post-tensioned work, since many of the units designed for this method of prestressing are too large to be placed in one operation with H.A.C.

From the early days of prestressing, a rich H.A.C./sand mortar has been used for making the male and female anchorage cones employed in the Freyssinet system, and similar mortars or concretes are used as joints between prefabricated units which have been erected for post-tensioning[33]. The wires, cables, or bars can then be stressed within 12 hours if necessary. The end-faces of the concrete to be jointed should be wetted before the joint is packed and the H.A.C. mortar or concrete should be kept wet while it hardens. For thin joints a rich mortar may be employed so that adequate workability is obtained at a relatively low water-cement ratio, and thicker concrete joints are also placed with an H.A.C. mix which has a generous cement content and the minimum amount of mix water consistent with obtaining good compaction.

The highest quality of H.A.C. concrete should always be used for prestressed work and this entails vibratory methods of consolidation.

170

With this efficient method of compaction and a good system of factory control[34], commercial pre-tensioned units are manufactured with low water-cement ratios (below 0.40) even when the concrete mix is lean (e.g. $7\frac{1}{2}$: 1 by weight). When equipment is not available for achieving such vigorous consolidation, the necessary workability should be obtained by increasing the cement content and not the water content of the mix. Information on other properties of H.A.C. concrete used for prestressed construction e.g. resistance to slip of wires, and anchorage and bond stresses, has been obtained by laboratory work[35].

Prestressed H.A.C. concrete is not recommended for subsequent use in situations where it is known that a major degree of conversion is certain or probable e.g. in tropical seas or in industrial situations where it will be under water (or in saturated conditions) while at a temperature higher than about 30°C. (86°F.). It is also considered of primary importance that when H.A.C. is used for prestressed construction the water-cement ratio should never exceed 0.45 and should preferably be below 0.40. Reference has previously been made to the relatively high fluidity of the H.A.C. paste at low water-cement ratios and it is therefore easier with H.A.C. to obtain the requisite workability at low water contents than it would be with Portland cement or, in particular, with rapid-hardening Portland cement. In practice, most of the H.A.C. prestressed beams made in England are cast with mixes having water-cement ratios not exceeding 0.40, and in view of the good physical properties obtained from this type of concrete even after full conversion, it was decided to carry out tests on commercially manufactured beams of this quality which had been deliberately converted by subsequent storage in hot water.

Works labour and equipment were used in making the test beams and the materials, water-cement ratio and mix proportions (1 : 2.3 : 4.6 by weight) were the same as those employed each day for commercial manufacture[36]. The beams were 5 ft. or 13 ft. long with a depth of 7 in. and a flange width of 6 in., stressed by 8 indented wires of 0.2 in. diameter. After the wires had been cut at about 1 day after casting, control beams were stored in the yard while the remainder were placed in a large tank containing water thermostatically controlled at 45°C. $\pm$ 5°C. (113°F.), where they remained for about a month. Concrete cubes also stored in the hot water revealed that full conversion had occurred before the end of this period. The beams which had been cured normally were then directly compared with those which had been fully " converted " under hot water, by testing, in most cases to failure, under third-point loading.

171

It was realised that, apart from any effect due to conversion, the prestress in the beams stored in hot water would be reduced in any case because of increased creep of wire and concrete at the higher temperature. However, the behaviour of the "converted" beams made with a low-water-cement ratio was quite satisfactory and Fig. 25 is an example of the results obtained with one pair of 5 ft. units[37]. Both curves depart from the straight line load-deflection section at values close to the loads calculated to give zero stress in the bottom fibre. Assessment of the transmission lengths showed that these had

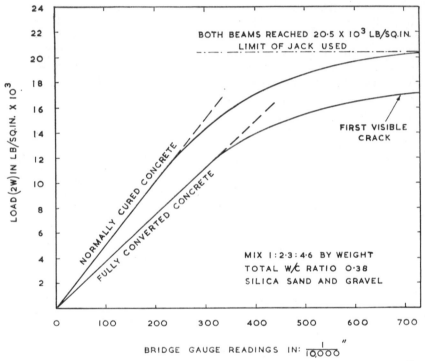

FIG. 25. Loading tests on H.A.C. concrete prestressed beams, normally cured or fully converted.

not been appreciably affected by conversion of the concrete, but the average strain-increase during the storage period was considerably greater from the "converted" beams. The colour of the concrete after storage in hot water was still black throughout indicating that no excessive permeability had been produced.

It therefore appears that prestressed H.A.C. concrete made with a sufficiently low water-cement ratio (not more than 0.40) is capable of giving satisfactory service for its designed duty even if *complete* conversion of the hydrates is brought about. Nevertheless, in spite of this favourable conclusion, it is not considered prudent to relax the restrictions on the use of H.A.C. for prestressed concrete in situations causing full conversion. H.A.C. prestressed concrete should always be made and used under conditions which avoid rapid conversion, and the insistence on low water-cement ratios is therefore intended to provide an assurance of continued satisfactory service in the event of any conceivable conversion which might take place either during hardening (e.g. in hot weather) or in subsequent normal use.

(a) *Fire-resistance of prestressed H.A.C. concrete.*

Fire-resistance tests on prestressed beams, carried out according to B.S. 476, A.S.T.M. E.119, or similar specifications of other countries, indicate the length of time for which the assemblage will fulfil its necessary function under the conditions of a fire. The high-tension steel used in prestressed concrete beams loses half its strength at 400°C. (752°F.) and it can usually be assumed that collapse is imminent when the wires reach that temperature. The efficiency of the concrete in delaying the advent of high-wire temperatures depends on its thermal conductivity, heat capacity and, to a certain extent, on its resistance to spalling. The type of aggregate, depth of concrete cover for the steel, and the presence or absence of plaster coats on the heated face, are therefore the chief factors. Other things being equal, it could thus be expected that the behaviour of prestressed concrete constructions, in brief rising-temperature tests of this nature, would be little influenced by the nature of the hydraulic cement. This appears to be confirmed by tests carried out with constructions based on H.A.C. prestressed beams, since the results indicate the same behaviour as would be obtained with Portland cement units.

In one fire test[38] the assemblage consisted of H.A.C. prestressed concrete beams (1 : 2 : 4 sand and gravel) placed at 2 ft. centres with hollow clinker blocks filling the intervening spaces. An insulating plaster coat (1 in. thick) was appplied to the underside (which formed the roof of the test furnace) and the top surface was covered with a 2 in. mortar topping. The beams were 7 in. deep with flanges 6 in. wide, and they contained six indented wires (0.2 in. diameter) having an initial prestress of 143,000 lbs./sq. in. After 4 hours 6 minutes the furnace temperature was about 1120°C. but there was no failure of the roof under the designed load of 112 lb./sq. ft.

6. Pipes and Tunnel Segments

H.A.C. concrete pipes have been made on all the usual pipe-making equipment. H.A.C. is not usually ground as finely as ordinary

Portland cement and is much coarser than rapid-hardening Portland cement, therefore the optimum spinning-time tends to be shorter for H.A.C. pipes made by the centrifugal process.

H.A.C. concrete pipes are employed for sewers, especially in sulphated ground or clay, or as drains carrying slightly acid solutions[39] and effluents containing agents aggressive to ordinary concrete. In many cases they must resist both external and internal attack. Very high strength pipes, with increased resistance to external attack are obtained by coating with glass fibres and polyester resin[40]. When the possible attack is limited to the interior of the pipe, H.A.C. concrete linings are spun into Portland concrete pipes and these composite units, in diameters up to 5 ft., have been extensively employed for sewers particularly in Malaya and Singapore[41]. Spun linings of H.A.C. concrete or mortar are also used to protect the interior of cast-iron or steel pipes and H.A.C. compositions are also employed on the outside of metal pipes for protection against corrosive soil conditions or sea-water[42]. Minchin[43] records that iron pipes in Holland were coated in 1928 with coal-tar pitch followed by a layer of H.A.C., and after 18 years the condition was still perfect.

Large diameter concrete pipes, which have been corroded on the inside are frequently repaired by cutting back to unaffected concrete, fixing a mesh reinforcement, and applying a gunited coat of H.A.C. mortar. In the case of a refinery pipe-line which had been corroded internally by condenser water, a repair to the soffit was effected by guniting H.A.C. mortar over the outside surface[44].

H.A.C. mortar is also employed for jointing pipes which have sockets, since hydraulic tests or smoke tests can then be carried out with the minimum delay. It has also been used as a packing in certain proprietary flexible joints[45].

Precast concrete tunnel and sewer segments are made in H.A.C. concrete because of the greater output from moulds or because of aggressive soil or atmospheric conditions in service. H.A.C. mortar (1 : 1) is usually used for joints between the units and for packing behind them[46].

7. BRICK-JOINTING

Unless a plasticiser is present in H.A.C. or has been added at the mixer, mortars made with sand and this type of cement have relatively poor water-retention properties. When they are used for jointing ordinary building bricks there is a tendency for water to be absorbed quickly into the porous brickwork and the mortar layer does not retain its plasticity for long. In such cases it is helpful if the suction

174

of the brick is reduced by dipping them in water, or if a small amount of suitable plasticing agent is added to the mix.

Semi-vitrified bricks e.g., blue engineering bricks and some types of facing brick, have a low porosity and suction, so that no trouble is experienced in jointing them with ordinary H.A.C. mortar[47]. Indeed certain advantages are gained since a greater height of brick-work may be quickly built. The H.A.C. mortar is not squeezed out of the joints by the weight of super-imposed bricks because it is less plastic than masonry cement and it hardens much more rapidly. H.A.C. mortar is most commonly used with this particular type of brick since resistance to chemicals or dilute acids usually requires a dense impermeable brick as well as a corrosion-resistant mortar.

Attack by acids arising from combustion of fuels is resisted well by H.A.C. mortar joints and suitable applications therefore include jointing and re-pointing in railway tunnels[48], and low-temperature brick flues, chimneys or stacks where condensation occurs[49]. The acid resistance of H.A.C. mortar, although limited, is sufficiently high also for similar uses in boiler plants but Catchpole[50] found that even H.A.C. mortar was attacked by the very acid gases produced when firing bricks made with clay of high sulphur content.

H.A.C. mortar is frequently employed for jointing brickwork in sewers, sewer manholes, drains, flumes, effluent or process-liquor tanks[51], and it is also used for laying brick linings in coal bunkers and ash-hoppers or applied as a gunite lining. Much greater resistance to acids and alkalis is obtained by using H.A.C./rubber latex mortars for jointing brickwork in the chemical industry. Such joints have great adhesion to the bricks and their resilience reduces the risk of hair-cracks between brick and mortar, even under fluctuating temperature conditions[52].

8. MISCELLANEOUS APPLICATIONS

The chemical resistance and rapid-hardening properties of H.A.C. are utilised in the provision of floors[53], tanks, sumps, drains, machine-bases and foundations in a wide variety of industries where aggressive effluents or liquors are encountered, and the suitability of H.A.C. for resistance to any particular chemical can be assessed from the information given in Chapter VI. Massive foundations or concrete bases should not be placed with lifts deeper than those recommended, and good water-curing is essential for this type of application and also for floors or floor-toppings. The latter may be cleaned with any of the usual detergents which do not contain more than about 4 per cent. alkalis[54], but caustic soda or potash should not be employed.

Many foundations and floors are composite structures built partly with Portland cement concrete and partly with H.A.C. concrete so that effective bonding is required. When a Portland cement mix is to be joined to an existing H.A.C. concrete it is usually recommended that the latter should be at least 1 day old, and conversely, that an existing Portland cement concrete should be at least 7 days old before an H.A.C. mix is placed upon it. A rapid-hardening Portland cement concrete need be only 3 days old. Further recommendations are that the surface of the existing concrete should be chipped, dampened, and then brushed with a slurry (or 1 : 1 mortar) of the other cement before the fresh mix is placed.

An excellent bond between the two types of concrete can be obtained in this way and evidence of this has been given by several investigators[55]. In fact the bond of H.A.C. concrete to Portland cement concrete is usually found to be greater than that of one Portland cement concrete to another. An equally satisfactory bond should be obtained when guniting H.A.C. mortar linings in Portland cement concrete tanks, chimneys, etc., or with gunite repairs of any concrete structure. The reservations of Burgess[56] with regard to this last application have not been confirmed in practice.

Although it has always been recommended that the existing concrete should be substantially mature before concrete made with a different type of cement is placed against it, there is strong evidence that this may be an unnecessarily conservative opinion. Biehl[57] compacted fresh earth-moist mixes containing H.A.C. and Portland cement to make composite prisms and showed that no bond defects developed after long exposure to the elements. Many manufacturers of concrete tiles regularly place a Portland cement backing onto an unset H.A.C. mix, or vice-versa, and a good bond results[58]. In a study of the methods of placing H.A.C. concrete toppings on a Portland cement concrete base (to provide runways resistant to the heat from jet or rocket engines) Hansen and Brandvold[59] found that the best strength was generally obtained when the topping was placed just after the concrete of the base course had taken its initial set, and there was no evident advantage in waiting for a greater degree of maturity in the latter. It therefore seems that an effective bond can be obtained between two freshly placed mixes so long as the compaction method and mix consistencies are such that no excessive mixing of the two cements occurs at the interface.

H.A.C. has shown certain advantages for atomic reactor shielding[60] since it retains a greater amount of combined water at moderately high temperatures. Accordingly the hydrogen content of the concrete is slightly increased and this is useful for shielding against fast neutrons. The effect is greatly accentuated by the use of hydrated aggregates such as serpentine or Colemanite, and a stronger and heavier concrete of this type would no doubt be obtained with hard diasporic bauxite as aggregate.

H.A.C. and suitable heat-resistant or refractory aggregates produce concretes which are suitable for temperatures higher than those yet required for shielding purposes, and such concretes have been patented[61] as a hot-face lining for gas-cooled reactors in which the pressure vessel and concrete shielding are combined in one unit. The refractoriness of concretes made with H.A.C. should also be useful in the case of high temperature insulating mixes (made with borated diatomite aggregate) for thermal and neutron shielding. H.A.C. may also be used with any of the heavier aggregates, such as basalt, iron shot, barytes or ferro-phosphorus, for attenuation of gamma radiation, and, in particular, this type of concrete has been successfully employed for shield plugs.

High-strength castings of H.A.C. concrete have been recommended for dies and shaping surfaces e.g. for plastics, since smooth polished concrete faces can be readily obtained. H.A.C. is also used for bonding abrasive grains in the manufacture of grinding-wheels. In most cases a proportion of pumice is added to the mix but a small amount of gas-forming agent has also been suggested as an addition to improve the grinding properties.

H.A.C. is commonly employed as a dehydrator in cement/water-emulsion mixes (see Chapter 5) but the absorption of water by the anhydrous cement has been utilised in other less usual applications, for example in measuring the suction and moisture content of soils by the electrical resistance method[62]. With other cements, H.A.C. can also be used as a dehydrator in organic chemical reactions involving condensation e.g. esterification or the formation of aliphatic and aromatic amines, amides and nitriles[63]. Calcium aluminate itself has been patented as a dehydrator/catalyst for condensing lower ketones to give higher unsaturated ketones, for example in the preparation of isophorone from acetone at 400°C.[64].

Before leaving the more unusual applications, calcium aluminate glass should be mentioned because of its good infra-red transmission. Alkali and iron are introduced into the batch composition in order to reduce the tendency to devitrification. Manganese and copper significantly increase the infra-red transmission but these glasses have a lower resistance to moisture than is the case with normal optical glass[65].

177

LITERATURE REFERENCES

1   A. V. HUSSEY. J. Soc. chem. Industr. 1936, **55,** (52), 1037. T. D. ROBSON. Contract. Rec. 1953, **64,** (48), 24. Architect. Sci. Rev. (Sydney). 1959, **2,** (1), 49. P. H. HARRIS. Engng. J. (Montreal). 1956, **39,** 219. T. J. VAN FLEET. Build. Progr. Dunedin. 1956, **21,** (2), 10. H. LAFUMA. Ann. Inst. Bâtim. 1939, **4,** (4), 1. F. M. LEA. J. Instn. sanit. Engrs. 1936, **40,** (6), 185. Royal Inst. Chem. Lecture 1944. J. L. MINER. Concrete N.Y. 1927, **30,** (4), 35.

2   P. B. HALL. West. Miner & Oil Rev. (Canada). 1957, 74. **Canad. Min. J.** 1957, 80.

3   L. E. HUNTER. Contract. Rec. 1952, 22. H. P. KAUFMAN. Civ. Engng. Lond. 1941. R. PESTELL. Gas World. 1952, **135,** (3530), 372.

4   G. WERNER. Proc. Amer. Soc. Test. Mater. 1958, **58,** 1166.

5   N. E. HENNING. J. Amer. Concr. Inst. 1961, **32,** (7), 851.

6   J. C. SÉAILLES & SOC. LAP. Brit. Pats. 217605 (1924), 222500 (1924). In France 1923. 231867 (1925), 234846 (1925). In France 1924. LAFUMA. Ref. 1.

7   ANON. Civ. Engng. Lond. 1954, **49,** (378), 821. Concr. constr. Engng. 1954, **49,** (10), 307.

8   ANON. Contract. Rec. 1955, 23. Concrete Quarterly No. 20 Cem. & Concrete Ass. London 1953. Idem 1958, 25. Concr. constr. Engng. 1936, 563.

9   J. W. MILLS. " Sculpture in Ciment Fondu." Contractors Record Ltd. London. 1959, pp. 52.

10 A. W. NORRIS, F. HOUSLEY & J. DUKES. 7th Inter. Ceram. Congress. London. 1960.

11 ANON. Génie. civ. 1939, **114,** (19), 399. A. R. COLLINS. Civ. Engng. Lond. 1950, **45,** (524), 110. M. DURIEZ. Rev. Gén. Routes Aerodr. 1960, **347,** 99. E. FREYSINNET. Mém. Soc. Ing. civ. France. 1935, 88, (8/10), 643. O. GRAF. Beton u. Eisen. 1934, **33,** (10), 156.

12 ANON. Contract J. 1954, 554.

13 ANON. Concr. constr. Engng. 1953, **48,** (1), 22. Idem. 1956, 530. Blast Furn. 1948, **36,** 94.

14 R. E. ROWE. Consult. Engr. 1957, 210.

15 L. E. HUNTER. Contr. Rec. 1952, 22.

16 J. A. C. ROSS. Trans. Canad. Min. Inst. 1950, **53,** 18.

17 ANON. Rds. Engng. Constr. (Canada). 1951, 75. Canad. Engr. 1931, 22. A. ECKARDT & P. W. KRONSBEIN. " Beton und Zement im Seewasser." Ernst & Sohn, Berlin.

18 H. J. DEANE. J. Instn. civ. Engrs. 1932.

19 L. G. SMITH & B. L. SHEPHERD. J. Instn. civ. Engrs. 1950, **33,** (3), 179

20 J. M. ANTILL. Commonwealth Engr. 1948, 471.

21 L. GRELOT & M. CHALOS. Génie. civ. 1935. July.

22 J. T. GUERITTE. Concr. constr. Engng. 1933, **28,** (7), Suppl. 21. ANON. Idem. 1931, **26,** (9), 503. ALLIN. Ref. 24.

23 ANON. Concr. constr. Engng. 1953, **48,** (1), 47.

24 R. V. ALLIN. Concr. constr. Engng. 1933, **28**, (7), 410 : (8), 449 : (9),
      509 : (10), 603. ANON. Iron Coal Tr. Rev. Special Issue " The
      Steel Co. of Wales Ltd. Technical Survey," p. 217, 232.
25 ANON. Concr. constr. Engng. 1950, **45**, (5), 168.
26 ANON. Travaux. 1948, **163**, 261.
27 F. M. LEA & C. M. WATKINS. D.S.I.R. Nat. Build. Studies. Res.
      Paper. No. 30. 1960. H.M.S.O.
28 J. C. BLACKMORE. Contract. Rec. 1951, 21. Prestressed Concrete
      Congress. Ghent. 1951.
29 ANON. Concr. constr. Engng. 1960, **55**, (10), 381.
30 ANON. Concr. constr. Engng. 1957, **52**, (8), 290. Idem. 1953, **48**,
      (10), 334. Idem. 1959, **54**, (1), 47. Contract. Rec. 1959, **70**,
      (40), 39.
31 C. W. GLOVER. Build. Digest. 1949, 3. Contract. J. 1950, **142**, 1023.
      J. SINGLETON-GREEN. Contr. Rec. 1949, 14.
32 K. C. HORTON. J. Instn. munic. Engrs. 1957, **83**, (11), 349. ANON.
      Concr. constr. Engng. 1950, **45**, (11), 398. C. W. GLOVER. Par-
      thenon, 1949, **24**, (3), 45.
33 W. M. SUTHERLAND. Contract. J. 1958, 620.
34 O. J. MASTERMAN. Mag. Concr. Res. 1958, **10**, (29), 57.
35 G. MARSHALL. Mag. Concr. Res. 1949, (3), 123. W. EASTWOOD &
      R. D. MILNE. Civ. Engng. Lond. 1953, **48**, (566), 741.
36 THE HOVERINGHAM CONCRETE CO. LTD., Notts, England.
37 LOWE & RODIN. Consult. Engrs. Victoria St., London, England.
38 L. A. ASHTON & P. M. T. SMART. " Sponsored Fire-Resistance Tests on
      Structural Elements." D.S.I.R. & Joint Fire-Research Org.
      H.M.S.O. London. 1960. A. W. HILL & L. A. ASHTON. Cem.
      & Concrete Assn. London. Tech. Rep. TRA/264. 1957.
39 D. WERNER & S. GIERTZ-HEDSTRÖM. Cement & Cem. Manuf. 1934,
      7, (7), 211.
40 ANON. Contract. Rec. 1956. Dec. 19.
41 C. C. COLLOM. J. Instn. civ. Engrs. 1951, (8), 418. C. HOGG & E. A.
      DYER. Int. Civ. Engr. & Contract. 1958, **10**, 32.
42 HUME PIPE (FAR EAST) LTD. Brit. Pat. 416466 (1934).
43 L. T. MINCHIN. Coke & Gas. 1956, 495.
44 ANON. Oil Gas J. 1955, 128.
45 ANON. Concr. constr. Engng. 1959, **54**, (7), 257.
46 ANON. Contract. Rec. 1959, 23. Concr. constr. Engng. 1953, **48**, (1),
      59. J. T. CALVERT, E. A. LEES & H. F. FRANKLAND. Proc. Instn.
      civ. Engrs. 1958-9, **12**, 269.
47 R. PESTELL. Gas World. 1952, **135**, (3530), 372.
48 S. C. BRITTON. J. Instn. civ. Engrs. 1940-41, **16**, (5), 65. H. E.
      ROBARTS. Instn. civ. Engrs., Railway Paper No. 23. 1947.
49 ANON. Steel. 1939, **105**, 64. Concr. constr. Engng. 1958, **53**, (1),
      404. E. J. STANKIEWICZ. Combustion N.Y. 1955, **26**, (8), 51.
50 F. CATCHPOLE. Trans. Brit. Ceram. Soc. 1953, **52**, (5), 259.
51 L. G. SMITH & B. L. SHEPHERD. Ref. 19. A. V. HUSSEY. Contract.
      Rec. 1950, 23.
52 L. H. GRIFFITHS. Symp. Materials of Construction. Birmingham Univ.
      1950. Soc. Chem. Industry.

[53] F. C. HARPER. Brit. Chem. Engng. 1956, **1**, (4), 212. A. E. HAMMOND. Food. 1952, 434. ANON. Dairy Engng. 1957, March, June. " Floor Finishes for Factories." H.M.S.O. Lond. 1960. A. J. BOASE. Industr. Engng. Chem. 1939, **31**, (11), 1435. G. W. DOUGLAS. J. Soc. Leather Tr. Chem. 1948, **32**, 398.

[54] F. C. HARPER. Dairy Ind. 1951, 1159.

[55] J. ROTHGERY. Bull. Mich. Engng. Exp. Sta. 1932, (4), Pt. 2. J. J. MANNING & W. F. WAY. Engng. News Rec. 1927, **98**, (9), 348. HELBLING. Bauingen. 1926, 514. H. LOSSIER. Bull. Soc. Encourag. Sci. 1924, 738.

[56] R. A. B. BURGESS. J. Instn. munic. Engrs. 1949, **75**, (9), 568.

[57] K. BIEHL. Address to Dtsch. Portl. Zem. Fabrikant. E.V. (Hanover). 1926.

[58] SOC. LAP. Brit. Pat. 231867 (1925). In France 1924.

[59] W. C. HANSEN & W. W. BRANDVOLD. J. Amer. Concr. Inst. 1958, **29**, (11), 1009.

[60] R. GRÜN. L'Industria Ital. Cemento. 1958, 3, 80.

[61] GENERAL ELECTRIC CO. LTD. Brit. Pat. 795826 (1958).

[62] D. CRONEY, J. D. COLEMAN & E. W. H. CURRER. Brit. J. appl. Phys. 1951, **2**, (4), 85.

[63] M. LEPINGLE & J. ELIAN. C.R. Acad. Sci. Paris. 1956, **242**, (16), 1989.

[64] W. A. BAILEY & W. H. PETERSON. Brit. Pat. 559682 (1944).

[65] S. A. LINDROTH. Zement-Kalk-Gips. 1956, 4, 20. Glastech. Ber. 1950, **23**, (9), 241. Jenauer Glaswerk Schott & Gen. Brit. Pat. 797573 (1958). CARL ZEISS STIFTUNG. Brit. Pat. 801163. R. A. WEIDEL. J. Amer. ceram. Soc. 1959, **42**, (9), 408. J. M. FLORENCE, F. W. GAZE and M. H. BLACK. J. Res. nat. Bur. Stand. 1955, **55**, 231. H. C. HAFNER, N. J. KREIDL & R. A. WEIDEL. J. Amer. ceram. Soc. 1958, **41**, (8), 315.

CHAPTER 8.—REFRACTORY CONCRETES AND HIGH-TEMPERATURE INSULATING CONCRETES

CONTENTS

CHAPTER EIGHT

Refractory Concretes and High-Temperature Insulating Concretes

When considering a concrete which may be subjected to temperatures very much higher than any possible atmospheric level, an important initial distinction must be made between circumstances in which the concrete is required to preserve useful properties during long service at high temperature, and those in which the temperature is accidental and non-recurring e.g. in the case of a fire.

The fire-resistance of a concrete construction depends on the ability of the concrete to protect the steel reinforcement for a limited period of time, and thus to retard the advent of excessively high steel-temperatures, which would cause collapse of the structure. Factors such as the thermal conductivity or diffusivity of the concrete are therefore of obvious importance in fire-resistance but others, such as thermal decomposition of the aggregate or cement and undue expansion of the aggregate, need not be harmful so long as they do not lead to premature exposure of the steel. After a fire, it is taken for granted that any part of the concrete which has been seriously affected must be replaced or repaired and therefore, if the concrete has fulfilled its relatively brief protective function, a seriously deteriorated physical condition is of little consequence. In these circumstances, the type of hydraulic cement used in the concrete does not greatly influence the fire-resistance rating of the construction.

On the other hand, a concrete which is deliberately designed for prolonged service at high temperatures (e.g. in furnaces or kilns) must have adequate refractoriness, it must maintain sufficient mechanical strength after continuous heating or after frequent heating and cooling cycles, and the fired concrete must not deteriorate or lose strength when subsequently exposed to moist air or contact with water. The refractory and refractory-insulating concretes, which will be the main subject of discussion in this Chapter, are those intended to give a satisfactory service life up to the maximum recommended temperatures and they consist of suitable aggregates bonded with high-alumina

183

cement. In general, the latter is the only type of hydraulic cement which confers all the properties required to meet the above conditions, and some of the reasons for this will be clarified by considering the effect of high temperatures on various kinds of concrete, and on the materials used in concrete.

1. THE EFFECT OF HIGH TEMPERATURES UPON ORDINARY CONCRETE CONSTITUENTS

(1) *Steel Reinforcement*

In reinforced concrete, made with the usual aggregates and any type of hydraulic cement, the thermal expansion of the steel is reasonably similar to that of the concrete, up to a temperature of about 100°C. As the temperature rises further, the expansion of the steel continues but that of the concrete diminishes owing to shrinkage caused by dehydration of the cement-hydrates. When the temperature of the steel is between 100°C. and 300°C. (570°F.)* it is therefore doubtful whether complete bond of concrete to steel can be relied on, and orthodox load designs based on this bond become increasingly uncertain. At high steel-temperatures the disparity in thermal expansion between steel and concrete may cause cracking and spalling, particularly if heavy-gauge reinforcement is present. The tensile strength of mild steel increases up to 200°-300°C. but drops rapidly from 400°C. (750°F.) and is reduced to about half its normal value at 500°C.(930°F.).

The properties normally expected from reinforced concrete and the full advantages gained from the presence of steel rod reinforcement, are therefore lost when the temperature of the steel rises to a level which is very modest by refractory standards. Thus, in concretes designed for high temperatures, it is nearly always impossible to use steel in the same manner and position as is customary for ordinary reinforced concrete. However, by using special techniques and observing certain precautions, it is still possible to employ steel usefully for reinforcing or supporting many high-temperature refractory concrete constructions, and some of these methods will be described in Section 9.

(2) *Cement*

The hydration of the calcium silicates which form the major part of Portland cements releases calcium hydroxide, and, if the hardened cement is heated above 450°C.(840°F.), calcium oxide begins to appear as the hydroxide is dehydrated. Re-hydration or " slaking " of this

---

* Approximate Fahrenheit temperature equivalents will be given frequently but not always.

free lime in presence of moist air or water involves a large increase in volume which may be sufficient to disintegrate or greatly weaken a fired Portland cement concrete or mortar.

Accordingly, even if Portland cement is used in conjunction with an aggregate suitable for much higher temperatures, the appearance of appreciable quantities of free lime in the concrete, after firing above 450°C., usually imposes a relatively low maximum temperature of service, or restricts the field of use. The addition of a pozzolanic material to Portland cement will reduce the amount of calcium hydroxide present in the concrete before firing (assuming that sufficient time is given for the pozzolanic action to become effective) and, during firing, the pozzolana may react with free lime which is formed. For these reasons it is considered that concretes made with refractory aggregate and Portland blast-furnace cement, trass cement etc. are more suitable for high-temperature use than similar concretes made with ordinary or rapid-hardening Portland cements.[1] The pozzolana may of course be added at the mixer, and it has been claimed that the addition of materials such as crushed granulated slag, boiler cinders, fly-ash, diatomite or brick dust, to a mix of Portland cement and refractory aggregate, yields a concrete able to give satisfactory service at 500°C. or even 1000°C. (1830°F.).[2] However, under the extremely varied conditions of use to which refractory concretes are submitted, it is doubtful whether the presence of a pozzolanic material will always eliminate the possible consequence of the reaction between water and free lime in the concrete. Grün and Beckmann found that cooling in water produced a marked deterioration in a variety of concretes, made with Portland cement or Portland blast-furnace cement, after they had been heated to temperatures over 300°C., and, more recently, Livovich[3] has shown that concretes made with crushed firebrick aggregate and Portland cement (Type I), rapid-hardening Portland cement (Type III) or Portland blast-furnace cement (Type IS), all expanded, cracked and lost most of their strength after repeated thermal cycles at or above 430°C.(800°F.), unless they were cooled each time in a desiccator. Similar concretes made with American H.A.C. did not crack or expand when cooled each time in moist air, and they retained a satisfactory level of strength. In addition, the refractory limits of concretes incorporating Portland cements are normally much lower than those containing H.A.C.,[4] and the latter cement is therefore generally used, with a wide variety of refractory aggregates, for preparing refractory concretes designed for service at temperatures between 300°C. and 1800°C. (3310°F.).

It should be noted that the preference for H.A.C. in such applications is not necessarily due to a greater retention of strength by H.A.C.

concretes at all higher temperatures. Initially, the proportional loss in strength of H.A.C. concretes at moderate temperatures (100°C.-500°C.) is often greater than that experienced by Portland cement concretes[5]. The general use of H.A.C. is due chiefly to the stability of the fired strength of H.A.C. refractory concretes when subjected, over a long period, to the very varied conditions encountered in service, including rapid temperature fluctuations, exposure to acidic gases and quenching in water. A concrete made with a calcium aluminate cement contains no calcium hydroxide after hardening and, if the fired concrete is cooled in moist air or quenched in water, there is no deterioration—in fact the strength is increased.

(3) *Aggregates*

The aggregates considered at this stage are limited to those which are used for concrete in ordinary practice, e.g. naturally-occurring quartzites or siliceous gravels and sands, limestone, igneous rocks such as granites, dolerites, basalts, whinstone or trap-rock, and certain light-weight manufactured aggregates including foamed slag, bloated shale, clay, slate or fly-ash.

The quartz in siliceous sands and gravels undergoes a structural alteration at 575°C.(1065°F.) and this is accompanied by a large reversible volume change which can disrupt any concrete made with this aggregate if it is repeatedly heated to the above temperature. At lower temperatures the thermal expansion of the aggregate, although regular, is relatively high, and if the concrete is required to withstand frequent temperature cycles a maximum service temperature of 250°C. (380°F.) is generally applied. For mortars, which do not contain the larger pebble-size aggregate, a limit of 300°C. may be allowed. In this type of concrete or mortar it is the aggregate which determines the limit of service temperature and the temperature restriction is therefore valid whether the concrete is made with a Portland-type cement or with H.A.C.

If any concrete containing limestone aggregate reaches a temperature sufficient to cause decarbonation, the subsequent hydration of the calcium oxide in moist air will almost certainly disrupt the bond. For this reason, limestone concretes should not be employed at temperatures higher than 600°-700°C. (1290°F.). Dolomitic limestones commence to decarbonate at a lower temperature than high-calcium limestones, and the consequences of exceeding the temperature limit can be so drastic that it may be considered prudent to apply a maximum temperature limit of about 500°C. (930°F.) to concrete containing any type of natural limestone aggregate. If kept safely below the decomposition temperature, limestone concretes have good temperature-resistance properties, provided that the cement component is also suitable for the temperatures which are reached in service.

Granites and other coarse-grained acidic igneous rocks, which contain appreciable quantities of free quartz, are not very suitable as high-temperature aggregates because of (a) volume changes in the quartz and (b) the disruptive effect of thermal cycles upon an assemblage of large crystals which have dissimilar thermal expansions. On the other hand, fine-grained basic igneous rocks, which contain little or no free quartz e.g. certain lavas, basalts and dolerites, provide excellent aggregates which can be used with H.A.C. in concretes for service up to about 1000°C. (1830°F.). Such aggregates are often classified as trap-rock or whinstone but it should be noted that these terms (and also " granite ") are used very loosely, and therefore any natural aggregate considered for use at high temperatures should be checked to ensure that both its geological type and its chemical nature are suitable.

Foamed slag, sintered or bloated shale, clay, slate and fly-ash aggregates, all of which may be found in concrete constructions for ordinary temperatures, are capable of use with a suitable cement at temperatures near their sintering point. With H.A.C. as bond, the maximum service temperatures of the corresponding concretes range from 1000°-1200°C. (2190°F.).

2. General Description of H.A.C. Refractory Concretes

Refractory concrete is essentially a mixture of a suitably graded refractory aggregate (replacing the stone and sand of ordinary concrete) and a high-alumina cement. The mixture is gauged with water, usually to a plastic consistency, and it is then cast within formwork or into moulds in the same general way as ordinary concrete. Alternatively, it may be rammed, vibrated, trowelled, or " gunned " into place. Since H.A.C. forms the bond, the concrete attains a high strength in the cold within 24 hours, and has the resistance to dilute acids, sulphates, etc. which is characteristic of concretes or mortars made with this kind of cement. The drying shrinkage in air is comparable to that of ordinary concrete and the total shrinkage, after firing to the service temperature, is still very small and occurs without distortion of the concrete.

Refractory concretes can be brought up to temperature, and submitted to the working conditions in a furnace or kiln, as soon as they have hardened sufficiently, i.e. they do not require to be pre-fired. Free water and water combined with the cement are driven off during the first firing, and this process should be carried out at a reasonably slow rate up to about 600°C.(1100°F.), particularly in the case of large units or those made with dense aggregates. Once the water has been eliminated, the concretes can be heated or cooled very rapidly, and characteristically exhibit a high thermal shock resistance.

Undoubtedly, the aggregate most commonly used is crushed firebrick (alumino-silicate), Indeed, if the term " refractory concrete " is employed without special qualification, it can usually be assumed that this type of aggregate has been incorporated. In the wider sense, the term is applied to all H.A.C. concretes required to give continued service at temperatures from 200°-300°C. upwards. It will become evident that there are a very large number of possible aggregates, some of which give concretes having a working temperature limit below that attainable with firebrick aggregate, and some which enable a refractory concrete construction to be used at much higher temperatures.

H.A.C. concretes made with certain light-weight aggregates (such as diatomite, vermiculite, bloated clay, etc.) can be employed at fairly high temperatures, and, because of their greater porosity, they possess excellent thermal-insulation properties. These concretes, with fired densities ranging from roughly 30 lb./cu. ft. to 100 lb./cu. ft. may be classified as high-temperature insulating concretes or as refractory-insulating concretes. The division between refractory and insulating concretes is quite arbitrary, since the two classes obviously merge together. Concretes suitable for high temperatures can in fact be made with fired densities lying between 25 lb./cu. ft. and 190 lb./cu. ft., and with thermal conductivities (K values) at 540°C. (1000°F.) of about 1.0-50.0 B.t.u./in./ft.^{2}/hr./°F. Since concretes made with crushed firebrick aggregates have fired densities of more than 100 lb./cu. ft., this provides a convenient line of demarcation, and any heat-resistant H.A.C. concrete of lower density may be placed in the refractory-insulating group. Such insulating concretes usually have lower strength, lower abrasion resistance, and lower ash or slag resistance than the common firebrick concretes.

The refractory concrete user can prepare his own mix by crushing new or used firebricks of any suitable type, or by buying crushed and graded aggregates. This gives the greatest latitude in the choice of aggregate-size or type, mix proportions etc., and frequently it is the most economical method. However, in most countries, a considerable trade has been developed in dry, prepared mixes consisting basically of suitably graded refractory or insulating aggregates together with H.A.C. The user has merely to add water and therefore these proprietary castable mixes ("castable refractories ") are most convenient to use. The factory control over aggregate quality, grading, and

188

proportioning should give a more reliable and consistent concrete than is frequently obtained when the user makes his own mix. In these prepared castable mixes, which are sold under a wide variety of proprietary names, there may be included smaller quantities of materials which favourably modify the properties of the concrete for certain uses, and the range of types available is sufficient to cover practically any application for which a refractory or refractory-insulating concrete is suitable.

One of the earliest patents involving these prepared refractory castable mixes was taken out by Kestner[6] for a mixture consisting of 2 parts H.A.C. and 1-10 parts of calcined bauxite, and, about the same time, a refractory concrete made with crushed firebrick aggregate was being used in the U.S.A. for lining combustion chambers and ash-pits, or for sundry refractory repairs in the steel industry. Indeed, for some time, refractory concretes or mortars were used chiefly in miscellaneous repairs to refractory brickwork constructions, or for special shapes difficult and more expensive to obtain in fireclay. As the convenience, speed, and economy of castable construction became apparent, more ambitious use was made of other favourable properties of the castable refractory (such as volume stability and resistance to thermal shock). As a result, refractory concrete is now viewed as a material of construction in its own right, and capable of being used for building complete refractory structures of the largest dimensions.

3. REFRACTORY " CONCRETES " NOT BONDED WITH HYDRAULIC CEMENT.

Monolithic constructions or moulded shapes can also be obtained by bonding refractory aggregates with materials other than a hydraulic cement. Such compositions often provide some degree of " set " or strength in the cold, but the resultant " concretes " usually require heating to some definite high temperature before the full strength is developed and, in this, they differ from the castable mixes with which we are primarily concerned.

For example, concretes with oxysulphate[7], chlorohydrate[8], oxychloride[9], or sodium silicate bonds have been reported. Considerable interest has also been shown in the use of phosphoric acid[10] or phosphates[11] for bonding various refractory aggregates (especially alumina aggregates). In some cases a small[12] proportion of a calcium aluminate cement is added (up to 5 per cent. by weight of the total mix). The reaction between the strong phosphoric acid and metal moulds, tools, etc. can be minimised by adding a complex amine as inhibitor[13]. A stable bond is developed after firing and the abrasion resistance of phosphate-bonded tabular alumina is particularly high.

The hydrolysis of ethyl silicate, in a mix with refractory aggregate, provides a high temperature bond[14]. A solution of the " silicon ester " in alcohol is usually employed, the setting-time being controlled with alkaline or acid catalysts. An aqueous emulsion of the ester and dilute hydrochloric acid can also be used as a binder[15]. In this case the elimination of the alcohol component obviously reduces the cost and removes the attendant fire risk during subsequent heating. Ethyl silicate has been found particularly satisfactory for bonding refractory powders or finely-crushed grogs and thus it permits the casting of thin-walled shapes, or precision moulds with intricate detail.

Refractory aggregates or grogs may also be mixed to a very stiff consistency with raw fire-clay or china-clay and a little water. Such products are called " ramming-mixes," " mouldables," " plastic fire-brick " or simply " plastics," since they are utilised by ramming successive thin layers into place or into a mould by means of hammers or pneumatic tools. A certain degree of cold strength is achieved on drying-out and this may be increased by additives, but baking or firing is necessary before the clay itself develops a strong bond. Pro-prietary products of this type are usually marketed in the plastic state ready for use, but they are also available in the dry condition and tem-pering with water is then required.

In comparing these products with castable (hydraulic-bonded) mixes, it is frequently found that the cost of materials for a ramming-mix is lower than that of a castable mix required to give the same refractory value. On the other hand, the successful placing of ramming-mixes or " plastics " usually requires more time and skilled workmanship, they must be slowly and carefully dried, and the total shrinkage is much greater than that of most castable mixes.

4. Types of H.A.C. used in Refractory Concretes

The commercial high-alumina cements, previously described, are all suitable for mixing with refractory or insulating aggregates to form mortars or concretes for use at high temperatures, and they are therefore incorporated in the main bulk of the proprietary castable mixes or refractory and refractory-insulating concretes employed today. These cements are all made from bauxite and consist of mono-calcium aluminate or CA (which is the main cementitious compound) together with a very variable proportion of other compounds derived from silica, iron oxides, titania and magnesia. When comparing one H.A.C. with another it will be seen from Table II, Chapter 2, that the variable amounts of other compounds cause colour differences (from very dark to very light grey) and the alumina contents range from 36 per cent. to over 50 per cent. In particular the iron oxide contents may vary from less than 1 per cent. to more than 16 per cent., and it is therefore not surprising that the refractoriness of the various neat cements extends from Seger Cone 9 to Cone 13-14 (i.e. from 1280°C. to 1400°C. approx). Of course, the cements are rarely if ever used in the neat condition at high temperatures, and the refractoriness of the corresponding mortars or concretes does not show nearly so much variation. Nevertheless, when other things are equal, the cements with the lowest iron oxide content will produce concrete mixes having the highest refractoriness. This is clearly noticeable when the cement content of the mix is relatively high but it is less marked in leaner mixes.

An obvious step towards the production of a cement with a refractoriness greater than any yet considered would be to substitute, as raw material, a purer form of alumina for the customary red bauxite and thus obtain a fairly pure mono-calcium aluminate composition. The pure CA compound is white, it has an alumina content of about 64.5 per cent. and it melts[16] at 1608°C. (2966°F.) which is far above the refractoriness of an ordinary H.A.C. made from bauxite and hence containing the associated " impurities." A pure cement of this type was made as early as 1856 by Sainte-Claire Deville[17] who heated together equal parts of powdered alumina and marble. Combination to calcium aluminate takes place at temperatures far below fusion point[18], and Sainte-Claire Deville found that crucibles moulded from his product and corundum aggregate were able to withstand the highest temperatures he could apply. In more recent times patents have been granted for castable refractory mixes which incorporate similar, relatively pure, calcium aluminate cements of alumina content ranging from 60 per cent. to over 70 per cent[19].

However, even this does not exhaust the possibilities since the melting-points of the various calcium aluminates rise with increasing alumina content, and calcium dialuminate (CA_2), which contains about 78.5 per cent. Al_2O_3, has a fusion point[16] of about 1770°C. (3258°F.). This compound, formerly thought to be tricalcium penta-aluminate or C_3A_5, was therefore soon considered as the basis for a still more refractory H.A.C. Pole and Moore[20] fused a composition corresponding to C_3A_5 and showed that the product had useful hydraulic properties when ground to cement fineness. The refractoriness of the neat cement was Cone 18 (1495°C. or 2714°F.) and a 1 : 3 mortar with crushed firebrick aggregate gave a refractoriness of Cone 30

191

(1650°C. or 3000°F.). Gitzen, Hart and MacZura[21] investigated substantially pure calcium aluminate compositions with alumina contents between 64 per cent. and 86 per cent. and concluded that the optimum refractory-cement properties were obtained from the composition corresponding to $CA_{2.5}$.

Cements of this general type, containing 72-80 per cent. Al_2O_3, and almost free from iron oxide, silica, etc. are now manufactured commercially in the U.S.A., France and England, either for sale as such, or as a necessary constituent of certain high-duty proprietary castable mixes[22]. These cements are much more costly than the ordinary high-alumina cements since they are made by sintering, clinkering, or fusing a pure grade of alumina and calcium carbonate, for example, in a tunnel kiln or a rotary kiln[23]. Their general properties, later to be studied in more detail, have been described by several writers[24] but the chief difficulty is to give this type of H.A.C. a name which is widely acceptable and which will provide a clear distinction from the ordinary high-alumina cements. They have been called tricalcium penta-aluminate cements but, since it is now known that this compound does not exist, such a designation is hardly appropriate. Although they may have a composition corresponding roughly to calcium dialuminate (CA_2) they do not in fact contain a major proportion of this compound because mono-calcium aluminate is still the main cementitious compound. The remainder consists of alumina or a mixture of alumina and CA_2. In the subsequent text this type of cement will therefore be called white H.A.C. (72-80 per cent. Al_2O_3). Trade names for such cements include ALCOA CA-25 or CA-25A and SECAR 250.

In Japan some H.A.C. is made by fusion of calcium carbonate and low-iron (white) bauxite. This gives a cement with a relatively low iron oxide content and very satisfactory refractory properties. It is also possible to raise the refractoriness of an ordinary H.A.C. by mixing with calcined alumina. This addition of alumina yields the best results when made to the high-alumina cements of lower iron content, e.g. those manufactured by reductive fusion of limestone and bauxite. Although cements containing a fairly high proportion of alumina can be obtained by either of the above methods, their derivation from bauxite is shown by the presence of appreciable amounts of silica etc. and this distinguishes them from the pure, white H.A.C. (72-80 per cent. Al_2O_3) which consists almost entirely of lime and alumina. Table I provides a summary of the available types of H.A.C. which have been discussed.

Aluminates of barium[25] and strontium[26] react with water and

192

TABLE I. SUMMARY OF TYPES OF H.A.C. USED IN REFRACTORY CONCRETES.

(Cement types listed in ascending order of refractoriness)

Type of H.A.C.	Derivation	Colour of Cement	Al$_2$O$_3$ %	CaO %	SiO$_2$ %	Fe$_2$O$_3$ %	FeO %	MgO %	TiO$_2$ %
(1) Ordinary grades of H.A.C.	From red bauxite (a) by fusion (b) by reductive fusion	Very dark grey to very light grey	36.0 to 54.0	36.0 to 42.0	3.5 to 9.0	0.1 to 14.0	1.0 to 7.0	0.5 to 1.0	0.5 to 2.5
(Not common)	From low-iron (white) bauxite		50.0 to 55.0	37.0 to 39.0	4.0 to 6.0	0.1 to 3.0	0.5 to 4.0	0.5 to 1.0	0.5 to 2.0
(2) Alumina-fortified H.A.C.	Addition of Al$_2$O$_3$ to H.A.C. made by reductive fusion	Grey-white	68.5	23.5	4.0	0.1	0.3	0.4	0.5
(3) White H.A.C. (72-80% Al$_2$O$_3$)	From Al$_2$O$_3$ by sintering or fusion	White (1) (2)	72 - 75	24 - 27	0.1	0.2	Tr.	0.25	Tr.
			79.0	18.0	0.1	0.3	Tr.	0.4	Tr.

G

some are capable of use as cements[27]. Strontium/barium aluminates[28], calcium/barium aluminates[29], and calcium/strontium aluminates[30] have also been investigated. Particular interest has been shown in the use of monobarium aluminate (BA) as a cement for refractory concretes since it has a much higher melting-point than mono-calcium aluminate (CA). There has been some disagreement about the actual fusion temperature which is given by different workers as $2000° \pm 40°C.$, $1820° \pm 20°C.$, and $1815°C$[31].

Patents have been granted for the manufacture and refractory use of barium aluminate[32], the compound being prepared in various degrees of purity by heating or fusing bauxite or alumina with barium sulphate, carbonate or sulphide. Braniski[33] indicates that the mechanical and refractory properties of a barium aluminate cement improve as the composition approaches that of pure BA, and that the proportion of silica, iron oxide and alkalis should therefore be as low as possible. It can be used with many refractory aggregates and is considered particularly suitable as a binder in refractory concretes containing basic aggregates such as chrome-magnesia and dead-burned magnesite. According to Braniski the refractoriness values of concretes made with barium aluminate cement and aggregates consisting of fire-clay, bauxite, corundum, chrome-magnesia and magnesia are 1670°-1690°C., 1750°-1790°C., 1865°-1900°C., 1880°-1960°C. and 1920°-1980°C., respectively[34]. The substitution of white H.A.C. (72-80 per cent. Al_2O_3) by a reasonably pure barium aluminate cement certainly raises the maximum service temperature of a refractory castable mix. However, mono-barium aluminate shows some anomalous characteristics during setting and hardening and the cost of manufacture is high. Therefore it is not yet certain that its advantageous refractory properties will justify a regular manufacture on the commercial scale, although substantial quantities have been used in experimental refractory castable work. This type of cement may also have possible applications in providing refractory concrete for the efficient shielding of atomic reactors at high temperatures.

5. TYPES OF AGGREGATE FOR REFRACTORY CONCRETES.

Table II gives a summary of the various kinds of aggregate which may be considered for use with H.A.C. at higher temperatures, and points of interest raised by some of these aggregates are discussed below. The values given for the maximum service temperatures and for the fired densities of the concretes depend on several factors and they can be used only as a general guide to the properties obtained from the more usual mix proportions.

The reasons for the temperature limitations imposed by the use of natural silica aggregates or of limestone aggregates have already been mentioned. H.A.C./silica sand mortars are frequently employed as linings in low-temperature flues or chimneys (maximum temperature never greater than 250°-300°C.) and in this application their resistance to dilute acidity is the most important factor. For higher-temperature operation a more suitable aggregate (e.g. crushed firebrick) is substituted. The accidental inclusion of pebbles of quartz in an otherwise suitable refractory concrete may cause " pop-outs," or even minor explosions, when the unit is heated to high temperatures. Silica firebrick (over 92 per cent. SiO_2) must also be considered unsuitable for use in refractory concretes, and therefore if used refractory bricks are crushed to provide aggregate, care should be taken to eliminate any silica brick. The volume changes associated with the low-temperature transformations of tridymite and of cristobalite can cause serious expansion in any refractory concrete containing a considerable quantity of silica firebrick aggregate. However, a small proportion of H.A.C. (up to 10 per cent. by weight) is sometimes added to ganister or to ganister-ramming mixes in order to improve the cold strength, and a special fused-silica aggregate is said to have given successful results in a refractory concrete for boiler furnace linings[35].

The olivine series of minerals are solid solutions of forsterite ($2MgO-SiO_2$) and fayalite ($2FeO-SiO_2$). Dunite[36] is the name given to those members of the series containing a low percentage of fayalite. Aggregates of this type have frequently been used in castable mixes for lining aluminium melting furnaces because they are not wetted by the molten metal and "pick-up" of impurities is thus minimised. It will be seen later that this property is shared by refractory concretes made with several other aggregates including ordinary crushed firebrick. Pyrophyllite is a hydrated aluminium silicate ($Al_2O_3.4SiO_2.H_2O$), and the properties of some refractory castable mixes, composed of this aggregate and H.A.C., have been given by Gower and Bell[37].

Air-cooled blast-furnace slag yields a hard abrasion-resistant aggregate often used in conjunction with a siliceous sand to form H.A.C. concretes suitable for floors subjected to moderate radiant heat. If the fine aggregate also consists of slag it is best to make a preliminary trial since some slags in the finely divided condition have a deleterious effect on the setting and hardening of the concrete. The process of " foaming " slag[38] produces a light-weight aggregate and eliminates some of the sulphur compounds which affect the set of cement. Therefore, foamed slag can usually be used for both

TABLE II. SERVICE-TEMPERATURE LIMITS FOR VARIOUS H.A.C. CONCRETES

Aggregate Type	Fired Density of concrete lb/cu. ft.	Maxm. Hot-Face Temperature of Concrete (°C)		Notes
		Ordinary H.A.C.	White H.A.C. 72-80% Al_2O_3	
A. NATURALLY-OCCURRING Silica gravel and Sand	130	250°-300°	—	The temperature limit is set either by expansion of aggregate or by thermal decomposition of aggregate
Limestone	125-135	500°	—	
Basalt, Dolerite (Whinstone, Traprock) Emery	130- 150	1000°- 1100°	— —	Aggregate must be fine-grained and basic (little or no free silica)
Olivine, Dunite Pyrophyllite	130-150 100-110	1000°- 1300°	—	Dunite may require calcination before use.
Pumice	50-90	1000°	—	Useful insulating aggregate where available.
B. HEAT-TREATED (DENSE) Blast-Furnace Slag (air-cooled)	130-145	800°- 1000°	—	Slag " fines " may affect setting and hardening of concrete
Building-brick (clay) Clay-tile Saggars (Pottery)	110-125	800°- 1100°	—	Useful heat-resistant concretes for low-duty use.
Saggars (Porcelain) Firebrick 26-45 % Al_2O_3 Flint-clay Chamotte Fired Kaolin	110- 125	1200°- 1350°	1300°- 1500°	Refractoriness of concretes increases with Al_2O_3 content of aggregate. Chamotte generally superior to crushed firebrick as aggregate.
Fired Kyanite Sillimanite Firebrick (> 60 % Al_2O_3 Mullite Calcined bauxite	130- 145 160	1400°- 1500°	1600°- 1650°	Sillimanite and Andalusite can be used without heat-treatment. Kyanite must be pre-fired to high temperature.

TABLE II—*continued*

Aggregate Type	Fired Density of concrete lb/cu. ft.	Maxm. Hot-Face Temperature of Concrete (°C)		Notes
		Ordinary H.A.C.	White H.A.C. 72-80% Al$_2$O$_3$	
Dead-burned Magnesite Chromite-magnesia Chromite	160- 170	1400°- 1600°	1500°- 1650°	Chromite occurs naturally but is given here since it may be used in the form of crushed chrome-brick
Silicon carbide	140-150	1600°	1700°	Gives concretes with the highest " K " values.
Corundum Fused Al$_2$O$_3$ Tabular Al$_2$O$_3$	175- 180	1500° - 1600°	1800°	Gives concretes of high strength, refractoriness and abrasion resistance
Zirconia	250-260	—	Not de-termined	Expensive. Used for special purposes.
C. HEAT-TREATED (LIGHT) Foamed Slag	90-100	800°-1000°	—	Give lower strengths but better heat-insulating pro-
Expanded clay, shale, slate or fly-ash	65-90	1000°-1200°	—	perties than concretes made with the denser aggregates above.
H.T. Insulating Brick (38-45% Al$_2$O$_3$)	70-85	1200°-1350°	1300°-1450°	
Bubble Alumina	90-95	—	1700°	Relatively high strength concrete for insulation at the highest temperatures
Calcined Diatomite	50-60	800°-1000°	800°-1000°	Medium to low strength. Good insulation properties
Vermiculite	25-40	900°-1000°	1000°-1100°	Low strength but highest insulation values.
Perlite	30-45	900°-1000°	1000°-1100°	

coarse and fine aggregate without undue effect on the hardening of H.A.C. concrete.

Crushed building brick, semi-vitrified or " blue " engineering brick[39], clay tile, pottery saggars, etc. all provide H.A.C. concretes for use up to about 1000°C.(1830°F.), and, in brick works, the broken or reject products of manufacture can often be employed economically in refractory concrete mixes for constructing or repairing all parts of the kiln where a high-duty refractory is not required. For temperatures over 1000°C. crushed alumino-silicate firebrick (26-45 per cent. Al_2O_3) may be used as aggregate and the refractory qualities of the concrete improve as the alumina content of the firebrick aggregate increases. Aluminous firebrick (38-45 per cent. Al_2O_3) is the material most commonly employed, and a best-quality firebrick aggregate of this type (42-45 per cent. Al_2O_3) gives H.A.C. concrete capable of resisting a hot-face temperature of about 1350°C.(2450°F.). The use of white H.A.C. raises the maximum service temperature of the concrete by at least 100°C. Other aggregates in this group include fired flint-clay (which is extensively used in the U.S.A.) and chamotte which is a first-class aggregate when prepared by the thorough firing of an aluminous fireclay. Fired china-clay or kaolin is practically free from iron oxide and is therefore specially suitable for use with white H.A.C. (72-80 per cent. Al_2O_3) in castable mixes designed to resist carbon monoxide attack.

The minerals sillimanite, andalusite and kyanite, all have the formula $Al_2O_3.SiO_2$ and decompose into mullite and siliceous glass at temperatures ranging from 1300°-1450°C. In the case of kyanite this change is accompanied by a considerable volume expansion and therefore the mineral cannot be employed as aggregate until it has been thoroughly fired at 1450°-1500°C. (2770°F.). However, a small proportion of raw kyanite is sometimes incorporated in refractory castable mixes because its expansion at high temperature can be utilised to counteract the firing shrinkage of a concrete. It should be noted that fired kyanite is often called " sillimanite." True silli-manite and andalusite can usually be used without prior calcination since the decomposition to mullite occurs with much less expansion. Mullite firebricks and high-alumina firebricks (over 60 per cent. Al_2O_3) also make excellent high-duty aggregates for use with ordinary H.A.C. and particularly with white H.A.C. (72-80 per cent. Al_2O_3). Calcined low-iron bauxite has been widely used as aggregate in refractory castables since (after firing at 1400°-1600°C.) it contains over 85 per cent alumina, the rest consisting of silica, iron oxide and titania. When calcined bauxite is the sole aggregate in a refractory concrete, excessive shrinkage on firing is occasionally experienced and this can be attributed to insufficient calcination of the bauxite. On other occasions, after-expansion may be found when the concrete has been fired, and this is probably due to the expansive formation of mullite. According to McGee and Dodd[40] this reaction can be greatly reduced by a small addition of sodium fluoride.

Certain slags obtained in metallurgy have a very high alumina content (e.g. ferro-alloy production by the Thermit process) and they may have a high refractoriness[41]. Although apt to vary in composition even when obtained from the same source, they have been successfully used as aggregates in refractory concretes for quite high-duty applications. Brown fused alumina and the purer white fused alumina represent the end-point in the process of increasing the refractoriness of castable mixes by raising the alumina content of the aggregate. Refractory concretes containing white H.A.C. (72-80 per cent. Al_2O_3) and white fused alumina or tabular alumina (a dense sintered form), may contain 96 per cent. by weight of alumina and they can be used at or somewhat above 1800°C. (3310°F.). Such concretes are heavy and strong, with a relatively high thermal conductivity. Aggregate consisting of hollow bubbles of fused alumina can be used when greater insulating properties are required at very high temperatures.

Refractory castables with enhanced resistance to iron scale, slag and ash are made with chromite, chromite-magnesia, magnesia-chromite, or dead-burned magnesite aggregates. The addition of calcium aluminate greatly reduces the refractoriness of the periclase in dead-burned magnesite[42] and the service temperature limit of magnesia concretes, although high, is not what might be expected. Concretes made with fused magnesia aggregate and the white type of H.A.C. may show considerable expansion on firing owing to spinel formation. When aggregates are being prepared for refractory concretes care must be taken (particularly in steel-works) to exclude any unfired magnesite or dolomitic material. If any appreciable amounts are incorporated in refractory concrete the latter will be liable to crumble and crack after undergoing heating and cooling cycles. This is due to rehydration of the magnesium oxide in damp air, and therefore all magnesite must be thoroughly dead-burned before use in refractory castables.

Carborundum (silicon carbide) aggregate gives concretes with an extremely high thermal conductivity, and the cement content probably has some influence in reducing the oxidation of the carborundum at high temperatures. Zircon ($ZrO_2.SiO_2$) is a rather disappointing aggregate since relatively low-melting eutectics are formed with calcium aluminates. On the other hand, stabilized zirconia (ZrO_2)

is an excellent aggregate for use with white H.A.C. (72-80 per cent. Al_2O_3) since the eutectics it forms with both lime and alumina have extremely high melting-points[43]. Except for special purposes, however, this aggregate is too costly.

The use of H.A.C. for bonding carbon aggregates or for impregnating carbon refractories has been patented[44], and mixes of graphite aggregate and H.A.C. have been proposed for moulds or cores used in the casting of metals, glass, etc.[45]

Most of the light-weight aggregates[46] have been mentioned previously and the H.A.C. concretes in which they are contained give greatly increased thermal insulation for a given thickness. In general, the lighter the concrete the lower is its strength but H.A.C. concretes made with expanded slate[47], clay or shale[48] aggregates have fired strengths which are little lower than those of firebrick concretes, and the same is substantially true of concretes incorporating high-temperature insulating brick, aggregates (porous fireclay and porous kaolin)[49]. On the other hand, the extremely light-weight H.A.C. concretes obtainable by the use of vermiculite[50] or perlite[51] cannot be expected to resist heavy loading or severe abrasion, and they are therefore often used as backing to stronger and more refractory types of concrete. It is of course possible to mix aggregates such as vermiculite and crushed firebrick[52] or alumina bubbles and fused alumina[53] in order to produce a single concrete having intermediate values of density, strength and thermal insulation. An addition of perlite to a relatively dense refractory aggregate yields a concrete of greater insulation value at the cost of some loss in strength. A reduction in the unit weight of concretes made with the denser aggregates can also be effected by omitting all " fines " from the material[54] or by " foaming " the mix[55] prior to placing (the latter method is the same as that described in Chapter V, Section 3).

6. THE FORMULATION OF REFRACTORY CONCRETE MIXES.

(1) The Grading of the Aggregate

The maximum size of aggregate included in refractory concretes, as in ordinary concretes, is determined primarily by the thickness of the unit, and it should not be much more than $\frac{1}{4}$ - $\frac{1}{5}$ of the minimum concrete dimension. In practice, it is not common to utilize pieces of aggregate larger than $1\frac{1}{2}$ in. diameter, even in massive refractory concrete, and for mixes prepared by the user the aggregate is usually graded downwards from $\frac{3}{4}$in., $\frac{3}{8}$in. or $\frac{1}{8}$in. according to the concrete thickness or minimum dimension.

Since users of proprietary castable refractories (pre-mixes) may require them for moulding small or very thin units as well as large units, these mixes do not normally contain aggregate larger than $\frac{1}{4}$in., $\frac{1}{6}$in., or, in some cases, $\frac{1}{8}$in. However, some manufacturers supply alternative grades containing aggregates of larger maximum size. Other factors may of course determine the maximum size of aggregate ; for example, perlite is not commonly available except in fairly fine sizes, and some placing techniques (e.g. guniting) limit the maximum size of any aggregate to about $\frac{1}{4}$in.

There is considerable controversy about the best particle-size grading within the aggregate used for refractory concretes or mortars, i.e. should there be a continuous grading containing all the sizes between maximum and minimum, or should the aggregate be gap-graded into coarse aggregate and fine aggregate by omitting a range of intermediate sizes ? The disadvantage of gap-grading is the greater tendency for segregation of the coarse aggregate in the dry mix or, if too much water is added, during the placing operation also. On the other hand, gap-graded mixes undoubtedly make the most efficient use of a given cement content and they are specially suitable for vibratory method of compaction. The manufacturing control which can be exercised during the preparation of proprietary castables has produced many excellent gap-graded compositions and Wygant and Bulkley[56], who examined a range of commercial castable mixes for their suitability in fluid catalytic cracking plants, concluded that one of the best contained 60 per cent. by weight of coarse aggregate (mainly 8-14 mesh) and 15 per cent. by weight of fine aggregate (mainly 50-100 mesh).

In preparing his own aggregate, the user is most frequently recommended to aim at a continuous grading[57] since suitably sized material of this type can be readily obtained by passing the raw material through a jaw-crusher adjusted so that only a small proportion of oversize need be subsequently removed. The product is then conveniently separated into coarse aggregate ($\frac{3}{4}$in. to $\frac{1}{4}$in.) or ($\frac{3}{8}$in. to $\frac{1}{8}$in.) and into fine aggregate ($\frac{1}{4}$in. to dust). The latter is suitable as such for making refractory mortars and, for concretes, the customary combinations of coarse and fine aggregates are 3 vols. ($\frac{3}{4}$in. to $\frac{1}{4}$in.) with 2 vols. ($\frac{1}{8}$in. to dust), or 2 vols. ($\frac{3}{8}$in. to $\frac{1}{8}$in.) with 2 vols. ($\frac{1}{4}$in. to dust). Ideally, the aggregate should be graded to conform to the curves of Fuller, Bolomey, Féret, etc. but, in practice, the grading of the final aggregate is likely to be suitable when (a) the proportion by weight of the whole aggregate passing $\frac{1}{8}$in. mesh amounts to about 40 per cent. in the case of $\frac{3}{4}$in. aggregate, or to about 50 per cent. for $\frac{3}{8}$in. aggregate, and when (b) the weight of the aggregate passing 100 mesh is about 10-15 per cent. It will be noted that this percentage of material through 100-mesh (fines or dust) is higher than that normally recommended for ordinary aggregates, but, in refractory concrete, this is usually essential in order to give good workability and to facilitate the thermal reaction between aggregate and cement which leads to ceramic bond. However, a large excess of fines in the aggregate will give a much weaker concrete unless the proportion of cement is correspondingly increased.

(2) Cement content

The densities of the refractory aggregates normally vary over a much greater range than those of aggregates used in ordinary concrete and therefore, in any discussion of the whole field of refractory castables, the aggregate/cement ratio by volume is more uniform and more convenient to employ than the corresponding aggregate/cement ratio by weight. The latter fluctuates greatly according to the type of aggregate, as shown below. The variations in the aggregate/cement ratio by weight would of course be still more extensive if very lightweight aggregates (such as vermiculite or perlite) had been included in the comparison.

Aggregate	Aggregate/cement by volume	Corresponding ratio by weight
Firebrick (42/44 per cent. Al_2O_3)	4 : 1	4.8 : 1
Fired kyanite	4 : 1	5.8 : 1
Fused alumina	4 : 1	8.5 : 1

For any refractory concrete mix in which the maximum size of aggregate is about $\frac{3}{4}$in. or $\frac{3}{8}$in., the most common proportions are 3-4$\frac{1}{2}$ volumes of aggregate to 1 volume of cement, but if a strong mortar is required, the mix may consist of 2-3 volumes of fine aggregate to 1 volume of cement. The following mixes therefore cover most of the standard applications for refractory concretes[58].

Type of Concrete	$\frac{3}{4}$in.-$\frac{1}{8}$in. (by vol.)	$\frac{3}{8}$in.-$\frac{1}{8}$in. (by vol.)	$\frac{1}{8}$in. dwn. (by. vol)	H.A.C. (by vol.)	H.A.C./cu.yd. of concrete.
> 4in. thick	3	–	2	1	730 lb.
> 2in. thick	–	2	2	1	770 lb.
Mortar	–	–	2$\frac{1}{2}$	1	940 lb.

In the case of ordinary high-alumina cements all the aggregates usually employed (e.g. firebrick, chromite, sillimanite, calcined bauxite, fused alumina etc.) are more refractory than the cement, and the refractoriness of the concrete therefore increases as the cement content is reduced. When the refractoriness of the aggregate is not greatly different from that of the cement (e.g. in the case of clay building brick, vermiculite, perlite, diatomite, etc.) the cement content has a minor influence on the refractoriness of the concrete. This is illustrated by Fig. 26 which contrasts the effect of cement content on the refractoriness of a concrete containing building brick aggregate with the effect on the refractoriness of concretes containing highly refractory aggregates. The influence of different types of aggregate upon the refractoriness of the concretes is also clearly shown. At the same time the strength of the concrete (before and after firing) is increased when the cement content is raised so that the proportion of cement in a mix is frequently a compromise between obtaining adequate strength and ensuring the desired refractoriness. The contrasting effects of different cement contents on strength and on refractoriness

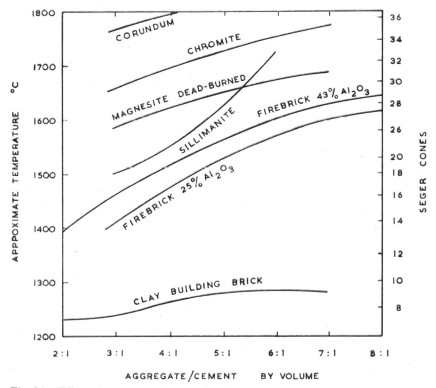

Fig. 26. Effect of cement content and of type of aggregate on the refractoriness (P.C.E.) of castable mixes.

203

are demonstrated in Fig. 27 which is adapted from work by Eusner and Hubble[59].

Increasing the proportion of white H.A.C. (72-80 per cent. Al_2O_3) in a mix similarly increases the strength of the concrete but, in this case, the refractoriness of the cement itself is much higher, and therefore a major reduction in the refractoriness of the concrete due to increasing cement contents, commences only with aggregates which have a higher refractoriness than that of firebrick (42-44 per cent. Al_2O_3).

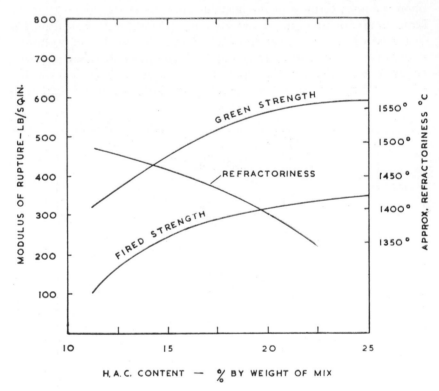

Fig. 27. Effect of cement content on the refractoriness and strength of a castable mix·

(3) *Additives for modifying the Properties of the wet Mix*

Most refractory aggregates are angular and give a mix with H.A.C. which is rather " harsh " to work. The plasticity and water-retention of the wet mix can be greatly increased by incorporating raw fireclay (10-15 per cent. by weight of the cement) or a smaller proportion of bentonite (2-3 per cent. by weight of the cement), and in mixes containing white H.A.C. (72-80 per cent. Al_2O_3) the same effect is best obtained by the use of raw china-clay. A much greater amount of fireclay or china-clay is sometimes added (20-100 per cent. by weight of the cement) e.g. for reducing the rebound of aggregates in guniting or in the preparation of mixes for trowelling and refractory-brick jointing. Other effects produced by additions of plastic clays[60] are discussed later.

Wetting agents, inorganic suspending colloids[61], and pro-prietary plasticising agents (most of which have been mentioned in Chapter V) can also be added in order to give freely workable mixes[62]. Salts of poly-hydroxylic acids, such as sodium citrate or sodium glu-conate can be used as water-reducing agents or set-retarding agents and synthetic poly-electrolytes (originally developed as soil con-ditioners) have been shown to impart greater cohesivity and to reduce the " bleeding " of a wet mix[63]. They may therefore be useful in refractory concrete mixes designed for guniting[64].

If a slight reduction in concrete density and strength is acceptable, a minor addition of vermiculite or perlite to an otherwise harsh castable mix also improves the workability to a marked degree. In the case of proprietary refractory castable mixes it should be noted that the manufacturer has already designed the mix to give certain properties and no additions (other than water) should be made to these compositions without consultation.

7. PROPERTIES OF THE HARDENED CONCRETE

(1) Strength before firing

The cold strength of a refractory concrete mix develops at the same rate shown by H.A.C. concretes containing ordinary aggregates, so that adequately high values are obtained within 24 hours. Low water-cement ratios, thorough compaction and good water-curing have a favourable effect upon refractory concrete strength also, and the latter is increased (within limits) as the mix is made richer in cement.

The cube compressive strength given by refractory concretes at 24 hours vary widely according to the physical characteristics of the aggregate, and range from 7000-10,000 lb./sq. in. (with strong dense aggregates such as fused alumina, silicon carbide, sillimanite, basalt, etc.) down to 500-1500 lb./sq. in. (with very light-weight aggregates such as diatomite, perlite and vermiculite). Concrete units made with weak and porous aggregates, which retain large quantities of water, take longer to " dry out " and cannot be demoulded, handled, and transported at such an early age as those made with denser aggre-gates. According to Ruedi[65], the 24-hour strength of vermiculite/

H.A.C. mixes is increased by 18-290 per cent. when 0.5-3.5 per cent. of magnesium chloride is incorporated. A standard refractory concrete made with a well-graded fireclay aggregate and containing 750 lb. H.A.C. per cu. yd. should give a cube compressive strength of about 2000 lb/sq. in. at 12 hours and 5000-6000 lb/sq. in. at 24 hours. Refractory concretes made with white H.A.C. (72-80 per cent. Al_2O_3) give somewhat lower cold strength than equivalent mixes made with many of the ordinary high-alumina cements.

The flexural strength (modulus of rupture) follows the same pattern as the compressive strength and it usually lies between 500-1500 lb./sq. in. for concretes made with the stronger aggregates but very little flexural or tensile strength can be expected from light-weight refractory-insulating concretes, even before firing.

The dynamic modulus of elasticity is naturally very dependent on the type and proportion of aggregate. A mix of white H.A.C. and fused alumina (1 : 8 by weight) gives a dynamic modulus (longitudinal) of over 13×10^6 lb./sq. in. but $4-6 \times 10^6$ lb./sq. in. is a more typical range for concretes made with chamotte or crushed firebrick.

(2) *Strength after firing*

When a refractory concrete or refractory-insulating concrete is heated, the free water, and ultimately the combined water[66], is driven off so that the hydraulic bond which is responsible for the high cold strength, is weakened. Some of the combined water is lost even below 100°C. and a drop in compressive strength on oven-drying is common but not invariable. The changes occurring in the structure of the hydrated cement or of the cement/aggregate complex have been studied by differential thermal analysis and by X-ray diffraction[67] and the loss in strength with rising temperature is definitely associated with dehydration of the cement-hydrates and of the alumina gel. Dehydration studies show that only about 2-3 per cent. of the combined water remains at 700°C. (1300°F.). At higher temperatures the cement can begin to react with the aggregate, first in the solid state, and then more quickly as traces of eutectic liquid appear. This produces a " ceramic bond " which results in an increase in the strength (after cooling) of concretes which are fired above the appropriate temperature. When ordinary H.A.C. is used in conjunction with an aggregate of comparatively low refractoriness, the temperature at which ceramic bond formation commences may be as low as 800°C. (1500°F.) but, with a good crushed firebrick aggregate, the concrete must usually be heated to above 1100°C. (2000°F.) before an appreciable effect is seen on the strength after cooling. The substitution of white

H.A.C. (72-80 per cent. Al_2O_3) for the ordinary type of H.A.C. may delay the start of ceramic bond formation until a temperature of 1300°-1400°C. is reached.

The effect of the dehydration process followed by ceramic bond formation is shown in Fig. 28, which is due to Heindl & Post[67]. It will be seen that when a crushed firebrick/H.A.C. concrete is heated for some time at increasing temperatures, and then tested after cooling, the strengths show a characteristic drop which is succeeded by an increase when the fired temperature has been sufficient to cause reaction between cement and aggregate. The strength after firing is at a minimum when the temperature (and its duration) is sufficient to dehydrate the hydraulic bond without being high enough to produce appreciable ceramic bond.

Many workers[68] have studied the factors which affect this minimum level of strength. It is obviously dependent to some extent on the physical characteristics of the aggregate and hence on the strength of the concrete before firing. It is true that a series of specimens showing large differences in initial cold strengths will yield fired strengths which more nearly approach each other[69], nevertheless the influence of the initial strength is by no means negligible, and there is every inducement for the user to make a good quality concrete in the first place, by employing well-graded aggregates, by avoiding unduly "sloppy" mixes, and by ensuring thorough compaction of the mix. The effect of cement content on the fired strength is also shown clearly in Fig. 27, and the stronger refractory concretes intended for furnace construction should be designed so that the minimum fired compressive strength is above 1000-1500 lb/sq. in. and the modulus of rupture above 200 lb./sq. in.

Hansen and Livovich[70] determined the compressive strength of crushed firebrick/H.A.C. concretes while the specimens were at elevated temperatures and found that, up to the point of ceramic bond formation, the hot strengths were equal to or higher than the corresponding strengths after cooling. Beyond this point the incipient thermal softening of the bond (which is a sign of active ceramic bond formation) resulted in lower strengths at the test temperatures but the strengths obtained after cooling naturally show an increase. West and Sutton[60] showed that the flexural strength of specimens fired at 1000°C. was also higher when tested hot than after the concrete had been cooled to room temperature.

The dynamic modulus of elasticity is also reduced when the concrete is heated, first during the elimination of free water and, secondly, during dehydration. Values obtained after firing are in the region of 1.5-2.0×10^6 lb./sq. in.

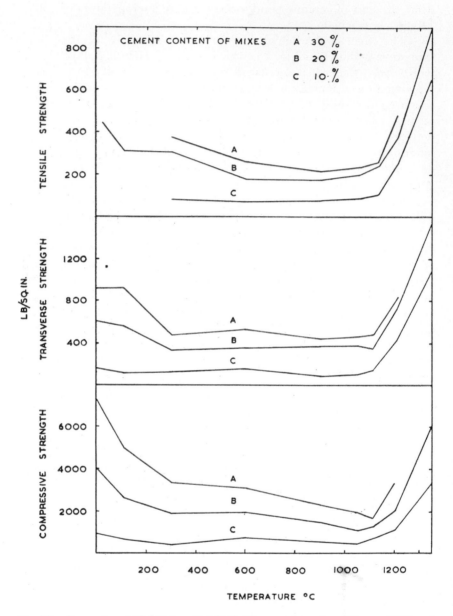

Fig. 28. Strengths of H.A.C./crushed firebrick concretes after 24hr. at 20°C and 110°C, 4 months at 300°C and 600°C, 5 hours at all higher temperatures (Heindl & Post).

(3) *Methods for increasing the fired Strength*

Suitably-made refractory concretes containing reasonably strong aggregates will give fired strengths which are more than adequate for the structural requirements of refractory design, even without the benefit of ceramic bond formation. In applications where it is known that the temperature will always be well below the refractory limit, the cement content of the mix can be increased (up to double the normal amount) because the concrete strength is thus improved at all temperatures, and the reduced refractoriness of the richer mix is immaterial in such circumstances.

It is preferable to use mechanical vibration when placing load-bearing refractory concrete since full consolidation can be achieved with a lower water-cement ratio, and both cold and fired strengths are increased. The use of a water-reducing additive, and/or plasticiser, is similarly helpful in mixes which are placed by hand. However, in many cases when refractory concrete is used at temperatures too low for ceramic bond formation, it is not the loss of strength which gives cause for dissatisfaction, but rather the corresponding reduction in other properties such as abrasion resistance, erosion resistance or ability to withstand impacts. Much work has therefore been devoted to improving the physical characteristics of refractory castables which are required for duty in intermediate temperature ranges. An apparently simple solution is to add finely-ground materials which soften and react with the aggregate or cement at comparatively low temperatures and the use of powdered glass cullet[71] or low-melting frits[72] has been suggested. The difficulty is that, below the reaction temperature, such materials act as inert additives and therefore reduce the concrete strength in the lower temperature regions. One must be sure also that the operating temperature of the concrete will never be greatly exceeded, otherwise high shrinkage or even fusion will occur. The addition of a low-vitrification clay (20-100 per cent. by weight of the cement) improves the strength of refractory castable mixes after firing at temperatures above 700°C. (1300°F.), and a high-vitrification clay increases the fired strength at 900°-1100°C. (1650°-2000°F.). The presence of a high proportion of raw clay in the mix reduces the cold strength and increases the firing shrinkage.

The mineral topaz, $(AlF)_2SiO_4$, (which has been used itself as an aggregate in refractory concrete) liberates fluorine[73] on heating, and it increases the fired strength of other refractory concretes in which it is contained as a finely divided powder. When added in amounts equal to that of the H.A.C. it is said to give a denser and less friable concrete[74] at temperatures above 870°C. (1600°F.). The concrete

209

strength, at or above this temperature, may be 3-6 times that of concrete without topaz addition[75]. Calcined aluminous material, containing absorbed hydrofluoric acid and obtained as a spent product from the alkylation of isoparaffins, has also been proposed for the same purpose[76].

The incorporation of small amounts of alkaline-earth carbonates (up to 2.25 per cent. by weight of the H.A.C.) often increases the concrete strength obtained after firing at moderate temperatures[77], and similar amount of sodium aluminate increase not only the fired strength but also the cold strength[78]. The sodium aluminate appears to act as a mineraliser in refractory compositions[79].

Finally, it should be mentioned that a proportion of raw kyanite (usually 100-mesh material) is frequently included in proprietary castable mixes. This addition can increase the refractoriness-under-load, modify the shrinkage characteristics at high temperatures and, it has been claimed, can increase the concrete strength by 50 per cent. at 950°C. (1750°F.).

(4) *Refractoriness and Refractoriness-under-Load*

The refractoriness (pyrometric cone equivalent) of neat hydrated high-alumina cements (ordinary type) is comparatively low, and does not exceed Seger cone 15-16 (approx. 1450°C. or 2650°F.). Nevertheless, in practice, the fusion point of the cement is raised by thermal reaction with alumina, or other refractory material present as the finer portion of the aggregate in a castable mix, and, therefore, it is the refractoriness of the fine aggregate/cement mixture which finally determines the behaviour of the concrete at high temperatures. A guide to the pyrometric cone equivalents of castable mixes containing various refractory aggregates is shown in Fig. 26, and the effect of type of aggregate and of cement content is quite clear. Of course, the mixes cannot be used industrially at the temperature shown since the maximum hot-face temperatures to which the concretes can be submitted are much lower (see Table II).

The range of refractoriness within the commercial types of H.A.C. has already been noted, and if the latter are all required to produce castable mixes of equal refractoriness, the cement content of the mix must be suitably adjusted, i.e. those mixes using H.A.C. of high iron oxide content should have a lower proportion of cement. In all cases when it is known that a refractory concrete will be submitted in service to a temperature approaching or slightly exceeding the normal refractory limit of the mix, the cement content can be reduced in order to increase the margin of refractoriness but, except in special

210

circumstances, the minimum cement content is usually about 500 lb./cu. yd.

The refractoriness of neat hydrated white H.A.C. is about 1650°C. (3000°F.) if it contains 72 per cent. Al_2O_3, and 1770°C. (3220°F.) if it contains 80 per cent. Al_2O_3. Values for the fusion points of the former type of cement, in normal mixes with various aggregates, have been given as follows[80].

H.A.C. (72 per cent. Al_2O_3)	Chamotte (40-42 per cent.Al_2O_3)	1640°C.
,,	/Chromite	1760°C.
,,	/Magnesia	1770°C.
,,	/Brown corundum . . .	1800°C.
,,	/White corundum . . .	1860°C.
,,	/Silicon carbide . . .	1940°C.

The refractoriness-under-load test, in which the temperature of subsidence of a refractory specimen loaded to 28 lb./sq. in. (2 Kg/sq. cm.) is determined, has given rise to much controversy and the methods used in various countries do not always give comparable results. In specimens cut from a refractory brick, the material, having been prefired in manufacture, undergoes little or no change until the original firing temperature is approached or exceeded. However, a specimen cast from a refractory concrete mix alters in character all through the test (e.g. by loss of free or combined water and by thermal reaction between cement and aggregate). The thermal reaction of many aggregates with H.A.C. (ordinary or white type) gives a bond of increasing refractoriness and therefore the refractoriness-under-load of a previously fired castable specimen is frequently much higher than that of a similar specimen tested in the usual unfired condition.

The temperature of subsidence under load of calcined fireclay/ H.A.C. concretes is often increased also when an addition of alumina, mullite, or raw kyanite fines is made to the mix, and when the proportion of cement is reduced. The use of white H.A.C. (72-80 per cent. Al_2O_3) in place of ordinary H.A.C. usually raises the refractoriness under load by 100-150°C.

Thin refractory concrete units (such as batts) which, in service, are supported on a span, will tend to sag in the middle whenever the temperature is high enough to produce some eutectic liquid in the composition. If such slabs are prefired to above the service temperature while supported on a flat surface, ceramic bond formation can proceed without causing deformation and the units will not sag in subsequent use until a higher temperature is reached. This type of application is one of the few for which pre-firing of refractory concrete may be advantageous or necessary.

Table III gives some indication of the temperatures at which rapid subsidence takes place when normal mixes of H.A.C. and various aggregates are submitted (unfired) to the rising-temperature test under a load of 28 lb./sq. in. The concretes containing white H.A.C. (72-80 per cent. Al_2O_3) and white fused alumina or silicon carbide aggregate show little sign of subsidence until the temperature collapse is almost reached, and in this respect they behave under load in the same way as silica firebricks. With other aggregates such as magnesia, or if the mix contains ordinary H.A.C., the subsidence occurs over a much wider range of temperature.

TABLE III. REFRACTORINESS-UNDER-LOAD CHARACTERISTICS OF H.A.C. CONCRETES

O = Made with ordinary H.A.C.

H = Made with white H.A.C. (72 % Al_2O_3)

Aggregate	Cement	Temperature of collapse under load of 28 lb./sq. in. (°C)
Basalt, Traprock	O	1050 - 1150
Chamotte	O H	1350 - 1400 1400 - 1500
Magnesia	H	1500
Chromite	O H	1400 - 1500 1450 - 1550
Chromite-magnesia	O	1500
Silicon carbide	H	1600
Brown fused alumina	O H	1600 1700
White fused alumina	O H	1650 1800

(5) *Thermal Expansion and Contraction*[81].

A refractory firebrick (unless chemically-bonded) has been fired to a high temperature during manufacture. When it is heated in service it must expand and, in accordance with the thermal expansion

212

characteristics of the material from which it is made, a suitable joint-allowance is therefore made in any large refractory brick construction.

Neat hydrated H.A.C. also expands with temperature while it is humid, but above 100°C. it begins to shrink due to elimination of combined water, and at 700°-800°C. there is a further contraction due to changes in the alumina gel and hydrate structure. After cooling it therefore does not return to the original dimensions (like a firebrick) but shows a nett contraction of about 2 per cent. White H.A.C. (72-80 per cent. Al_2O_3) behaves similarly.

When a refractory concrete is heated for the first time the expansion characteristics are the resultant of those shown by the aggregate and the neat cement. In Fig. 29, OA represents the reversible thermal expansion and contraction of an alumino-silicate firebrick (42-44 per cent. Al_2O_3), OBC shows the linear change in neat H.A.C. on firing to 1000°C. and cooling, the portion BC being reversible on subsequent re-heating. ODE represents behaviour of a concrete mix of H.A.C. and aggregate made from the firebrick. It will be seen that the dimensions of the concrete at 1000°C. are almost the same as the original dimensions as cast, because the shrinkage of the cement has counter-acted the expansion of the aggregate and, on cooling, there is a nett shrinkage of about 0.5 per cent. When subsequently reheated and cooled, the concrete expands and contracts reversibly according to the line ED or DE, i.e. it regains its cast dimensions at high temperature and shrinks to 0.5 per cent. below its original length on cooling again. For this reason a castable mix of this type can be placed in large lengths without expansion joints. Butt-joints or " cold " construction joints are conveniently made every 3-5 ft. and these will open slightly as the concrete cools and contracts after firing. A completely monolithic refractory concrete wall will tend to crack at similar intervals on cooling, and many users are prepared to allow the concrete to make its own *contraction* joints in this way. Others prefer to pre-determine the position of the cracks by the use of butt-joints during construction or by inserting very thin cardboard sheets, waterproof paper etc.

With other types of aggregate, or at higher temperatures, the total thermal expansion of the aggregate may exceed the shrinkage of the cement bond, and the thermal expansion and contraction curve of such mixes can be realised by moving point D in an upward direction. Conversely, if certain castable mixes are heated to a temperature near their refractory limit, the active reaction between cement and aggregate can cause excessive contraction and point D will then fall below the original base-line, and move towards B.

Aggregates which have a high thermal expansion include, dead-

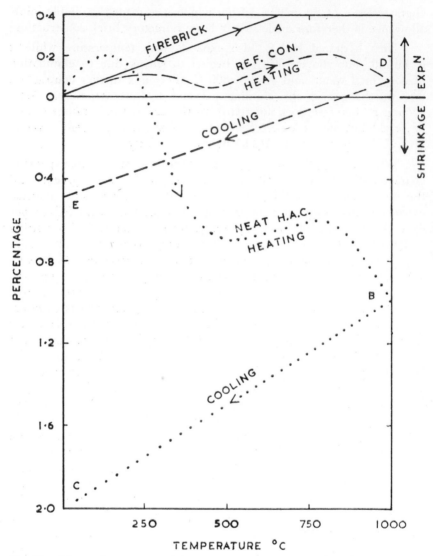

Fig. 29. Linear changes occurring on heating neat hydrated H.A.C. or refractory concrete for the first time.

burned magnesite, chromite-magnesite, pyrophyllite and siliceous firebrick, but the expansion of the corresponding concretes (from cast dimensions to hot dimensions) is always lower than the expansion of the firebricks up to the same temperature. In mixes which contain these aggregates or which contain materials with a tendency to bloat when heated near their refractory limit, some small provision for thermal expansion may be considered necessary. The service temperature of white H.A.C. castables is usually very high and the total expansion of the aggregate at that temperature is correspondingly greater so that in some cases an allowance for an expansion of 0.5–0.75 per cent. is sometimes recommended. However, much depends on the particular application since, if the concrete is under constraint while being heated, (e.g. a concrete lining in a steel shell), creep will probably relieve any expansion strains at high temperatures.

If the interior face of a refractory concrete furnace wall is heated and cooled, the firing shrinkage should theoretically make it concave towards the inside of the furnace. In practice however the differential shrinkage stresses are usually relieved by the formation of a network of hair cracks on the hot-face which may be visible after cooling but which disappear each time the furnace is brought up to temperature.

(6) *Thermal Conductivity*[82]

The thermal conductivity of refractory castables made with the denser aggregates (i.e. with fired densities of 100 lb./cu. ft. or more) is, in general, in accordance with the thermal conductivity of the aggregate, and the high conductivity of silicon carbide, magnesia, and fused alumina, is reflected in the concretes they form. In most cases the conductivity of silicon carbide, magnesia, and fused alumina, is reflected in the concretes they form. In most caes the conductivity of the concrete increases with rising temperature, but with some aggregates (e.g. magnesia) it is reduced at high temperatures. Owing to the elimination of water from the H.A.C., the fired concrete made with the denser aggregates shows a lower thermal conductivity than the material from which the aggregate is obtained. Outer sections of refractory concrete furnace walls, where the combined water may still remain, have higher conductivities than the fired sections and Table **IV** gives average values of conductivity which may be used for various concretes under the conditions and temperatures of normal use.

The conductivity of light refractory-insulating concretes depends less on the nature of the aggregate and more on the fired density obtained. Rich mixes, although stronger, therefore give higher conductivities than lean mixes. Hansen and Livovich[83] found that it was possible to predict fairly accurately the thermal conductivity of most insulating concretes from the fired density, and Fig. 30, showing this relation, is similar to their results.

If the concretes are saturated, not with air, but with a highly conductive gas, the thermal conductivity rises. Wygant and Crowley[84]

215

TABLE IV. THERMAL CHARACTERISTICS OF CONCRETES MADE WITH H.A.C.
AND VARIOUS AGGREGATES

Aggregate	Typical Fired Density (lb./cu. ft.)	Heat Capacity BTU/cu. ft. /°F.	Average Thermal Conductivity BTU/hr./ sq.ft./°F./in.	Thermal Diffusivity (sq. ft./hr.)
Vermiculite	35	9	1.2	0.011
Diatomite	55	14	1.7	0.010
H.T. Insulating Brick	85	21	3.2	0.013
Expanded clay	90	22	3.5	0.013
Firebrick	115	29	6	0.017
Fired Kaolin	120	31	8	0.021
Sillimanite	135	33	10	0.025
Calcined bauxite	160	45	12	0.022
Chromite-magnesia	165	37	8	0.018
Silicon carbide	145	40	50	0.013
Bubble fused alumina	95	22	6	0.023
Brown fused alumina	175	52	16	0.026
White fused alumina	175	52	16	0.026
Fused magnesia	170	50	24	0.04
Magnesite (dead-burned)	160	45	20	0.037
Zirconia	260	44	6	0.011

Note : For the thermal emissivity of white H.A.C./fused alumina see J.
Segall. Verres et Réfractaires, 1957, (4), 203.

showed that it more than doubled in pure hydrogen at moderate
temperatures. At atmospheric pressure the conductivity of a crushed
insulating firebrick/H.A.C. concrete rose slightly above the value in
air but the increase was much greater at elevated gas pressures, no
doubt owing to greater penetration of the gas.

One of the benefits of castable construction is the ability to produce a concrete with practically any desired thermal conductivity

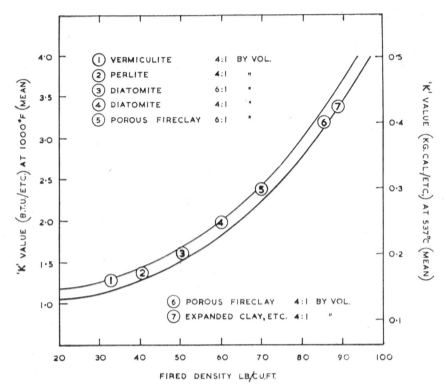

Fig. 30. Relation between the fired density and the thermal conductivity of refractory-insulating concretes.

by choice of aggregate, by mixing dense aggregate with light-weight aggregate, and by varying the cement/aggregate proportions. It is also possible to produce composite concrete units with a hot-face consisting of a stronger and more refractory mix backed by a sufficient thickness of an insulating concrete mix to give the required overall conductivity value. If one mix is compacted on top of the other while both are in the unset condition, they will harden together to give an integral unit which will not separate even when submitted to severe thermal cycling. Vertical walls are prepared by casting the two mixes on each side of a thin metal separating-plate which is withdrawn as the concrete is placed.

The specific heat of refractory concrete is substantially the same as that of the aggregate used and usually lies between 0.22-0.25.

(7) *Porosity and Permeability*

The apparent porosities of dense firebricks vary according to the type of refractory, the method of brick manufacture, and the degree of firing. Alumino-silicate firebricks usually have porosities within the range 20-26 per cent. and most other refractories give similar values. Porosities as low as 10-15 per cent. are not very common.

Although the apparent porosity of a refractory concrete (before firing) is influenced by the particular type of dense aggregate which is chosen, it depends mainly on the cement content of the mix. Within limits the higher the cement content the lower is the porosity after the concrete is air-dried. In this condition a refractory concrete of normal mix proportions can have a porosity which is similar to that of the brick which provided the aggregate. For example, if an alumino-silicate firebrick with a porosity of about 21 per cent. is the source of aggregate for refractory concretes containing various cement contents[67], the apparent porosities of these concretes after prolonged air-drying extend from 15 per cent. (when the cement content is 30 per cent. by weight) to 28 per cent. (when the cement content is 10 per cent. by weight).

If the concretes are heated however, their porosities increase proportionally to the amount of combined water which is eliminated and they soon reach values of 30-35 per cent. The apparent porosity of a dense refractory concrete *after* firing is therefore liable to be much higher than that of the refractory brick from which it is made.

In spite of the relatively high porosity produced in refractory concrete by heating at 300°-500°C. or higher, it is important to note that the permeability to gases is extremely low up to about 1000°C. Wygant and Bulkley[56] found that the permeability of refractory concrete to air at room temperature was only 0.002-0.05 cu. ft./hr./ sq. ft. per inch of differential water pressure per inch of concrete thickness. Corresponding values for dense fireclay brick, alumina refractory brick and recrystallized silicon carbide were 0.08-20.0, 50.0, and 90.0, respectively. Eusner and Hubble[59] concluded that castable refractory mixes had lower permeabilities than other refractories tested, with the possible exception of some types of carbon brick. Other results indicate that refractory concretes have about one-twentieth the average permeability of high-duty or super-duty firebricks. In practice, an additional factor is the absence of joints in a castable construction, and the resulting low overall permeability combined with a relatively high porosity (which increases the thermal insulation value) has resulted in the extensive use of refractory concrete for lining vessels containing hot gases.

Unlike the porosity, which increases rapidly as the temperature is raised above 100°C., the permeability of refractory concrete remains at a fairly constant low value[59] until a temperature of about 850°C.

218

(1550°F.) is reached, when it begins to increase markedly (see Fig. 31). This increased permeability may be due to reduction of the internal surface area owing to crystal growth and structural changes in the alumina and gel constituents of the bond. Nevertheless it has been found that the permeability at over 1200°C. (2250°F.) is still below that of the average firebrick[56]. To obtain a concrete with low permeability a plastic constituency appears to be the best for placing by hand. A " dry " mix will give a higher permeability unless thoroughly and completely compacted, e.g. by vibratory methods.

The apparent porosities of refractory-insulating concretes made with the usual light-weight aggregates are mainly in the 50-80 per cent. range after firing but such concretes again exhibit the property of lower permeability if compared with insulating-brick refractories of comparable thermal insulation value.

(8) *Thermal Shock Resistance*

In practical use, refractory concretes show a characteristically high resistance to thermal shock and this is borne out by laboratory

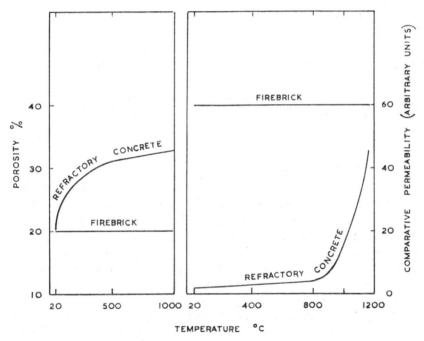

Fig. 31. Changes in the porosity and permeability of H.A.C./firebrick concrete on heating for the first time, and comparison with firebrick. (*Only diagrammatic*).

tests in which specimens are rapidly heated to high temperatures with intervening periods of rapid cooling in air or quenching in cold water[85]. Naturally, the type of aggregate has an influence on the spalling properties[86], and a concrete made, for example, with magnesite (which, in brick form, has a poor spalling resistance) also has lower thermal shock resistance. However, in all cases it appears that the concrete has an appreciably greater resistance when compared with refractory bricks from which the aggregate may be derived. It is probable that the concrete structure, after firing, is specially favourable for spalling resistance since it consists of an assemblage of small units of aggregate bonded by semi-resilient dried gel, and therefore relatively large stresses and strains can be absorbed internally. According to Longchambon[87], H.A.C. concretes prepared with alumino-silicate aggregate show cracks only after 30-40 cycles of heating to 1000°C. and quenching in cold water, but concretes containing a low proportion of cement do not perform well in this type of quenching test although their behaviour under practical conditions of rapid heating and cooling may be quite satisfactory.

There is some evidence that if a refractory concrete is placed by vibration with the lowest water-cement ratio, its spalling resistance may be lower than when placed with a very plastic consistency, since the latter type of concrete has a more porous internal structure after firing. When thermal shock resistance is the main property required, and particularly when the spalling characteristics of the aggregate are not favourable, it is therefore best to use a water content which gives this plastic consistency, and a further improvement can probably be obtained by incorporating in the mix a small proportion of vermiculite, perlite, or alumina bubbles.

(9) *Erosion Resistance and Abrasion Resistance*

In some industrial applications (particularly in fluidized-bed reactors) refractory concrete linings for vessels, pipes, etc. may be subjected to erosion which takes place by the impact, abrasion, and cutting action of solid particles moving freely in a gas or other fluid[56]. It is the cutting action which is the most important erosive force, since particles moving at an angle to the general fluid flow can quickly undercut and expose the larger aggregate particles by attacking the softer matrix in which they may be embedded.

A good correlation has been found[56] between erosion resistance and the compressive strength of refractory concretes. Accordingly, factors which tend to improve the latter (e.g. strong aggregate, low water-cement ratio and increased cement content) also increase the erosion resistance. The results of Wygant and Bulkley indicate that the erosion rate of a castable mix containing 20-25 per cent. H.A.C. was about one-tenth that of a mix containing only 15 per cent. H.A.C. There is evidence also that the erosion resistance of refractory mortars is better than that of concretes, i.e. aggregate of large maximum size is not an advantage when erosion has to be resisted.

Gitzen, Hart and MacZura[21] found that the erosion resistance of a castable made from tabular alumina and one type of white H.A.C. (80 per cent. Al_2O_3) was comparable to that displayed by a phosphate-bonded alumina mix. However, most of the commercial H.A.C. castable refractories show much lower erosion resistance than the phosphate-bonded type. Venable[88] showed that, if the erosion resistance of best silicon carbide brick is given a value of 100, the average refractory concrete has a maximum erosion resistance of 35.

Abrasion (i.e. rubbing or friction only) takes place on the high points of the concrete surface, and refractory concrete has its highest abrasion resistance when the surface is composed mainly of (coarse) aggregate particles which are strong and dense. A castable which has a good abrasion resistance need not necessarily show a good erosion resistance. Avoidance of laitance on the concrete surface during placing and thorough water-curing greatly improve abrasion resistance. Various surface treatments applied to the dry or fired refractory concrete are also effective and, for example, solutions of sodium silicate[89], magnesium silicofluoride, borax/sodium carbonate, or ethyl silicate, may increase both abrasion and erosion resistance.

(10) *Electrical Resistivity*

The electrical resistivity of refractory concretes, before firing but after drying for some days in air, is about 0.1-1.0 megohm-cm. (depending chiefly on the humidity of the concrete). Oven-dried concretes show an extremely high electrical resistivity but conduction increases at furnace temperatures. Concrete structure and the cement bond are probably responsible for the fact that fired refractory concretes usually possess a greater electrical resistivity than the material which forms the aggregate. The nature of the aggregate can be important, for example the resistivity of silicon carbide concrete is relatively low in comparison with that of concretes compounded with most of the other refractory materials.

Resistivity values for some H.A.C. refractory mortars at different temperatures have been given by Sauzier[90] and they are reproduced in Table V.

TABLE V.   ELECTRICAL RESISTIVITIES OF H.A.C. REFRACTORY MORTARS AT
HIGH TEMPERATURES
(in Megohms-cm.)

Aggregate in Mortar	500°C.	700°C.	900°C.	1000°C.
Crushed Firebrick	16.0	3.0	0.25	0.10
Calcined Bauxite	11.0	1.0	0.20	0.05
Chromite	1.0	0.035	0.005	—

8.   PLACING, CURING AND BRINGING INTO SERVICE.

Proprietary castables in which the cement and aggregate are already mixed should always be used according to the manufacturers' instructions, and, even when less than one bag of material is required for a particular job, all should be tipped out and remixed before the necessary quantity is taken.

When the user prepares his own mix the technique of making the mortar or concrete is similar to ordinary practice. The gauging water should be of drinking quality and all tools, mixers and receptacles, should be free from soluble salts, Portland cement, plaster, etc. Old firebricks which are contaminated with soluble salts should not be used for aggregates and slag or jointing cement must also be removed. The aggregates should not contain silica brick, unfired magnesite, or dolomitic material. In many cases the refractory aggregate is more absorptive than is usual in ordinary structural concrete and it is often recommended that such aggregate should be pre-soaked and drained before the cement is mixed with it. The reason for this is that, after perfunctory mixing of aggregate, cement, and water to the correct consistency, the larger particles of aggregate may continue to absorb water and alter the mix consistency so that complete compaction in the mould is not likely to be achieved. Except in the case of very porous aggregates it is doubtful, however, whether pre-soaking is really necessary unless the maximum size is above ¾in. Instead, a really adequate mixing time should be given so that the water-requirements of the aggregate can be almost completely satisfied before placing commences.

When placing the concrete by hand-tamping, spading or rodding, a plastic but not too " sloppy " consistency is desirable, and a lower water content is used for mixes which are consolidated with immersion vibrators or mould vibrators. The vibration technique is recommended when structurally strong refractory concrete is required, e.g. for walls and arches of furnaces and kilns. Refractory concretes may also be placed by gun[91]. In one type of machine the dry or relatively dry mix of aggregate and cement is blown through the hose and the necessary amount of water is added to the materials at the nozzle ; in another type the wet mix is extruded from the nozzle. Mechanical vibration is not usually suitable for placing light-weight concretes made with diatomite, vermiculite, perlite, etc. These aggregates should first be mixed with a major portion of the gauging water and then the cement is added. A final mixing is then given, during which further water is slowly added (if necessary) in order to obtain the desired consistency. With such aggregates the tamping into moulds or formwork should not be too vigorous so that the aggregate is not crushed and the full heat-insulation properties of the concrete are realised.

Absorbent wood moulds are thoroughly oiled and made waterproof before use, and metal moulds also require a light coating of mould oil. Cores are more easily removed if covered with waterproof paper and they should be gently eased out as soon as the concrete has set sufficiently. When keying to existing brickwork is required, most of the suction of the bricks should be satisfied with water before the concrete mix is placed. When no key to an absorbent surface is wanted, the latter should be painted with any reject oil or covered with waterproof paper, otherwise it may abstract too much water from the mix.

Concretes made with the denser aggregates should be cured by lightly spraying any large exposed areas as soon as the surface is sufficiently strong, thus keeping them wet for 24 hours. Porous and light-weight aggregates retain so much water that sprinkling in this case may be unnecessary unless the mass of concrete is large and cooling is required. Conversion of the H.A.C. hydrates, which can occur if the cement hardens at high temperatures (see Chapter 4), does not present the same problem in refractory concrete that it does in ordinary structural H.A.C. concrete. It has been shown that if refractory concrete is fully converted (e.g. by allowing it to harden in very hot water) and if it is then heated to furnace temperature (say 1000°C.) the fired strength obtained is equal to, or usually greater than, that obtained at the same temperature from similar concrete which has been perfectly cured[92]. However, whenever possible, refractory concrete should be kept cool during hardening by limiting the depth of lift and by appropriate curing. There are two reasons for this (a) the whole of a refractory concrete structure does not usually reach a high temperature in service and the higher cold strengths obtained by good curing may be useful in the outer (cold-face) sections of furnace walls, (b) if the temperature within the concrete reaches a very high level during hardening, the thermal stresses produced during cooling may be sufficient to cause cracking particularly if the concrete is made with one of the weaker insulating aggregates.

As with ordinary H.A.C. concrete, the strength of refractory concrete continues to increase at ordinary temperature so long as water is present, but substantially the same fired strength is obtained whatever the maturity of the concrete. In emergency, the refractory concrete can therefore be raised to furnace temperature at the same rate as the surrounding brickwork even if the concrete has only recently set. If water remains long enough in the mix to provide " steam-curing " the result is usually satisfactory. For the same reason hot patching can be effective, and successful stack repairs have been carried out with gunited refractory castables in blast-furnaces which were still under (reduced) working conditions.

After the concrete has hardened and dried out it still contains a large amount of absorbed and combined water. There is an obvious danger that, if the temperature throughout the mass is raised too quickly, the sudden steam formation may cause explosive spalling. It is almost impossible to cause this with normal concretes which contain aggregate of reasonable porosity (e.g. calcined fireclay), but any factor which tends to give a dense, impermeable internal structure will increase the risk. Mixes of very fine-ground white H.A.C. with dense sintered alumina aggregate may occasionally show a susceptibility towards this phenomenon[93], and a decrease in the cement fineness or a reduction in cement content and curing at 70°-90°F. (21-32°C.) all reduce the possibility of hazard. It has also been claimed [94]that the addition of 0.2-1.5 per cent. boric acid to a castable permits very rapid initial heating without danger of explosive spalling. Although such occurrences are rare, any thick section of refractory concrete should be heated up for the first time at a reasonably slow rate (e.g. 50°C. per hour) until it has reached a temperature of about 600°C. Precast shapes can be taken up to temperatures at the same rate as new furnace brickwork and, in all cases, once the bulk of the combined water has been eliminated, a refractory concrete can be heated or cooled as rapidly as desired.

9. DESIGNING WITH REFRACTORY CONCRETES AND METHODS OF REINFORCING.

We have seen that when refractory concrete is heated, strength is lost due to dehydration of the hydraulic bond but, at higher temperatures, ceramic bond formation will raise the strength when the concrete has been heated sufficiently. Whenever possible the type of aggregate and cement, and the cement content of the mix, should always be selected to give some ceramic bond, at least on the hot face. Three zones of strength will usually be found in a refractory concrete furnace wall which has been heated to a high temperature on the inside only. The outer " cold " zone of the wall will retain a high proportion of strength obtained on casting, the hot-face zone will develop ceramic bond and should also be relatively strong, and an interior zone of the wall will have the lowest strength since it has been dehydrated but not ceramically bonded.

Knowing the thermal gradient through a given furnace wall it is possible to assign a strength to each inch of thickness, based on the compressive strengths of the concrete at each temperature interval[95]. In the case of firebrick/H.A.C. concrete any thickness of the wall which is above 1260°C.(2300°F.) is ignored because it will be deformable under load. In practice however it is found that a refractory concrete wall or arch usually behaves in a satisfactory fashion if it is cast to the same thickness as would ordinarily be used for refractory brickwork and the thermal insulation value of the concrete will be higher than that of similar brickwork which it replaces.

Furnace walls may be cast with butt-joints or construction joints every 3-4 ft. length and alternate sections are often cast and allowed to harden, after which the intervening sections are filled in. If the furnace operates at well above 1000°C. or if the aggregate has high expansion characteristics, thin strips of cardboard or several thicknesses of waterproof paper can be inserted between the units. With chamotte or crushed firebrick aggregate such joint formers are rarely necessary except perhaps in a long run of wall, and one section of concrete is usually cast directly against another.

After the concrete has been taken up to the operating temperature and cooled down, butt-joints or construction joints will tend to open up a little. When the furnace is again put into operation the joints tend to close (see Section 7). If bogie or kiln-car tops are constructed with refractory concrete containing a series of butt-joints, the two sides of each joint will still be in contact at the operating temperature but will separate on cooling. If these joints are made as in Fig. 32 (A and B) any sand, scale, or brick dust which enters the crack can be blown out before the car re-enters the kiln.

Refractory concrete sprung arches are usually constructed with transverse butt-joints every 3-4 ft. run. Only a single travelling section of formwork is therefore essential. If longitudinal butt-joints are left in the arch they are made at the third points or in the centre of the arch, and they may be rebated (Fig. 32 C) or constructed with a slot which is sealed by insulating bricks or a vermiculite/H.A.C. mix (Fig. 32 D).   When a large wall area consists of a light-weight insulating concrete it is often best to pre-determine the position of contraction cracks by scoring or incising lines into the surface, immediately after removal of the formwork, and while the concrete is still " green."

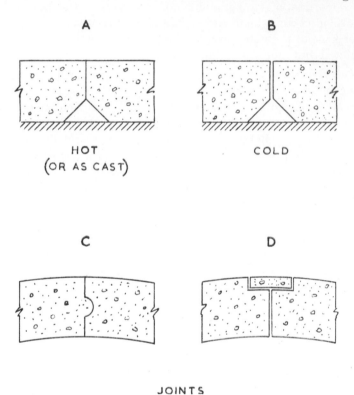

A   B

HOT   COLD
(OR AS CAST)

C   D

JOINTS

Fig. 32.   Refractory concrete butt-joints.

The volume stability of refractory concrete (i.e. the lower expansion on heating) results in less side-thrust from a sprung arch at the operating temperature and, whereas a brickwork arch is usually designed as the arc of a circle, much greater latitude is possible with refractory concrete.   Elliptical arches, giving the minimum side-thrust and more even radiation of heat, can be constructed with a refractory castable mix.   Conversely, concrete arches with a very high rise do not lack stability and catenary arches, which require a large number of different brick shapes, can be readily cast.   Concrete skew-backs can of course be adjusted to any angle.

Sprung arches do not require any reinforcement but there are many other applications in which steel can be usefully employed. In flat arches which are supported by the side-walls, I-beams may be embedded in the top surface but some parts of the steel must always be exposed to the air. Ordinary steel should never be completely embedded in refractory concrete when the position is such that it will reach a temperature of more than 300°-350°C. However if part of the steel is exposed to the air, or is joined to other steel members which are similarly exposed, the embedded portion of the reinforcing is kept cooler by conduction and it will operate satisfactorily in a hotter zone within the concrete. This is illustrated by Fig. 33 which shows suitable positions for rolled-steel joists in the flat roofs of furnaces operating at different temperatures[96], and Fig. 34 shows a more complete picture of a suggested construction method[96] for furnaces operating at relatively high temperatures.

Fully-suspended refractory concrete flat arches may be cast monolithically (Fig. 35)[97] or composed of several individually hung units (Fig. 36)[98]. When a furnace is operating at the highest tem-

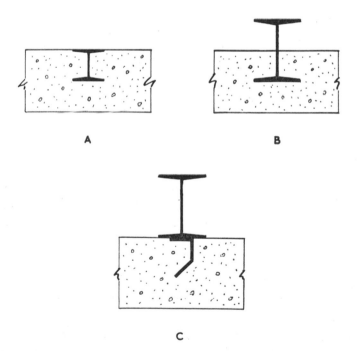

Fig. 33. Methods of reinforcing or supporting refractory concrete roofs with steel joists. As drawn, the under-side of the concrete is the hot face, and the furnace temperature increases from A to C.

CAST-IN-SITU REFRACTORY CONCRETE FLAT ARCH ROOF

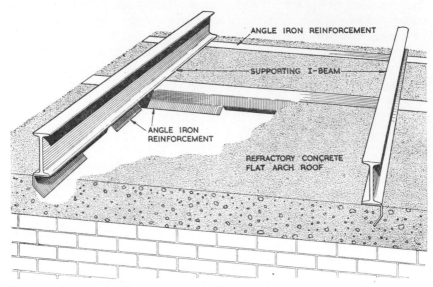

Fig. 34. Arrangement for reinforcing a flat arch refractory concrete furnace roof. (*After Universal Atlas Cement Div., U.S. Steel Corp.*)

peratures, support can be given through the depth of the roof to the hot-face itself by means of refractory anchors (Fig. 35) of which there are many patented types[99]. In some cases alloy steel hangers may also be employed[100].

Heavy-gauge steel in refractory concrete should always be avoided except when its temperature can be kept relatively low. When employed it is probably best to paint it with a thick coat of bitumastic or similar material which, on burning, will allow a little play for expansion. On the other hand a 10-gauge 2 in. x 4 in. or 3 in. x 3 in. mesh gives no trouble in the concrete at much higher temperatures if it is connected to an external steel shell. Fig. 37 B and C illustrates how the mesh may be anchored to the furnace, kiln, or reactor shell by means of hooks or studs welded to the shell at 12-18 in.centres. Other methods of keying the castable in doors etc. are shown in A and D.

Any of these anchorage methods can be used in the " tilt-up " form of furnace construction[101] which has effected a great saving in labour costs and which largely dispenses with the need for expensive formwork and scaffolding. Large refractory panels for furnace walls and roofs are cast on a steel plate lying on the ground and after the units have hardened they are tilted into the vertical position or lifted

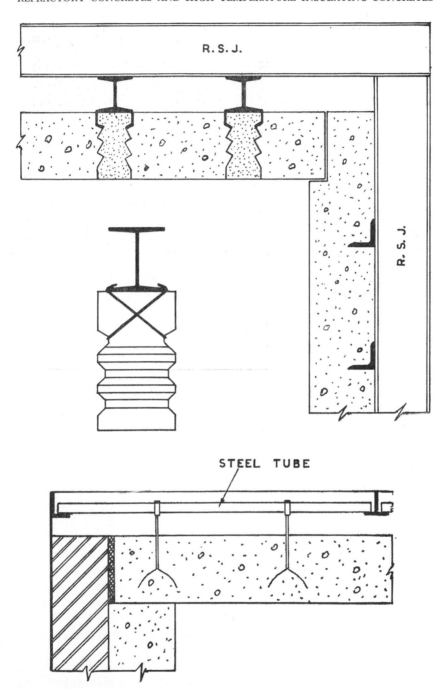

Fig. 35. Freely suspended flat refractory concrete furnace roof, showing use of patented refractory or alloy steel anchorage and suspension systems.

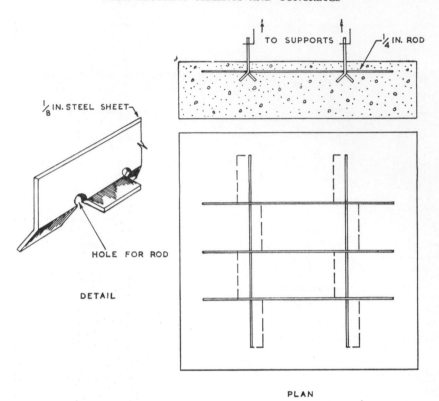

TO SUPPORTS

¼ IN. ROD

⅛ IN. STEEL SHEET

HOLE FOR ROD

DETAIL

PLAN

Fig. 36. Method of suspending one precast unit (e.g. 4ft. × 4ft.) of a flat refractory furnace roof. Use of steel sheet or angle-iron and steel rod.

into place. Only simple wooden formwork is required round the perimeter of each panel, and burner ports or other openings are easily formed by means of cores placed on the steel plate.

10. Survey of Applications

The scope for the utilisation of H.A.C. refractory castables will be evident from previous discussion of these materials and the field is now too wide to be treated in any great detail. Fortunately there are many excellent reviews of practical applications, some general and others dealing with specific aspects or industries[102], so that an adequate number of literature references can be given to facilitate the study of any particular use.

For convenience, the following general account will be divided among the main industries but many applications of refractory concrete are of course common to several manufacturing activities and therefore

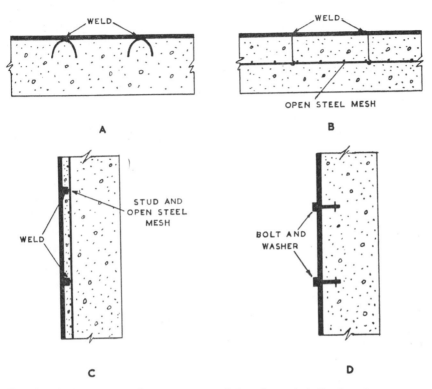

Fig. 37.   Anchorage for refractory concrete linings in steel shells, door frames, etc.

they cut across this classification.   For example, refractory concrete
doors, dampers, and burner blocks can be used in practically any type
of furnace stove or kiln.   Brickwork doors may fail when one or two
bricks loosen or fall out, and the advantages of castable methods lie
in the monolithic construction, thermal shock resistance and ease of
placing.   Refractory or insulating concrete door linings cast in frames
less than about 4 sq. ft. in area require no anchorage but, in larger
doors, hooks studs[103] or mesh are usually welded to the shell.   Floors
laid with a castable mix will withstand high radiant heat, hot coke or
ash, and the spillage of molten metal or slag[104].   They are therefore
used in many industries, the aggregate being crushed firebrick, or a
less refractory material if the conditions are not severe.

Users of raw fireclay for refractory brick-jointing obtain a high
cold strength by adding H.A.C. to the clay (e.g. 2 parts fireclay, 1
part H.A.C.) and a hydraulic bond remains in those parts of the brickwork which never reach a temperature sufficient to bake the clay
bond.   A refractory mortar consisting of grog and H.A.C. (usually

with an addition of raw fireclay) is also employed for brick-jointing and in this case the joints can be $\frac{1}{4}$in.-$\frac{1}{2}$in. thick in order to take up any inequalities in the bricks.

Cast-in-place monolithic linings are often preferred in rotary kilns since this usually ensures greater shell stability. Casting proceeds in sections along the kiln and covering up to one-third of the circumference, the kiln being turned after the concrete section has hardened. Only butt-joints are required between sections and they are often rebated. In order to obtain a good key for the concrete, hooks, studs or light angle-iron may be welded to the shell before casting starts. The kiln can be equally well lined with concrete shapes, of any convenient dimensions, precast or pressed in simple gang-moulds whenever labour is available. Lining with precast shapes is considered most suitable when there is an appreciable " whip " in the shell or when the shut-down time for repairs is very limited. Crushed firebrick is the aggregate usually used in castables for lining a wide variety of rotary kilns but other types of aggregate may sometimes be necessary to suit special operating conditions. Satisfactory applications include sand driers or sand colouring kilns, grass driers, calciners for the chemical industry (alumina, chrome-ore, phosphates etc.), rotary lime kilns and plaster kilns, iron-ore sintering kilns, and parts of cement kilns including desiccator kilns.

The use of crushed firebrick concrete in cement kilns is normally confined to the sections before and after the clinkering zone, although the behaviour, in this zone, of castables incorporating white H.A.C. (72-80 per cent. Al_2O_3) is at present being investigated. Russian work[105] indicates the suitability of chrome ore as an aggregate in castables for lining cement kilns and it is stated that for this purpose the content of silica in the chromite should not be too high. Several patents have been accepted which cover the use of other aggregates such as corundum, zirconia, and calcium aluminate clinker[106]. A mix of ordinary H.A.C. and traprock or whinstone aggregate has been found ideal for compacting by pneumatic hammer between the helically disposed rows of hooks to which the kiln chains are attached, and monolithic refractory concrete heat-exchangers may be cast directly against the kiln shell on the burner side of the chains. A chrome-magnesite aggregate may be used with high-alumina cement for lining rotary copper-melting furnaces and a magnesite aggregate has been recommended for monolithic concrete linings in rotary or semi-rotary furnaces melting lead.

(1) *Iron and Steel Industry*[107]

In the blast-furnace, refractory concrete has been extensively used for forming a heat-resistant foundation in the shape of a large " plug " below the hearth. This cylindrical base for the hearth may be over 10 ft. deep and up to 36 ft. in diameter, protecting the underlying structural foundations from the soaking heat[108]. A mortar of fine crushed firebrick and H.A.C., or in some cases the neat cement itself, is used for grouting cooling plates. Arches over cigar-type coolers are cast in place with refractory concrete.

The floor round the blast-furnace at casting level has also been covered with refractory concrete in order to provide a smooth working surface which will not spall or fly in the event of an accidental breakout or spillage of molten metal. The underside of the casting-house floor is frequently protected by refractory or insulating concrete from heat radiated by ladles passing below[109]. This concrete is applied as a gunned layer, or in the form of precast slabs laid in the bottom of the formwork before the structural floor concrete is placed.

Blast-furnace metal runners in refractory concrete have been quite successful. A fairly " lean " mix is used to enhance the refractoriness of the firebrick concrete, and the runners have been constructed with precast shapes or, especially at bends, by casting in place. Castable mixes have also been employed for slag dampers or skimmers, slag troughs and for lining the slag pots[110].

A mix of chrome ore and H.A.C. has been employed as a filling in the hearth jacket but internal conditions in the hearth and bosh are probably too severe for concrete made with ordinary H.A.C., although in 1942 in the U.S.A. an 8 : 1 firebrick mix was used (apparently successfully) to cast the lining of the bosh in two blast-furnaces[111]. However, the advent of the more refractory white H.A.C. (72-80 per cent. Al_2O_3) has opened up new possibilities for castable linings at this level in the furnace[112].

Trouble is often experienced at or above the inwall of a blast-furnace because catalytic decomposition of carbon monoxide leads to the deposition of carbon within the brickwork. The use of white H.A.C. (72-80 per cent. Al_2O_3) in conjunction with an aggregate which is also substantially iron-free (e.g. fired kaolin, sillimanite, etc.) gives a lining resistant to these conditions.

Higher up the blast-furnace, ordinary firebrick concrete is extremely useful for bedding the wearing plates or armouring bars[113] and, in mortar form, a castable mix is used for jointing brickwork in the throat or upper inwall where the temperature is insufficient to produce a good ceramic bond in fireclay cements. A " gunned " lining of refractory concrete is particularly suitable for the top cone.

A greatly increased use of castable mixes is evident for lining pipework associated with the blast-furnace and stoves, e.g. for bustle-pipes, goose-necks to tuyéres, off-takes, bleeders, downcomers, dust-catchers, hot blast mains[114] and valves. In pipes of small diameter the lining is cast or trowelled but in larger pipes the lining is conveniently applied by gun over a light mesh tacked at intervals to the shell. When the dust burden is high and the conditions are highly abrasive, hexagonal metal reinforcement is fixed to studs welded to the shell and the castable is brought to a flush finish[115]. Apart from the above applications, refractory castable mixes have been invaluable in effecting speedy emergency repairs such as patching of hot-blast mains, sealing breakouts at the bath[116], or stopping hot spots in the shell.

Considerable savings have been effected in blast-furnace stoves[117] by replacing the brickwork base and gas-ports with refractory concrete. In one case the use of concrete allowed semi-skilled workers to complete the job in one day in contrast to the eight days required for skilled bricklayers. Refractory concrete has also been effectively used for manhole shapes and linings and for backing the brickwork in the combustion chamber of the stove.

The use of refractory castables in the open-hearth shop has not been so extensive, nevertheless several applications are well established[118] and the use of white H.A.C. (72-80 per cent. Al_2O_3) will doubtless extend the scope for refractory concrete in steel-making[119]. Castable mixes are at present in use for heat-resistant, insulating foundations and slag-pocket bases, for charging floors, for plastering on the shell of the open-hearth furnace before laying the hearth, and for insulation of the regenerators. Precast refractory concrete shapes have been used for the soot-blowers in regenerators, and cast-in-place concrete serves for lining ladle-drier hoods. One of the largest uses for refractory concrete is in the construction of monolithic underground flues such as gas and air-reversing flues, or flues from regenerators to the stacks, etc[120].

White H.A.C. (72-80 per cent. Al_2O_3), in conjunction with fused alumina or kaolin aggregates, is being increasingly used for skew-backs, ports, and complete roof linings in arc-melting furnaces[121] and also for lining rocking-arc furnaces. Castable hot-tops for ingot moulds appear to have been thoroughly investigated but opinions on this application are not always favourable[122].

High-temperature castable mixes incorporating white H.A.C. have been employed for building complete soaking-pits[123], (bottoms, walls, arches and flue-dampers), and accounts have been published of the construction and service behaviour of large pit-covers filled with this type of concrete[124]. Slow-cooling pits may be constructed with castables containing ordinary H.A.C. and all foundations can be conveniently cast with H.A.C. insulating concrete.

Reheating furnaces also show scope for refractory concretes, mixes made with the white cement being used for higher temperature duties such as burner blocks, and mixes containing the ordinary cement for doors, walls, and arches. In many cases a chrome or chrome-magnesite aggregate is employed for concrete hearths or bogie-tops[125]. It has been claimed that precast shapes used to insulate the water-cooled support pipes in under-fired bloom heating furnaces, resulted in 20 per cent. saving in fuel costs, and 10 per cent. increase in output[126].

There are few conditions in annealing or heat-treatment furnaces which are beyond the range of ordinary refractory or insulating concrete. Indeed, periodic annealing furnaces for the malleable iron industry have been built entirely of light-weight insulating concrete[127], and good accounts of the use of castable mixes in many other types of heat-treatment furnaces have been published[128].

Refractory concrete floors or gangways contribute to safety in foundries by providing a smooth hard surface which does not spall in contact with molten metal, and castable mixes are also particularly suitable for the areas beneath cupolas. Conditions in the melting zone of cupolas are too severe for ordinary refractory concrete linings but the latter are used in the upper zone. A patented lining for the top of a cupola[129] consists of sections of metal with castable refractory between the sections. Castable mixes are also used for arches and linings in spark arrestors.

Ordinary refractory concrete has been used to some extent for semi-permanent foundry[130] moulds and mixes containing white H.A.C. (72-80 per cent. Al_2O_3) have been attracting considerable attention in the field of investment or precision casting[131].

Mould and core drying stoves, japanning furnaces and other low-temperature furnaces can be constructed entirely with H.A.C. insulating concretes, and white H.A.C., together with an aggregate which is free from iron, is employed for furnaces with a controlled reducing atmosphere.

(2) Non-Ferrous Metal Industry

Many of the applications in this industry are similar to those in the iron and steel industry, and castable mixes are used for pit-furnaces, reverberatory furnaces, or rotary furnaces for melting copper, bronze, zinc, lead and aluminium[132].

Molten aluminium does not readily " wet " refractory concretes made with many aggregates and white H.A.C./alumina mixes can be employed for processing super-purity aluminium since there is no possibility of adding silica impurity to the metal[133]. Reverberatory bale-out furnaces for aluminium have given extremely satisfactory service, with low heat loss, when constructed with refractory and insulating concretes, and castable linings are used for ladles, launders and spiders[134]. Large furnaces for baking carbon electrodes used in electrolysis have been erected in firebrick/H.A.C. or traprock/H.A.C. concrete and the same material is used for discharge-ports, burner hood linings and kiln lining repairs in rotary kilns calcining alumina.

White H.A.C. (72-80 per cent. Al_2O_3) is sometimes required in castables for furnaces meling copper[135], bronze, etc. and magnesia/ chromite aggregate has been recommended. Dead-burned magnesite castable mixes are also in use as covers for arc-furnaces melting magnesium alloys. The same aggregate is incorporated in castables for lining lead melting furnaces but lead oxide is very reactive with refractories including most refractory concretes.

Roasters (of the multi-hearth or fluidised-bed types) can be lined or constructed with firebrick/H.A.C. mixes when used for treating copper concentrates, zinc sulphides or zinc plant residues[136]. This application is widely duplicated in the sulphuric acid industry where multi-hearth pyrites roasters have been constructed entirely in refractory concrete[137]. The precision in casting allows the minimum gap to be left between rabble teeth and the bed, thus preventing the formation of pyrites agglomerations. It has been found that these kilns can be quickly shut down and restarted without deforming the concrete hearths and the material is resistant to the action of sulphur dioxide or dilute sulphuric acid in flues, gas offtakes etc.

(3) Oil Refining Industry

Castable monolithic linings insulate and protect the shells of the vessels and allow the latter to be made of carbon steel in place of the more expensive alloy steels. Refractory and insulating concrete linings are therefore used for reactors, regenerators and cyclones, catalyst transfer lines, and for gas coolers[138]. The cost of lining refinery vessels with a castable refractory mix is said to be 50-60 per cent. less than the cost by any other method[139]. Ancillary plant in the refinery, such as stacks and chimneys, flues, ducts, and breechings, explosion doors, vacuum and barometric condensers, continuous-still evaporator towers, pipe-still bubble towers, flash columns, sour water strippers and cooler boxes, are also protected by castable linings. Oil-still furnaces are often built on ventilated refractory concrete hearths topped with insulating concrete, and the latter material is also used for the panel-type steel encased walls and roof of the heaters[140]. A castable mix assists in preventing corrosion round the U-bend headers in the heaters[141].

Reactors may contain a high concentration of carbon monoxide, carbon dioxide, hydrogen, methane and water vapour. Carbon is deposited within the reactor lining but since it is not normally produced in the refractory by catalytic decomposition of carbon monoxide there has not been much evidence of disruptive action. However, recent work suggests that, at least for some types of reactor (e.g. gas-oil hydroformers), a substantially iron-free concrete lining should be used[142]. This consists of white H.A.C. (72-80 per cent. Al_2O_3) and a low-iron aggregate such as fired kaolin. Pre-heaters, converters, reactors, and transfer lines in the petrochemical industry are similarly lined with castable mixes.

Refractory and insulating concrete linings are usually applied in this industry by means of a cement gun[143]. In many cases metal reinforcement is fixed level with the interior surface of the lining to improve its resistance to the abrasion and erosion[144] caused by the moving catalyst. A common method of lining a vessel is to weld studs (4 in. long and $\frac{3}{8}$ in. diameter) to the shell at 9 in.-12 in. centres. The first 3 in. depth of gunited lining may consist of a light-weight insulating castable[145]. Metal mesh of various types is then fixed to the ends of the studs and the final layer of denser refractory castable mix is gunned through the mesh until the metal and concrete surfaces are flush. If one-coat linings are employed, the aggregate frequently consists of expanded clay, a mixture of expanded clay and vermiculite, or crushed insulating firebrick.

(4) *Gas and Coke Industry*[146]

Application in coke-ovens include heat-resistant foundations and stack linings, oven doors (precast shapes or cast monolithically), coke-hopper linings, ascension-pipe and gas off-take linings, top-paving on the battery, and for floors resistant to hot coke[147]. Refractory concrete has successfully replaced heavy cast-iron tops on vertical retorts and has found many applications in gas producers.

White H.A.C. castables have been used for the base and domes of reactors in oil or coal gasification plants[148], and a porous insulating concrete made by foaming fused alumina and white H.A.C. is a suitable refractory for special high-duty tunnel burners[149].

(5) *Boiler Industry and Combustion Chambers*[150]

One of the major uses of castable refractories in steam-generating plants is for tube baffles. The castable form of construction solves many problems here which are difficult or costly to overcome by the use of refractory clay tile. Refractory and insulating concretes are also used in water-tube boilers for front and rear walls, insulating behind the tubes and as a backing to the tangent base tubes[151]. Stoker arches and particularly ignition arches may require the use of white H.A.C. (72-80 per cent. Al_2O_3) together with an aggregate of high refractoriness, and divisional walls between grates can be quickly cast or repaired. Large ash-hoppers below coal-fitted water-tube boilers are now largely constructed with firebrick/H.A.C. concrete[152]. A chromite/H.A.C. castable is used for Bailey or stud walls, and for stoker surrounds.

In shell-type boilers, foundation slabs are insulated with refractory or insulating concretes and other applications include stoker and ignition arches, guillotine doors, rear walls, downtake walls, flat rear roofs and flue baffles[153].

Precast refractory concrete units comprise the rear combustion chamber of several packaged boilers[154] and castables made with white H.A.C. are employed in marine boilers[155], chiefly for burner quarls. The same cement is necessary in concrete linings for high-heat-release combustion chambers[156] used, for example, in the concentration of sulphuric acid by submerged direct heating, and the life of combustion arches in coal-fired locomotives has been greatly prolonged when cast with mixes containing ordinary or white H.A.C.[157]

Small combustion chambers for domestic oil-furnaces, linings for solid-fuel stoves, and firebacks for open coal-firegrates are all readily cast in refractory concrete[158].

(6) Ceramic and Brick Industries[159]

The use of refractory concrete in Europe for brick-kiln construction has been well described by Sauzier[160]. In this industry it is often possible for the brick manufacturer to use his own product as source of concrete aggregate, although a good-quality crushed firebrick will be necessary in parts of kilns exposed to the higher temperatures. Most types of kilns[161], including tunnel kilns, have now been built completely in refractory concrete and these structures show excellent stability. A design has also been produced for a continuous Hoffmann-type kiln with pre-fabricated moveable walls and roof cast in refractory concrete[162].

Wicket-arches and wicket sealing blocks[163] are often a convenient starting point in the use of refractory castables, and feed-holes, hot air off-takes etc. can be quickly cast on site. The flat base on which the clamp-firing of bricks takes place is another useful application for refractory concrete.

Although refractory concrete absorbs large quantities of fluxes without much visible effect, its behaviour in salt-glaze kilns has not been entirely satisfactory, and it does not appear to have any advantage in durability for this application.

Refractory castables are widely used for tunnel kiln car-tops which may be cast in situ or made up with pre-cast slabs[164]. Insulating concrete is usually placed first in the bottom of the car in order to reduce weight and heat loss.

(7) *Glass Industry*

Most refractory castables are not very suitable for use in contact with molten glass although a monolithic castable lining for a glass-melting furnace has been patented[165], and a sodium silicate furnace has also been constructed in refractory concrete. This had an inner lining of white H.A.C./fused alumina, backed by firebrick/H.A.C concrete. Laboratory tests on white H.A.C./fused alumina and silli-manite castables have shown that their resistance to corrosion by soda-ash is relatively high.

Most of the applications in this industry are in parts out of contact with the molten glass, e.g. for hearths in pot furnaces, rafts under regenerators, heat-resistant floors, burner blocks, flue linings, furnace doors, and as insulation in annealing or cooling tunnels for plate glass. Refractory concrete tiles are also used for conveying glass-ware through the lehrs.

(8) *Applications in newer Industries*

The trend towards higher operating temperatures in atomic reactors has developed interest in the possible use of refractory concrete for the interior of the reactor pressure-vessel[166]. Light-weight insulating H.A.C. concretes also present advantages in this situation. H.A.C. retains a somewhat higher amount of combined water than does Portland cement at moderately elevated temperatures, and con-cretes made with H.A.C. and a heavy aggregate have therefore been used for shielding-plugs etc.

The testing of gas-turbine engines at manufacturing plants situated in populated areas presents a noise problem, and sound-absorbing mufflers or silencing cells must be provided for the exit gases. Many large refractory concrete or insulating concrete structures have been built to serve this purpose[167]. In one type the gases first pass through a refractory concrete venturi pipe, thus becoming diluted with cold air drawn in from the exterior. They then pass through a labyrinth of refractory concrete blocks before escaping to the atmosphere.

Refractory concrete has also been used for parking-bays where air-craft jet engines are " run-up " and it may be bonded to a Portland cement concrete base placed at the same time[168]. Refractory concrete pads were also used for the test area in trials of vertical-take-off aircraft.

Reference has been made to the use of H.A.C. for bonding ceramic bodies in the combustion chambers of uncooled non-regenerative rocket engines[169]. A mix consisting of fused silica and H.A.C. has also been patented as a castable material for forming rocket nozzles and turbine blades. It is claimed that the product has low thermal expansion, low conductivity and that it has an extremely high thermal shock resistance[170]. However, one of the most successful uses for refractory concrete is the casting of rocket-exhaust deflector pads. The issuing gases from a rocket motor are at an extremely high temperature, move with supersonic speed, and disintegrate or fuse most of the materials tested as deflectors. Firebrick/H.A.C. or white H.A.C./fused alumina concretes have given excellent service in this duty and are therefore particularly useful for test-sites or launching areas which do not have the abundant water supply required for the alternative water-cooled metal deflector systems. An interesting account of experimental tests in England on various refractory concrete deflection surfaces has been given by Landon and Thackray[171].

The extensive use of refractory castables for laboratory or pilot-scale development work is no doubt due to the facility with which any desired refractory shape can be cast in moulds constructed by the user in wood, plaster, concrete, etc. Necessary changes in design can therefore be quickly tried and evaluated. Furnaces heated by oil, gas, or electricity[172] are readily constructed or repaired and many manufacturers have standardised the use of refractory or insulating castables in commercial models.

The survey of applications in this last section of Chapter VIII is necessarily very incomplete. In particular there has been little mention of the use of refractory concretes within the chemical industry as a whole, but in this case and in others also omitted, the possible applications can probably be deduced from those examples which have been briefly described.

LITERATURE REFERENCES

[1] Suppl. Ann. Inst. Tech. Bâtim. 1961 (Feb.), No. 158. "Comportement du Beton entre 80° et 300°C."

[2] R. GRÜN & H. BECKMANN. Cem. & Cem. Mfr. 1930, 3, (3), 430. G. FRANKE & F. KANTHAK. Silikattech. 1959, 10, (9), 445. V. A. AL'TSHULER, G. D. SALMANOV, A. D. SOKOLSKII & P. P. KARASEV. Ogneupory 1957, 22, (9), 425. K. D. NEKRASOV. Communication 46/7, Lab. for Structural Materials, Publ. No. 3. Stroizdat Narkomistroya. 46 pp. Issle. po Zharoupornym Betonu i Zhelezobetonu, 1954, 315. LUDERA. Zement-Kalk Gips, 1959, (12). G. N. DUDEROV. Byull Stroit. Tekh. 1946, 3, (23-24), 20.

[3] A. F. LIVOVICH. Bull. Amer. ceram Soc. 1961, 40, (9), 559.

[4] F. ZAPP & F. DRAMONT. Ber. dtsch Keram. Ges. 1955, 32, 97. M. LEPINGLE. Verre. & Silic. industr. 1937, 8, (34-36), 403, 416, 425.

[5] H. L. MALHOTRA. Mag. Concr. Res. 1956, 8, (23), 85. H. LEHMANN & G. MALZIG. Tonindustr. Ztg., 1960, 84, (17), 414. N. G. ZOLDNERS, Canad. Dept. Mines & Tech. Surveys Res. Reports R64. Ottawa 1960. G. C. MUDROV & A. V. MIKHAILOV. Betonu i Zhelezebetonu 1959, (7), 318. A. CLAUDON. Industries Thermiques 1957, (11), 666. S. KIMURA. Rev. 13th Ann. Gen. Meeting, Jap. Cem. Engng. Assn. 1959, 65. J. C. SALMANN & G. W. WASHA. J. AMER. concr. Inst. 1957, 29 (5), 385.

[6] P. J. F. KESTNER. Brit. Pat. 231141 (1925). In France 1924.

[7] A. CSER. Epitoanyag. 1957, 9, (6), 293.

[8] THERMAL SYNDICATE LTD. & A. E. J. VICKERS, J. B. MALONEY. U.S. Pat. 2818345 (1957).

[9] A. A. PIROGOV. Ogneupory. 1958, 23, (10), 445.

[10] W. D. KINGERY. J. Amer. ceram. Soc. 1950, 33, 239. W. H. GITZEN, L. D. HART & G. MacZURA. Bull. Amer. ceram. Soc. 1956, 35, (6), 217. ANON. Industr. Heat, 1960, 27, 1694. HARBISON-WALKER REFRACTORIES Co. & K. W. HANSEN, D. F. KING. U.S. Patent 2852401 (1958). C. H. WATTS, U.S. Pat. 2928749 (1960). U.S. Pat. 2928750 (1960). W. F. ZIMMERMAN. Bull. Amer. ceram. Soc. 1959, 38, (3), 97.

[11] BASIC. INC. & E. P. PEARSON, S. RUSOFF. Brit. Pat. 850655 (1960). METROPOLITAN-VICKERS. Brit. Pat. 812352 (1959).

[12] G. J. GROTT, A.J.M.E. Electric Furnace Steel Proc. 1959, 17, 391. Industr. Heat. 1960, 27, 834.

[13] H. D. SHEETS, J. J. BULLOFF & W. H. DUCKWORTH. Brick. Clay Rec. 1958, 133, 55. Refract. J. 1958, 34, 402.

[14] ANON. Chemical Industries 1936, 39, (2), 145. A. E. WILLIAMS. Cheap Steam 1950, 34, 129. E. A. K. PATRICK. Gas. J. 1950, 261, 711, 717.

[15] ANON. Steel Processing 1947, 33, 121. See also D. F. B. TEDDS. J. Inst. Brit. Foundrym. 1959, 52, (1), 10.

[16] A. AURIOL, G. MAUSER & J. G. WURN. Battelle Mem. Inst. (Int. Dev.) Report 1961.

[17] H. SAINTE-CLAIRE DEVILLE. Ann. Phys. Chim. 1856, 46, (3), 196.

[18] B. ADOUZE. Silicates Industr. 1961, 26, 179. Thesis, Clermont-Ferrand 1958. W. L. DE KEYSER. Bull. Soc. Chim. Belge, 1951, 60, 516. D. P. MCHEDLOV-PETROSYAN & V. V. I. BABUSHKIN. Silikattech. 1958, 9, (5), 209.

19 H. N. Clark & Refractory & Insulation Corp. U.S. Pat. 2407135 (1946). R. P. Heuer. Brit. Pat. 765482 (1957). S. Kondo, T. Yamauchi & Y. Inamura. J. Jap. ceram. Ass., 1937, **45**, (532), 227 : (533), 313 : (534), 373.

20 G. R. Pole & D. G. Moore. J. Amer. ceram. Soc. 1946, **29**, 20.

21 W. H. Gitzen, L. D. Hart & G. MacZura. J. Amer. ceram. Soc. 1957, **40**, 158.

22 C. L. Norton, Jr., V. J. Duplin & Babcock & Wilcox Co. U.S. Pat. 2527500 (1950). Anon. Iron Age 1947, **159**, 45. Babcock & Wilcox Co. Brit. Pat. 669044 (1952). In U.S.A. 1947. Morgan Crucible Ltd. & Babcock & Wilcox Co. Brit. Pat. 667969 (1952). T. W. Ratcliffe & Babcock & Wilcox Co. U.S. Pat. 2558782 (1951).

23 Anon. Cement & Lime Manuf. 1958, **31**, (2), 29.

24 J. Arnould. Chim. et Industr. 1953, **70**, (6), 1081. L. Longchambon. Rev. univ. Mines. 1957, **13**, (10), 619. E. Eipeltauer & G. Bayer. Berg-u-Hüttenm. Monat. 1956, 129. E. Eipeltauer. Idem. 1958, **103**, 29. T. D. Robson. Refract. J. 1954, (5), 203. Gitzen, Hart & MacZura. Ref. No. 21.

25 E. Martin. Mon. Sci., 1915, **5**, 225. H. Gunther. Feuerungstechnik 1930, **18**, 138. G. Grube & G. Heintz. Z. Elektrochem. 1935, **41**, 797. N. A. Toropov. C. R. Acad. Sci., U.R.S.S. 1935, **1**, (2/3), 147, 150. G. Purt. Radex Rdsch., 1960, (4), 498.

26 F. Massazza. Chim. e industr. (Milan), 1959, **41**, (2), 108.

27 V. F. Zhuravlev. Tsement 1939, (8), 41. H. V. Wartenburg & H. J. Reusch. Z. anorg. Chem. 1932, **207**, 1. N. A. Toropov & F. Y. Galakhov. Dokl. Akad. Nauk U.R.S.S. 1952, **82**, 69.

28 A. Braniski. Zement-Kalk-Gips, 1957, **5**, 176.

29 A. Braniski. Rev. Matér. Constr. C., 1949, (404), 154. A. Braniski &. T. Ionescu. Zement-Kalk-Gips., 1960, **13**, (3), 109.

30 Kerr Dental Manuf. Co. & O. T. Zimmerman. U.S. Pat. 2445052 (1948). Brit. Pat. 578702. E. T. Carlson. J. Res. nat. Bur. Stand, 1955, 54, 329.

31 Wartenburg & Reusch Ref. No. 27. Toropov Ref. No. 25. Purt Ref. No. 25. G. H. Mohanty. Thesis, Univ. of Missouri, 1954.

32 Ciments Lafarge. French Pat. 1125983 (1956). R. R. Matveev. Russ. Pat. 55383. F. J. Williams. U.S. Pat. 2375715 (Applicn. 1941). P. S. Roller. U.S. Pat. 2469413 (Applicn. 1946).

33 A. Braniski. Rev. Roum. Metall (Bucharest) 1960, **5**, (1), 165 : Tonindustr. Ztg. 1961, **85**, (6), 125, 129. Int. Symp. on Chemistry of Cement, Washington 1960.

34 A. Braniski. Studii Cerc. Metal (Bucharest) 1959, **3**, (4), 413.

35 Anon. Brick Clay Rec. 1960, **137**, (6), 58.

36 V. M. Goldschmidt. Brit. Pat. 597845 (1945).

37 I. W. Gower & W. C. Bell. Bull. Amer. ceram. Soc. 1956, **35**, (7), 259.

38 J. Singleton-Green. Contract. Rec. 1945, **56**, (3), 115. Meyer. Zement. 1935, **24**, (10), 148.

39 A. V. Hussey. Struct. Eng. 1945, **23**, (1), 1.

40 T. D. McGee & C. M. Dodd. Industr. Heat. 1960, 1265. J. Amer. ceram. Soc., 1961, **44**, (6), 277.

[41] V. A. Bron & A. A. Bichurina. Ogneupory (Fireproof Mater.) Moscow 1959, **24**, 216.

[42] K. N. Repenko. Ogneupory, 1952, **17,** 27. A. Chadeyron & W. J. Rees. Bull. Brit. Refract. Assn., 1937, (42), 24.

[43] Eipeltauer & Bayer. Ref. No. 24.

[44] C. D. Patents Ltd. & A. Hilliard. Brit. Pats. 646524 ; 646534 (1950).

[45] J. Robinson. Brit. Pat. 492718 (1937).

[46] F. T. Moyer. U.S. Dept. Interior, Bur. Mines Info. Circ. 7195, 1942.

[47] E. H. Coleman. Concr. constr. Engng. 1936, **31**, (1), 47. Brit. Pat. 401685. J. E. Conley. Amer. Inst. Mining & Metal Engrs. Tech. Publ. 1512. Mining Tech. 1942, **6**, (5).

[48] P. E. Cox. Ceram. Age. 1947, **49,** 109. W. C. Smith. J. Canad. ceram. Soc. 1948, **17,** 69.

[49] General Refractories Ltd. & W. E. Hemmings. Brit. Pat. 496861 (1938). H. Shaw. Ceram. Digest, 1948, **1**, 82.

[50] Anon. Chem. & Industr. 1948, **(13)**, 200. Mining Mag. 1946, 269. R. B. Sen. Indian Concrete J., 1953, **27**, (8), 308. N. C. Jones. Chem. & Industr. 1946, 195. G. R. Gwinn. U.S. Bur. Mines, Mineral Mkt. Rept. No. 1184, 1944. T. Wathey. Ceramics, 1954, **6**, 65.

[51] J. J. Brouk. J. Amer. concr. Inst., 1954, **25**, 857 ; 1949, **21**, (3), 185. R. D. Hill. Construct. Rev. 1953, 25, (3), 33. A. L. Renkey & Harbison-Walker Refractories Co. U.S. Pat. 2963377 (1960).

[52] British Zonolite Products Ltd. Brit. Pat. 485508 (1937).

[53] Norton Co. & H. F. G. Ueltz. U.S. Pat. 2965506 (1960).

[54] H. Shaw. Refract. J. 1945, **21**, 243.

[55] R. C. Valore, Jr. J. Amer. concr. Inst. 1954, 25, 773. A. Moser. Tonindustr. Ztg., 1939, 762, 775, 789.

[56] J. F. Wygant & W. L. Bulkley. Bull. Amer. ceram. Soc. 1954, **33**, 233.

[57] R. A. Heindl & Z. A. Post. J. Amer. ceram. Soc., 1950, **33**, (7), 230.

[58] " Refractory Concrete " Lafarge Aluminous Cement Co. Ltd., London, England.

[59] G. R. Eusner & D. H. Hubble. Bull. Amer. ceram. Soc., 1960, **39**, (8), 395. G. R. Eusner & J. T. Shapland. J. Amer. ceram. Soc. 1959, **42**, (10), 459.

[60] R. R. West & W. J. Sutton. Bull. Amer. ceram. Soc. 1951, **30**, (2), 35. Zapp & Dramont. Ref. No. 4.

[61] Armstrong Cork Co. N. A. Johnson & P. H. Stern. U.S. Pat. 2419684 (1947).

[62] Master Builders Co. & E. W. Scripture. U.S. Pat. 2099176.

[63] G. M. Bruere. Austral. J. Appl. Sci., 1960, **11**, (1), 205.

[64] Ann. Report. Refractories Institute, Pittsburgh, Pa., 1960.

[65] A. F. Ruedi. U.S. Pat. 2469081 (1949).

[66] R. Nacken. Zement 1936, **25**, (34), 565 ; 1937, 26, (44), 701.

[67] S. J. Schneider. J. Amer. ceram. Soc., 1959, **42**, (4), 184. R. A. Heindl & Z. A. Post. Idem., 1954, **37**, (5), 206. H. Lehmann & H. Mitusch. " Feuerfester Beton aus Tonerde-Schmelzzement." H. Hübener Verlag, Goslar, Germany, 1959. J. Ando, G. Hiraoka & S. Matsuno. Yogyo Kyokai Shi. 1958, **66**, (755), 253.

[68] Nat. Bur. Stand. Tech. News Bull. 1950, **34,** (8), 119. HEINDL & POST. Ref. Nos. 57, 67. EUSNER & HUBBLE. Ref. No. 59. H. LAFUMA. Ann. Inst. Tech. Bâtim, 1939, **4,** (4), 1. M. LEPINGLE. Industr. chim belge. 1937, **8,** (3), 79. G. V. KUKOLEV & A. I. ROISEN. Ogneupory. 1949, **14,** (2), 65. F. ARREDONDO. Inf. de la Construc. (Madrid). 1954, **7,** (64), 684. GITZEN, HART & MACZURA. Ref. No. 21. WYGANT & BULKLEY, Ref. No. 56.

[69] R. T. GILES. Bull. Amer. ceram. Soc. 1939, **18,** (9), 326.

[70] W. C. HANSEN & A. F. LIVOVICH. Bull. Amer. ceram. Soc. 1955, **34,** (9), 298.

[71] W. S. RAMSAY. U.S. Pat. 2562477 (1951).

[72] UNIVERSAL ATLAS CEMENT CO. & F. E. LOBAUGH. U.S. Pat. 2516892 (1950).

[73] K. FEARNLEY. Refract. J., 1944, **20,** 205.

[74] UNIVERSAL ATLAS CEMENT CO. & D. W. KOCHER. U.S. Pat. 2416700 (1947). F. E. LOBAUGH. Blast. Furn., 1947, 35, 868.

[75] F. E. LOBAUGH. J. Amer. ceram. Soc., 1947, **30,** 349.

[76] R. T. GILES. U.S. Pat. 2537218 (1951).

[77] ALUMINUM CO. OF AMERICA & R. W. RICKER. U.S. Pat. 2912341 (1959).

[78] PITTSBURGH PLATE GLASS CO. & D. E. EMHISER. U.S. Pat. 2793128 (1957).

[79] CHAMPION SPARK PLUG CO. U.S. Pat. 2531397.

[80] " Les Betons Réfractaires à base de SECAR 250." SOC. ANON. S.E.C.A.R. Paris.

[81] S. J. SCHNEIDER & L. E. MONG. J. res. nat. Bur Stand, 1957, **59,** (1), 1. R.P. 2768. G. R. RIGBY & A. T. GREEN. Trans. Brit. ceram. Soc., 1943, **42,** (5), 95. M. S. CROWLEY. Bull. Amer. ceram. Soc. 1956, **35,** 465.

[82] E. GRIFFITHS, R. W. POWELL & M. J. HICKMAN. J. Inst. Fuel, 1942, **15,** 107. " Heat Transmission through Furnace Walls." Universal Atlas Cement Co. SHAW, Ref. No. 54. E. C. PETRIE. Industr. Heat. 1953, **20,** (10), 2049.

[83] W. C. HANSEN & A. F. LIVOVICH. J. Amer. ceram. Soc. 1953, **36,** (11), 356. Bull. Amer. ceram. Soc., 1958, **37,** (7), 322.

[84] J. F. WYGANT & M. S. CROWLEY. J. Amer. ceram. Soc., 1958, 41, (5), 183.

[85] GILES, Ref. No. 69. CLAUDON, Ref. No. 5. WYGANT & BULKLEY, Ref. No. 56. A. V. HUSSEY, Chem. & Industr., 1937, **56,** (3), 53. Indian Concr. J., 1938, 257. H. G. PROTZE. J. Amer. concr. Inst., 1957, **28,** (9), 871.

[86] E. HAMMOND. Engineer, London, 1959, **207,** (5393), 878.

[87] L. LONGCHAMBON. 18th Congr. Industr. Chem. Nancy, 1938.

[88] C. R. VENABLE J. Bull. Amer. ceram. Soc., 1959, **38,** (7), 363.

[89] ANON. Oil Gas J., 1957, 61 (December). SMITH, Ref. No. 48.

[90] P. M. SAUZIER. Beton 1951 (1), 283.

[91] T. D. ROBSON. Mod. Pwr. Engng. (Canada). 1954, 134.

[92] LAFARGE ALUMINOUS CEMENT CO. LTD., London, England. Unpublished work.

[93] W. H. GITZEN & L. D. HART. Bull. Amer. ceram. Soc., 1961, **40**, (8), 503.

[94] HARBISON-WALKER REFRACTORIES CO., D. F. KING & A. L. RENKEY. U.S. Pat. 2845360 (1958), Canad. Pat. 578399 (1959).

[95] ANON. Industr. Heat., 1947, 14, 116. R. T. GILES. Idem. 1936. " Refractory Concrete Manual " Universal Atlas Cement Co. (Universal Atlas Cement Division, U.S. Steel Corp.).

[96] ANON. Industr. Heat. 1947, 14, 464, 820 (Universal Atlas).

[97] Acknowledgements to HARBISON-WALKER REFRACTORIES CO., U.S.A. MORGAN REFRACTORIES LTD., England. PLIBRICO LTD., England.

[98] CIMENTS LAFARGE, Paris.

[99] LACLEDE-CHRISTY CO. Brit. Pat. 796538 (1958). G. D. COBAUGH. Industr. Heat., 1959, **26**, 791.

[100] ANON. Industr. Heat, 1961, 28, 155. (Harbison-Walker Refractories Co.).

[101] N. M. THOMPSON. Industr. Heat., 1959, **26**, 362.

[102] C. R. PLATZMANN. Zement 1941, **30**, (18), 239. S. B. MACDONALD. J. Canad. ceram. Soc., 1938, 7, 15 ; 1948, **17**, 72. Industr. Heat, 1948, 15, 1210. R. T. GILES. Metals & Alloys 1934, **5**, (2), 28. G. T. HADDOCK. Idem. 1945, **21**, 395, 714. M. CROZEL. Flamme et Therm., 1948, (9), 3. Rev. Matér. Constr., 1950, (413), 46. K. D. NEKRASOV & G. D. SALMANOV. Ogneupory 1960, **25**, 219. A. NIERENSKI. Przeglad Tech., 1950, 374. A. E. WILLIAMS, Metal Industr., 1958, 3. E. EIPELTAUER. Neue Hütte, 1958, 5, 303. A. HIRT., Verr et Silic. Industr., 1949, **1**, 13. N. J. KENT. Heat Treat. Forg., 1935, **21**, 343. W. D. KINGERY. " Ceramic Fabricaton Process " Chap. 18. E. KUNTZSCH & G. RABE. Silikattech., 1959, **10**, 448. ANON. Industr. Heat., 1947, **14**, 1892. L. LONG-CHAMBON. Mem. Soc. Ing. civ. Fr., 1955, **2**, 135.

[103] O. L. BRAUN. U.S. Pat. 2705477 (1955).

[104] ANON. Iron & Steel, 1956, March.

[105] N. J. LEVIN & I. G. HANOVICH. Tsement, 1930, **6**, 10. N. I. VORONIN, Ogneupory, 1937, **5**, 790, 863.

[106] G. POLYSIUS. Brit. Pat. 276185 (1926). French Pat. 618089 (1926). J. H. JENNINGS. Brit. Pat. 588367 (1944). DIAMOND ALKALI CO. Brit. Pat. 668690 (1950).

[107] General or miscellaneous references. R. E. WOLSTENSPERGER. Iron Steel Engr., 1952, **29**, (5), 84. W. N. HORKO. Idem, 1952, 29, 83. C.O. RABINOVICH. Ogneupory 1960, **25**, 221. C. WOLSTENCROFT. Heat. Treat. Forg. 1936 (May). J. G. COLVIN, Iron Coal Tr. Rev., 1957. **175**, 1309. G. D. COBAUGH & C. R. HAUTH. Ref. No. 99. HARBISON-WALKER REFRACTORIES CO., U.S. Pat. 2961978 (1960). UNION CARBIDE & CHEMICAL CORP., U.S. Pat. 2776203 (1957). BIRMINGHAM ELECTRIC FURNACES LTD., Brit. Pat. 525513.

[108] " Technical Survey of Steel Co. of Wales." Iron Coal Tr. Rev., 232. E. W. VOICE, Iron Coal Tr. Rev., 1952, 1265 (June). Iron Steel Engr., 1952, **29**, (7), 125. E. J. WILLIAMS & E. J. BURTON. J. Iron Steel Inst., 1955, **179**, 17.

[109] Iron Coal Tr. Rev., 1954, 24.

[110] PETRIE. Ref. No. 82.

[111] G. T. HADDOCK. Metals & Alloys, 1945, **21**, 714.

[112] ANON. Iron Coal Tr. Rev., 1961, **182,** 187. P. COHEUR. M. FOUASSIN & E. FREMAY. Rev. univ. Mines, 1953, **9,** 482. ANON. Industr. Heat., 1960, 2641.

[113] H. G. W. DEBENHAM & W. H. TUBBS. Iron & Steel, Lond., 1953, **26** (12), 507. ANON. Claycraft, 1960, 68, 361. H. M. KRANER. Proc. Amer. Inst. Min. Engr., Blast Furn. Comm., 157, **16,** 4.

[114] R. N. AMES & Z. J. SCHIENE. Blast Furn., St. Plant., 1960, **48,** 357. J. E. DEEGAN. Iron Steel Engr., 1952, **29,** (5), 79.

[115] A. BRIDGE. J. Iron Steel Inst., 1961, **199,** (1), 52.

[116] J. W. THOMPSON. Iron Coal Tr. Rev., 1945, **150,** 467.

[117] FREYN ENGINEERING CO. & A. F. BURGESS. Brit. Pat. 512131 (1939).

[118] ANON. Blast. Furn. St. Plant, 1948, **36,** 94. H. M. KRANER, A.M.I.E., Open Hrth. Proc., 1958, **41,** 293. J. D. SLOANE, Idem, 291. R. R. FAYLES. Idem, 1953, **36,** 265. H. D. WATTERS. U.S. Pat. 2796652 (1957).

[119] S. O. SMITH. Industr. Heat., 1960, **27,** 1960. A.I.M.E. Electric Fce. Steel Proc., 1959, **17,** 396.

[120] W. F. CONLIN. Steel, 1947, **120,** (3), 94. J. C. WITHERSPOON, A.I.M.E. Open Hrth Proc., 1952, **35,** 90. R. E. WRIGHT. Idem., 1952, **35,** 92. ANON., Iron & Steel, 1951, 68. ANON. Concr. constr. Engng., 1956, 353.

[121] J. D. McCULLOUGH. Industr. Heat., 1958, **25,** (9), 1825 ; (11), 2325. A.I.M.E. Elect. Fce. Steel Proc., 1959, **17,** 73. S. A. ZHIKHAREVICH et al. Ogneupory, 1959, **24,** 309.

[122] OGLEBAY NORTON CO. Brit. Pat. 866703 (1961). U.S. Pat. 2833008 (1958). R. J. TATOUSEK & A. T. PETERS. A.I.M.E. Open Hrth. Proc., 1957, **40,** 158. R. L. BUNTING. Idem, 1958, 41, 338. U.S. STEEL CORP. & R. W. CARTER. U.S. Pat. 2843898 (1958). H. W. CLARK. J. Metals. 1957, 584.

[123] W. D. REES. Iron Steel Engr. 1954, **31,** 3. W. S. DEBENHAM. Blast. Furn. St. Plant, 1960, **48,** 169. H. C. HUSBAND & K. H. BEST. Struct. Engr., 1953, 301. U.S. Steel Corp. E. D. LARSON & H. H. NICHOLS. U.S. Pat. 2801099 (1957).

[124] W. B. SMITH. Steel, 1952, **131,** (3), 100. J. D. McCULLOUGH. Iron Steel Engr., 1953, **30,** 84. R. R. FAYLES. Idem., 1952, **29,** 79.

[125] VORONIN. Ref. No. 105. J. BERNSTEIN. Found. Tr. J., 1954, 169.

[126] J. E. HOVIS. Iron Steel Engr., 1951, 28, (11), 69.

[127] R. A. WITSCHEY. Brick Clay Rec., 1949, **77,** 62. Canad. Metals 1950, **13,** 26.

[128] E. HAMMOND. Indian Rly. Engr., 1957, **4,** (3), 16.

[129] L. A. GIONET. U.S. Pat. 2713481 (1955).

[130] E. HAMMOND. Foundry Tr. J., 1959, **107,** 169, 203. J. D. CUSTER & J. S. McDOWELL. Trans. Amer. Found Ass., 1952, 681.

[131] E. HAMMOND. Ref. No. 86.

[132] D. TURNER, W. B. LAWRIE, A. EYDEN & A. EDWARDS. Metal Industr., 1956, 413. G. A. HODGES. Foundry Tr. J., 1959, **107,** 453. S. GAMBLE. Industr. Heat. 1959, **26,** 1607. W. H. STEWART. Idem. 1959, **26,** 1959. E. AYRES & W. B. LAWRIE. Foundry Tr. J., 1960, **109,** 195.

133 E. EIPELTAUER. Ref. No. 102. D. F. STOCK & J. L. DOLPH. Bull. Amer. ceram. Soc., 1959, **38,** (7), 356. R. ITSCHNER. Swiss Pat. 319161 (1957). J. BOLFA & R. KERAN. Bull. Doc. Tr. Minéral. Cristall., 1960, **83,** 242.

134 W. H. HORSMAN. Metal. Industr., 1956, (15), 290.

135 E. EIPELTAUER. Ref. No. 102.

136 ANON. Chem. & Process. Engng., 1957, 307. A. R. GORDON, R. W. PICKERING & O. G. WOODWARD. Brit. Chem. Engng., 1961, **6,** (4), 261. See also A. W. NORDIN. Idem 1961, **6,** 260.

137 J. HOUDIN. Génie chim., 1955, **73,** 8. V. I. MURASHEV & D. E. UCHITEL. Centr. Sci. Res. Inst. of Industrial Structures, Moscow, 1954 (State Press for Literature on Building & Architecture).

138 WYGANT & BULKLEY, Ref. No. 56. ANON. Oil Gas J., 1957, 61. ANON. Found Tr. J., 1957, 83.

139 W. B. PAUL, Jr. Bull. Amer. ceram. Soc., 1954, **33,** 108. W. B. PAUL, JR. & D. L. GARRISON. Radex Rdsch., 1956, (2), 67. " Lumnite in the Oil Refinery." Universal Atlas Cement Divn.

140 P. VON WIESENTHAL. Oil Gas J., 1958, **56,** (48), 103.

141 F. GARNER &. A. R. HALE. Petroleum 1954, 17, (11), 407 ; (12), 440 ; **18,** (1), 12. E. J. M. TAIT. Corr. Prevent. Control. 1955, 25, 44.

142 C. M. VOGRIN & H. HEAP. Trans. Amer. Soc. Mech. Engrs., 1956, **78,** 1021. Petroleum Process. 1956, 72.

143 T. D. ROBSON. World Petrol., 1952, Ann. Refinery Issue, 128. R. A. WITSCHEY. Mod. Pwr. Engng. 1953, **47,** (11), 118.

144 C. R. VENABLE, JR. Ref. No. 88.

145 M. W. KELLOGG CO. & V. P. JOHNSON. U.S. Pat., 2982623 (1961).

146 T. D. ROBSON. Coke & Gas, 1952, **14,** (158), 241.

147 J. E. LUDBERG. Steel, 1945, **117,** 137. Blast. Furn. St. Plant 1945, **33,** 830. Brick Clay Rec., 1945, **107,** (3), 57. ANON. Gas World, 1939, 11. ANON. Coke & Gas 1956, 364. W. M. McGRUE, Blast Furn. St. Plant, 1937, 25, (6), 624. ANON. Coke & Gas., 1957, 230. A. E. WILLIAMS. Gas Times 1951, **68,** (743), 24. ANON. Steel, 1939, **105,** 64. G. T. HADDOCK. Pwr. Plant (Engng.) 1947, April.

148 J. M. REID, W. G. BLAIR & H. R. LINDEN. J. Inst. Fuel, 1958, 325. EMIL BLAHA. Industr. Engng. Chem., 1953, **48,** 183.

149 W. E. FRANCIS & B. JACKSON. Gas Council Res. Commun., G.C.44 pp. 1-51. London. GAS COUNCIL & J. H. WYLDE. Brit. Pat. 871428 (1961). W. N. SMIRLES. Gas J., 1957, **291,** 663, 667, 673. K. F. BRAY. Gas World 1958, 37 (1), 11. J. P. LIOTIER. J. Inst. Fuel, 1960, **33,** (230), 116.

150 ANON. Engng. Boiler Hse. Rev., 1960, **75,** (3), 74. A. E. WILLIAMS. Steam Engr., 1958, **28,** 75. ANON. Power, 1953, 97. C. S. DARLING. Steam Engr., 1955, 24.

151 W. L. GERMAN. Ceramics, 1955, **7,** (74), 296. T. G. ZAMSKII. Elekt. Sta., Moscow, 1955, **26,** 44. ANON. Chem. Age., 1947, **56,** 376. COMBUSTION ENGNG. CO. INC. & W. J. KUNZ. Brit. Pat. 636707 (1948). In U.S.A. 1947. R. R. B. HILTON. Brit. Pat. 802694 (1958).

152 ANON. Pwr. Works Engng. 1951, 338. Engng. Boiler Hse. Rev., 1950(1), 344.

153 A. E. MORDIN. J. Inst. Fuel. 1955, 441.

154 R. H. PIPKORN. Mod. Pwr. Engng. 1959, 52.

155 H. M. RICHARDSON & W. McCLIMONT. Refract. J., 1960, **36,** 273. W. McCLIMONT, H. M. RICHARDSON & B. TAYLOR. Trans. Inst. Marine Engrs., 1959, 71, 237.

156 G. F. J. MURRAY. J. Inst. Fuel, 1959, **32,** (221), 287. See also ANON. Insulation. 1961, **5,** (1), 17.

157 C. MARÉCAT & M. HOELLE. Rev. gén. Chemins de Fer 1957, 71. C. MARÉCAT. Usine nouv. 1959, 29. ANON. Railway Gaz., 1961, **114,** (9), 248. E. HAMMOND. Ref. No. 128.

158 H. L. PALMER. Prefabrication 1954, 34. ANON. Coal Merch. Shipp., 1952, **105,** 100, 268. A. CLAUDON, Ref. No. 5. J. K. TWINE. Building Materials, 1958, 69. ANON. Master Builder, 1954, **72,** 54. (Electric storage heaters).

159 F. E. LOBAUGH. Brick Clay Rec. 1946, **109** (6), 52. J. H. HARTLEY. Brit. Claywkr., 1955, **63,** 298. ANON. Idem. 1943, **52,** 85. ANON. Idem., 1960, **69,** 28. O. WEISS. Ost. ZieglZtg., 1954, **4,** 6. R. T. GILES, Brick Clay Rec., 1934, **84,** (7), 254, 257. H. J. ROLKE. Ceram. Age, 1959, **74,** (5), 26. A. C. MACDONALD. Ceramics, 1955, **7,** 255. T. D. ROBSON. Claycraft, 1955, **28,** (4), 244.

160 P. M. SAUZIER. L'Industr. Ital. Laterizi, 1953, **7,** (4), 173. T. D. ROBSON. Brit. Claywkr., 1954, **62,** (741), 302.

161 A. J. CAMPBELL. E. Afr. Industr. Res., Bd., Tech. Pamphlet, No. 15, 1947. N. M. THOMPSON & R. A. SAUNDERS. Brick Clay Rec., 1957, **131,** (5), 69, 77.

162 E. D. B. RUSSELL. Claycraft, 1958, **31,** 147.

163 ANON. Brit. Claywkr., 1945, **54,** 159. Idem., 1960, 69, 28.

164 N. M. THOMPSON. Bull. Amer. ceram. Soc., 1953, **32,** (1), 1. Ceramic Industr., 1936, **26,** (5), 356. ANON. Brick Clay Rec., 1949, 60, 74. ANON. Ceramic Age., 1956, **68,** (1), 25. W. L. STAFFORD. Brick Clay Rec., 1955, **127,** (3), 49. HARBISON-WALKER REFRACTORIES CO. & C. A. TATE. U.S. Pat. 2974374 (1961). S. SCHWARTZ & S. HEMPEL. Silikattech. 1960, **5,** 233.

165 NOBEL-BOZEL. Brit. Pat. 833238 (1960).

166 GENERAL ELECTRIC CO. LTD. & D. W. T. ANGWIN. Brit. Pat. 795826 (1958).

167 H. G. PROTZE. Ref. No. 85.

168 W. C. HANSEN & W. W. BRANDVOLD. J. Amer. concr. Inst., 1958, **54,** 1009.

169 R. C. KOPITUK. Metal Prog., 1958, **73,** (6), 79.

170 STEATITE RESEARCH CORP., G. E. KADISCH & J. M. KATZ. U.S. Pat. 2874071 (1959).

171 G. LANDON & R. W. THACKRAY. Engineer Lond., 1961, **212,** (5505), 133.

172 T. D. ROBSON. Ceramics 1952, (October), 134.

AUTHOR INDEX

253

SUBJECT INDEX

263